The Stephenson Method of Natural Health Care

Creative Healing

Patricia Blaine Bradley

Editor and Compiler
for the Joseph B. Stephenson Foundation

LP Publications ~ Scottsdale AZ

Published by LP Publications
7119 E Shea Blvd Suite 109
PMB 418
Scottsdale, AZ 85254-6107

Copyright © 2000 Patricia B. Bradley

All rights reserved. This book may not be reproduced or transmitted in any form or by any means, electronic or mechanical, including photocopying and recording, or by any information storage or retrieval system without permission in writing from the author, except for a reviewer who may quote brief passages or a single treatment for a review.

The Joseph B. Stephenson Foundation World Wide Web Site address is:
www.stephensonscreativehealing.org

To contact the Joseph B. Stephenson Foundation:
creativehealing@hotmail.com

Printed in the United States of America
First trade printing: May 2000
Second trade printing: January 2009

ISBN 13: 978-0-916-19252-5

Book design, typography and copyediting: Louise Lambert
Illustrations: Patricia Bradley, Bill Foland, and Tony Sourdry
Cover design: J. Bradley Design

This book is dedicated in gratitude
to the memory of a western Master,
Joseph Bestford Stephenson, 1874–1956.

Acknowledgments

The treatments in this workbook cover all of Mr. Stephenson's work to which the Stephenson Foundation has had access. I am grateful to many people in Northern and Southern California for their help and to two people for the preservation of the greater part of the work.

John Hunt studied with Mr. Stephenson and had the ability to memorize his exact words and teach in the same unforgettable way. During John's teaching sessions, audio tapes were made and Dr. Lulu Bechtolsheim had the foresight and patience to bring them into print, a wonderful gift of love and appreciation for John's Creative Healing for her husband and herself. These lessons were available to Creative Healing students but never formally published. They have been a strong foundation for this book.

Next, I acknowledge Mabel Gunderson Young, whom Mr. Stephenson chose to be his student; he also entrusted all of his writings to her keeping. Mabel and Mr. Stephenson published and copyrighted a pamphlet in the late 1940s that introduced the Four Principles and gave brief descriptions of some fifty treatments. It was through her influence that the first book of over forty treatments was published in 1989 by the Joseph B. Stephenson Foundation.

The accuracy of the workbook contents has been greatly enhanced by another third generation Creative Healer, Louise Hunt, R.N., whose life work and livelihood has been Creative Healing for nearly thirty-five years.

Helyn Cruikshank Foley, who also studied with Mr. Stephenson, has been a wonderful friend and has given great encouragement when I needed it.

Also, I thank Joseph B. Stephenson, Jr. and family for permitting the use of Mr. Stephenson's voluminous writings.

For meticulous editing and layout, Louise Lambert has my unending admiration and gratitude.

And finally, my husband John O. Bradley is here publicly acknowledged as the perfect partner, encouraging me when I felt overwhelmed, and assisting with writing, researching, publishing, distributing and all the other work associated with this project. I would be remiss if I did not also acknowledge his Creative Healing ability whenever my heart acted up or my back has hurt.

I thankfully bless all who have assisted this endeavor in any way.

Patricia Blaine Bradley

Santa Rosa California

January 2000

DISCLAIMER

The Joseph B. Stephenson Foundation, Inc., a not-for-profit California Corporation, is not a clinic and does not perform treatments.

Anyone using these techniques as treatments or therapy must already have the appropriate license to do so, depending on their location and application. The Joseph B. Stephenson Foundation does not qualify a person for such licensing.

For diagnosing or prescribing medicine for a cure for diseases, a medical doctor should be consulted. No book will replace the need for doctors, and no doctor can replace the need for people to take care of themselves.

Contents

Chapter 1 Basics of Creative Healing

Chapter 2 Head and Neck

Chapter 3 The Back

Chapter 4 Chest Cavity

Chapter 5 The Abdominal Cavity: Digestion and Elimination

Chapter 6 The Arms and Hands

Chapter 7 The Legs

Chapter 8 Men, Women and Children

Chapter 9 General Problems

Chapter 1 ♦ Basics of Creative Healing

Creative Healing, the Stephenson Method of Natural Health Care

Creative Healing, as Joseph Bestford Stephenson called his natural method of health care, was an ancient art practiced by many people over time, but lost today. Mr. Stephenson saw his mission as restoring these natural methods to the planet; however, he predicted before he died in 1956 that his methods would not be widely accepted for 50 years. It is appropriate, as we near the target of this fifty-year prediction, that all Mr. Stephenson's treatments, remedies and wisdom about the body and its functioning be offered to the world. This *Stephenson Method of Natural Health Care* workbook attempts to do this.

During his years as a healer, Mr. Stephenson healed family members of medical doctors and tried to teach doctors his simple hands-on methods, but they couldn't integrate them into their medical school thinking. Today, doctors search for complementary methods that work, and scientists invent machines that "see" into the body. The medical profession now acknowledges the powerful and subtle influence exerted by the mind over the physical world in creating change, for better or worse. While we envision the mind–body interaction as complex, Mr. Stephenson's methods model a simple mind–body connection for producing health. They can give hope to both.

The "Creative" in Creative Healing is the powerful image in the mind of the operators that their hands intend to create changes or remove blocks within the body that will allow the body to heal itself. For example, while performing the specific hand movements for the three-part kidney treatment, the mental image is that the hand actions will (1) reposition the nerve that nourishes the kidney, (2) remove the heat engendered by the ill-functioning kidney, and (3) drain the kidney into the bladder. The mind can easily envision these simple actions occurring inside the body while the hands are performing the work on the body. Thus, visualization is specifically taught and used with every finger or hand movement. Creative Healers work in a specific way on the body to obtain intended results and often accomplish other beneficial results as well.

The Creative Healing work rests on four principles that Mr. Stephenson felt he had learned in other lifetimes and followed intuitively until later in life when he gained a visual understanding of exactly how the body functioned.

The practice of combining and applying these four principles fosters creativity in the Creative Healer's power to visualize. Visualization, Mr. Stephenson said, is one of the greatest powers endowed to humans and is waiting to be developed to its fullest in a positive way. This is the true significance of the name Creative Healing, which Mr. Stephenson gave to his work; however, the casual observer may see nothing different from massage.

Mr. Stephenson advertised himself as a masseur, but he said he never "practiced medicine," he just did his healing work and charged two dollars for his time. If people couldn't pay, he treated them for free.

A Creative Healer summed it up this way: "Mr. Stephenson's methods give me a non-invasive, non-chemical, painless hands-on way to remove the blocks that cause many wellness problems whether circulatory, neural, structural, organic or respiratory. As I have become more aware of the part that my thoughts and actions play in creating problems in my own physical body, the gentle Creative Healing methods have brought fast resolution when I became ill. I consider these gentle methods to be my first line of defense. More invasive measures will be used as a last resort."

History and Growth of Creative Healing

Joseph Bestford Stephenson, a Man of Wisdom

At age five, Joseph Stephenson healed his own father of sciatica. He believed from an early age that he had healed the sick in many previous lifetimes and would do so again in this one. He was born in England in 1874, had an inquisitive mind, and experienced many unusual events in his childhood.

At age twelve he went to work in the coal mines near New Castle-on-Tyne becoming a pit boss at age seventeen. An inner voice was with him all his life and "guides" appeared on auspicious occasions. One such incident brought him to the USA in 1910 where he soon became a superintendent in the Berwin Coal Company in Pennsylvania. A mine accident when he was forty-nine directed him into full time healing work in Johnstown.

He knew from a very early age that his life would some day be devoted entirely to healing. At age forty-nine, after many years of healing friends and neighbors in his spare time, he began full time healing from his large three-story family home in Johnstown, Pennsylvania. He didn't need to ask his patients for symptoms—he knew what they needed the minute he saw them. His work as a healer came very naturally to him, as though he had always known how. According to records kept by his wife, he treated as many as 50 people a day.

From 1922 to 1944 Mr. Stephenson made healing his livelihood. In the 1930s he was prosecuted for practicing medicine without a license. Because of the high success rate of his work (close to 99%), the Grand Jury dismissed the case and the judge referred it to the State where he was finally protected by the State Law Enforcement Agency and given lifetime immunity in Pennsylvania.

Joseph Stephenson's work had become teachable when, at age fifty-five, he was given an unusual experience that taught him to see all the working parts of the body in motion and discover where the blockages were. He already "knew" what to do to remove the blockages but this gift of sight allowed him to accurately teach others.

Two hours of sleep at night allowed him to write about his lifetime search for wisdom, which he claimed was superior to education (only other people's thoughts). His book about educating children, *The Human Rosebud*, was published in Boston in 1936 and reviewed in newspapers across the country. After more than 22 years of work from early morning until evening in Johnstown, he retired in 1944 at age seventy to Long Beach, California and to find the students he would teach.

Stephenson's Method Grows

John Hunt and Mabel Gunderson were the two people he chose as students and they each made Creative Healing their careers by treating many people and by teaching several hundred people.

While Mr. Stephenson had a 99% success rate, he said that those who learned the work could be 65% effective if they had willing hands and a loving heart and that the rest could be learned by experience and intuition.

John and Mabel attended Dr. Cotner's Physical Therapy College in Los Angeles while they were studying with Mr. Stephenson. In fact, Mabel learned about Mr. Stephenson from John and asked him to introduce them. The arrangements were made and as Mabel stepped from a cab at Mr. Stephenson's door, he saw her from his office window and said, "That is the woman I saw at the 5th and Main bus stop in Long Beach. We have worked together before."

John Hunt's story about meeting Mr. Stephenson goes back to John's childhood in Pennsylvania where the Hunts and the Stephensons were neighbors. John's father was taking Vernon, a younger son, to Mr. Stephenson for help and 13-year-old John went along. As Mr. Stephenson worked, the father told him that John was scheduled for appendectomy surgery the next day. "That won't be necessary," Mr. Stephenson had said without even looking at John. When he finished, he told John to lie down and loosen his trousers, and he began working on him. The scheduled operation never took place and Mr. Stephenson promised to teach John, then a Boy Scout, several treatments he could use in emergencies and "all my work" someday. The Hunt family later moved to California.

This is certainly part of the reason Mr. Stephenson retired to California in 1944 with his wife, Mary, and son, Joe Jr, who was then 16. In the spring of 1945, John Hunt was on shore leave while his Navy ship was docked for repairs in San Diego. He visited Mr. Stephenson who told John he would come to him in September to learn Creative Healing. John reminded him that the world was at war and his ship would be in the Pacific by then.

But Mr. Stephenson was right—atomic bombs were dropped that August, the war ended and the ship never left the harbor. John Hunt became a student of the work that would change his life. Fortunately, John and Mabel both had the ability to repeat Mr. Stephenson's exact words, although to begin with he would not let them take notes during classes.

Mr. Stephenson did teach others the basic treatments from head to toe, answered questions, and later dictated his teachings to Mabel. He and Mabel published a small pamphlet, *Creative Healing,* in 1951.

A looseleaf notebook created by John Hunt and Lulu Bechtolsheim, and printed by Dr. Fred Andrews has been the basis for much of the work to preserve Mr. Stephenson's legacy and contained in this workbook.

Third Generation at Work

Patricia and John Bradley were inspired to study Creative Healing in 1980 when Patricia's excruciating back pain was cured in less than an hour by John Hunt and his companion, Hildreth Coulter. In 1983 and 1984, videotapes of the first 41 treatments and another tape on elaborations of other treatments were made by John Hunt and the Bradleys.

The Stephenson Foundation was co-founded in 1987 by Patricia and John Bradley, Louise Hunt, William Foland, Sharon and Stanley Bertsch, and Barbara Thompson. With Mabel Gunderson's encouragement and her writings, the first book edited by Patricia Bradley was given to and published by the Foundation. Another video on the head and neck treatments was made in 1989 and the foundation has published a quarterly newsletter since 1986.

Patricia and John Bradley have given classes around the USA and in England, Scotland, Greece and Australia. Patricia presented the work in 1989 at the First International Conference on Holistic Health and Medicine in Bangalore, India with the help of Stanley and Sharon Bertsch. Later a workshop was given for over 80 Indian doctors and nurses. The "Pink" Creative Healing book was accepted by Sri Sathya Sai Baba at his ashram in Puttaparthi.

Since receiving all the Stephenson papers, the Bradleys' work has been to read the handwritten pages, and catalog, type and preserve them as much as possible. This workbook covers everything found so far about Creative Healing treatments. With the valuable help of Louise Hunt, RN, and her experience in using and teaching this work over the years, the Bradleys have been able to make available for future generations this workbook of the *Stephenson Method of Natural Health Care.*

Many medical professionals have studied Creative Healing, most of whom integrate it with their other medical skills. Practitioners of complementary therapies use Creative Healing as part of their treatments. There are about twenty qualified teachers of Creative Healing. Dr. Gowri Motha, ObGyn in London, England is using and teaching the work. Those who study, perform and teach in the new millenium will be able to spread the Stephenson Method around the world.

Overview of Creative Healing

The Four Principles

The Four Basic Principles in the *Stephenson Method of Natural Health Care* are simple and must be understood before a healer can be really effective. These principles refer to the exact way the hands are used to accomplish the intended results and are applied differently in every treatment.

The mind–body complex is a closed interdependent system, one whole organism composed of tubes, liquids, solids, lots of space and various sized parts, all with the intelligence to operate correctly. Many of these components change size and shape as they interact with each other, and at the same time carry out their individual functions. While bodies appear to be a solid mass, they also enclose much empty space. In addition, much of what is inside the skin is movable even though located in specific places known to doctors and students of anatomy but not usually to the average lay person. Creative Healing uses these facts and also teaches the location of essential body parts to the novice.

Every treatment applies one or more of the four principles at the correct body location and with a clear picture in the healer's mind of what is to be achieved by each movement in the treatment. These procedures are explained in each treatment, making it possible for the layman or professional to follow the directions. All the treatments emphasize the use of such a gentle touch that they cannot be harmful even if they do not produce the intended result.

The illustrations of the front and back of the body on pages 1–12 and 1–13 were drawn by Mr. Stephenson to help students find the locations of the notches, spots, and indentations where the hand movements are performed.

Principle 1: Reposition substance

If a substance in the body is causing pain it may be because it is out of place. "Substance" is a catch-all word used by Mr. Stephenson and can include anything from a nerve to an organ, such as a bladder, or it can be cartilage, nerves, ligaments, muscles or tendons. Gentle movements of the thumb or the whole hand as described in the treatments can relieve the pain and/or reposition the substance back into place with ease. This principle of repositioning substance is applied extensively in treating the back along the spine, by replacing the substance between the vertebrae, not the bones themselves. A complete back treatment from the sacrum to the seventh or protruding cervical at the neck, will clear up most back problems; for an example, see sciatica treatment, page 3–23. For an example of repositioning an organ, see bladder treatment, page 5–49.

Principle 2: Restore the body to normal temperature

The palm of the hand detects areas of the body that are above or below normal temperature, indicating inflammation or low blood circulation; oiled hands on the skin withdraw or add heat as needed. Heat can be removed with the palm of the oiled hand with fingers extended, either touching or not touching the body. Restoring heat is done with less oil on the palms and the use of both hands to create friction. The palms can effectively ease pain quickly in an emergency.

Everyone's hands can help another person if the mind and heart are willing. The pain from a finger caught in a door or from a child's skinned knee can be quickly removed at the spot that hurts without touching the injured place. The palm of the hand with fingers extended, not even touching the body can remove pain with only a dozen passes in a downward direction over the painful area.

If a sick person complains of an aching leg or painful shoulder, the hands of a friend or relative can become loving instruments that remove the pain by passing the palms, one following the other in a downward direction, about an inch above the aggravating place. This will remove the heat from the area and ease the pain.

A Creative Healer uses the palms of the hands with a little oil on them to detect temperatures above or below normal and sore throats are quickly relieved by specific movements of the hand to remove the heat and drain; see page 2–13. Asthma patients need heat restored to the lower lung area by the use of less oil where the palms create friction that warms up the mucous so that it can be coughed up; see page 4–13.

Principle 3: Create a vacuum

As noted earlier, there is space inside the body and blockages can occur anywhere in the body and they must be dissolved and/or removed for perfect functioning. A natural law says if you create a vacuum something has to flow through it. Anyone who has drawn water from a glass beaker or gasoline from a can with a flexible tube inserted, knows how to create a vacuum by using the thumb or fingers to lower the pressure and let the water or gas flow out the other end of the tube. Creating a vacuum is another Creative Healing Principle.

When a vacuum is created inside the body, undesirable matter drains into the elimination system and is replaced by fresh blood or other body fluids. The body's own healing system takes over. The vacuum stroke is usually done with fingers or a thumb with a light pressure. It can clear a jaundiced liver (see page 5–5), or stuffy sinuses (see page 2–2), and is part of many other treatments.

Principle 4: Break up congestion

When there is a visible or palpable lump or bruise, we often touch or rub it without thinking. Any congested place needs to be broken up but in the correct way that will aid the healing power of our bodies. Breaking up congestion is done with one or two fingers in a circular movement that does not glide over the skin but moves the skin with it in tiny circles and only around the edges of visible lumps or bruises; see page 9–5. In other breaking up movements, though done on the surface of the body, the intention and visualization is to penetrate to a congested place deep inside the body. Even though used in a gentle way, the finger at the right spot with the arm extended acts like a drill, the congestion is broken up and disperses, and again the body's healing system takes over; see flu spot treatment, page 3–12.

The General Treatment, a Basic Technique

The general treatment is given to everyone—as a specific treatment or as a preliminary or followup to other treatments—to improve circulation and to keep the back of the neck clear of obstruction. The general treatment can be given any time during the session, whenever it best fits in. For very nervous patients, it is best to give it at the beginning along with stroking down the back and shoulders and half-way down the upper arms.

The internal organs of our bodies are nourished with vital nerve energy through the spinal column and through the correct circulation of blood. Mr. Stephenson viewed the Creative Healer's duty as that of seeing that these two forces reached their destinations: blood circulation is sent out by the heart through the circulatory system and nerve life emanates from the brain throughout the nervous system. Creative Healers perform a great service any time that they correct the flow of nerve life because it is the "governor" and director of all vital functions, even that of the circulation.

Location of filter areas

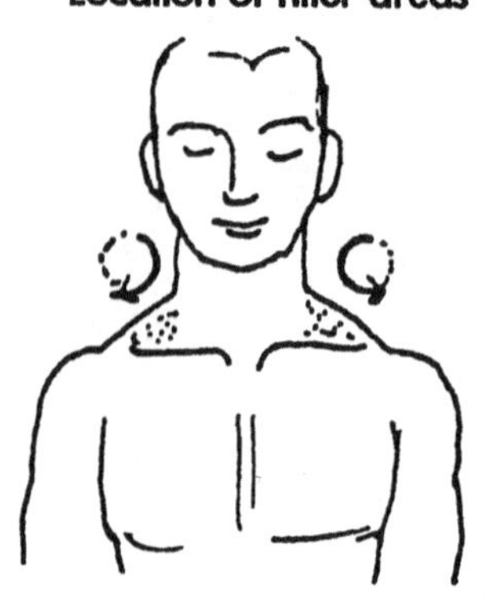

Creative Healing makes good use of the upright spine, so the patient is seated on a flat bench, the most effective posture for all the back treatments. If you sit quietly behind patients before the treatment and place your hands on their shoulders, you will become aware of tensions, vibrations and sometimes heat in that area.

You can relieve tension on any tight muscles that lie parallel to the spine between the spine and the shoulder blades by using the thumb vertically to gently exert a light pressure from the sides to the center back.

Position

The patient sits on a bench; the Creative Healer stands behind.

Clear the filters

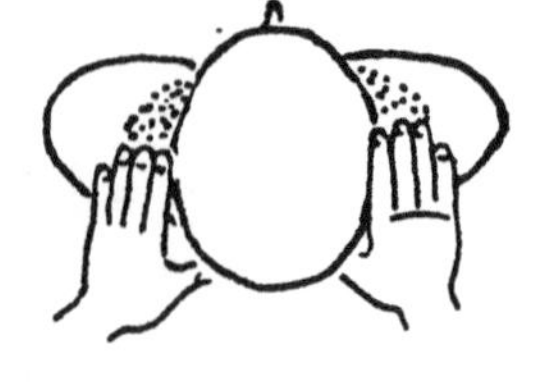

➧ **Step 1: Clear the filter areas.** The filter areas lie on each side of the neck in a triangular area bounded by the ridge of the shoulder, the collarbone and the base of the neck. With olive oil on your hands, stand behind the seated person and place three fingers of each hand on the filter areas. The palms rest lightly on the patient's shoulders and the thumbs touch at the back of the neck.

Now, very gently, make breaking up circles slowly over the entire filter areas with the flats of the fingers in lengthwise contact moving the skin rather than gliding over it. As seen by the operator the movement is clockwise on the right and counterclockwise on the left. A slight pressure is applied on the downward movement (toward the heart). Continue for 1 or 2 minutes.

These circles force thickened blood to break up finely enough to prevent it from posing a threat to vital areas of circulation. Visualize this happening as you work.

Step 2: Decongest channels in the back of the neck. Much of the return circulation from the head to the heart is regulated through the channels that lead from just below the mastoid bones to the filter areas just relieved. Here the two sides of the back of the neck must be treated separately. Treating both sides simultaneously could, in serious cases, cause the patient to faint. This vacuum ensures good drainage so that the poisons or wastes drawn from the head may be carried away.

Vacuum downward

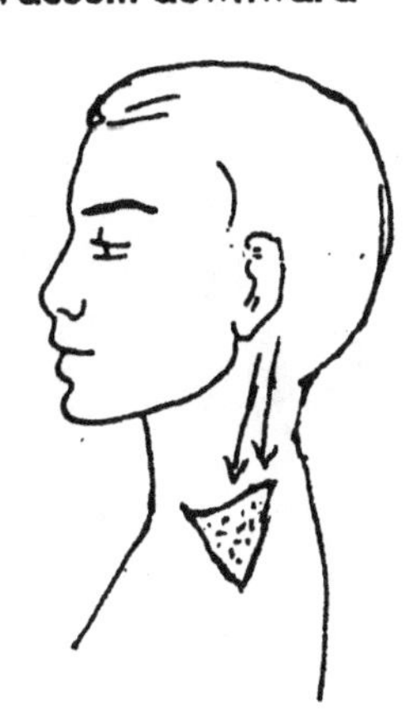

To treat the right side, support the person's head gently with the left hand while the first 3 fingers of the right hand create a vacuum by stroking only downward. With the middle finger prominent, repeat this movement for 1 or 2 minutes gently and rapidly to create the vacuum that will clear the channels on the right side of the neck behind the ear, from the base of the skull to the filter area you have just cleared.

Treat the left side correspondingly and then clean out the triangular filter areas again as in step 1 before proceeding to step 3.

Step 3: Loosen back tension. The third step of the treatment relaxes the muscles of the upper back and feels good to the patient.

Relax back muscles

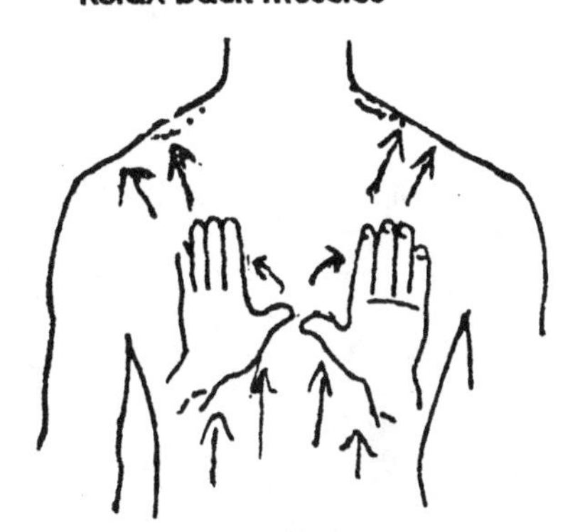

Place your palms on the back, below the shoulder blades and work up very gently to the shoulder ridge in a circular motion with the whole of the hands. As the hands glide upward, move the thumbs in and out toward the base of the fingers in a kneading motion. Maintain the palms in contact with the skin. This combined movement by its rhythm creates a gentle jiggling motion that eliminates from the tissues of the shoulder region the contractions that could spread upward to impair the work previously done.

Duration

As a guide, this treatment should take from 3 to 5 minutes, but may be longer depending on the built-in tension in the neck and shoulders.

Using the Bench in Treatments

Mr. Stephenson impressed on his students the importance of treating the head, neck, and back, and many leg and foot problems with the patient sitting upright on a bench. He said that because humans are endowed with an upright spine, the circulation of blood and nerve life is enhanced and returned to normal function throughout the whole body in this sitting position. This hastens whatever healing must take place with the hands-on treatment.

The Importance of Olive Oil

Mr. Stephenson favored olive oil above the many other oils available. After washing the hands, the Creative Healer applies olive oil to them. This is analogous to putting on a pair of invisible gloves that protect the patient and the healer. When finished with a treatment, the gloves are washed off again. Mr. Stephenson claimed that olive oil is too "dense" for a germ to live in. His strong statement was, "I have treated more than 250,000 people and have never, to my knowledge, transmitted or contracted anything. I give the credit for this to the olive oil."

Moreover, he found that olive oil is the softest oil and as such not only provides a consistent lubricating medium allowing the hands to glide smoothly even when perspiration is present, but also furnishes a most effective medium for heat transfer, both for detecting hot spots and for withdrawing heat from the body as in the pneumonia treatment. It is also one of the most compatible oils for the great variety of skins presented to a Creative Healer.

Olive Oil Nourishes the Tissues

Olive oil has been known to "feed" or nourish the body, providing nutrition acceptable to the body when it seems to reject or fails to respond to any other form of nutrition. By immersing as much of the body as possible in olive oil, warmed to a comfortable degree, people who were "skin and bones" have again become plump and strong. Such a bath should be used at least once a day for 20 to 30 minutes.

Olive Oil Heals Withered Limbs

Olive oil is also beneficial after surgery where there has been a severe accident or injury. In this condition, the affected limbs are often left withered. This is true especially when there has been a disturbance of the circulatory channels and tissues. The olive oil bath seems to enable the tissues to reconstruct. See Chapter 8 for uses of olive oil in treating men and women problems.

Mr. Stephenson's View of the Body

The illustations shown on pages 1–12 and 1–13 show all the spots and treatment points on the body as identified by Mr. Stephenson and drawn by him, and which he called the Creative Healing System. He published these diagrams under U.S. Copyright 8227.

These points and spots are the ones referred to in the treatments contained in this Stephenson Method Creative Healing workbook.

From the writings of Joseph B. Stephenson

All my desires and goals in life were based on three great principles: Wisdom (not education); Power (not dominating power but the power to heal the sick, the power to restore hope where it was lost); and Love (love that would embrace all the human race). These are the things for which I have lived.

I have watched the process of time and evolution in the creation of this wonderful world, the Creator's gift to man. As in Creative Healing, all of man's greatest inventions have been based on the "Creative Principle," perhaps unconsciously. How much more could be done if the Principle were consciously applied?

Where did the Creative Principle originate? It is the Creator's (God's) Principle—a gift to man that can be passed down through the ages to anyone who would help suffering humanity.

Through this Principle we don't "try" to do something. We do it. We don't "think" something, we know it. We don't try to see, we see and as we follow on that path we advance in Wisdom and create our own Power. Eventually we become so strong and healthy in ourselves that we are able to help those less fortunate; we are able to love them, and the three principles of wisdom, power and love so intermingle in our lives that we cannot help but use our selves for the benefit of a greater humanity.

For me the highest and most noble end that can be attained is total health. There is so much sickness in the world today and the creative instincts of most people have been channeled into scientific research. Science claims wonderful credits and discoveries, yet I feel the toll of experimentation has been too great. With much scientific experimentation one has to take a life in order to discover how to give a life.

Front

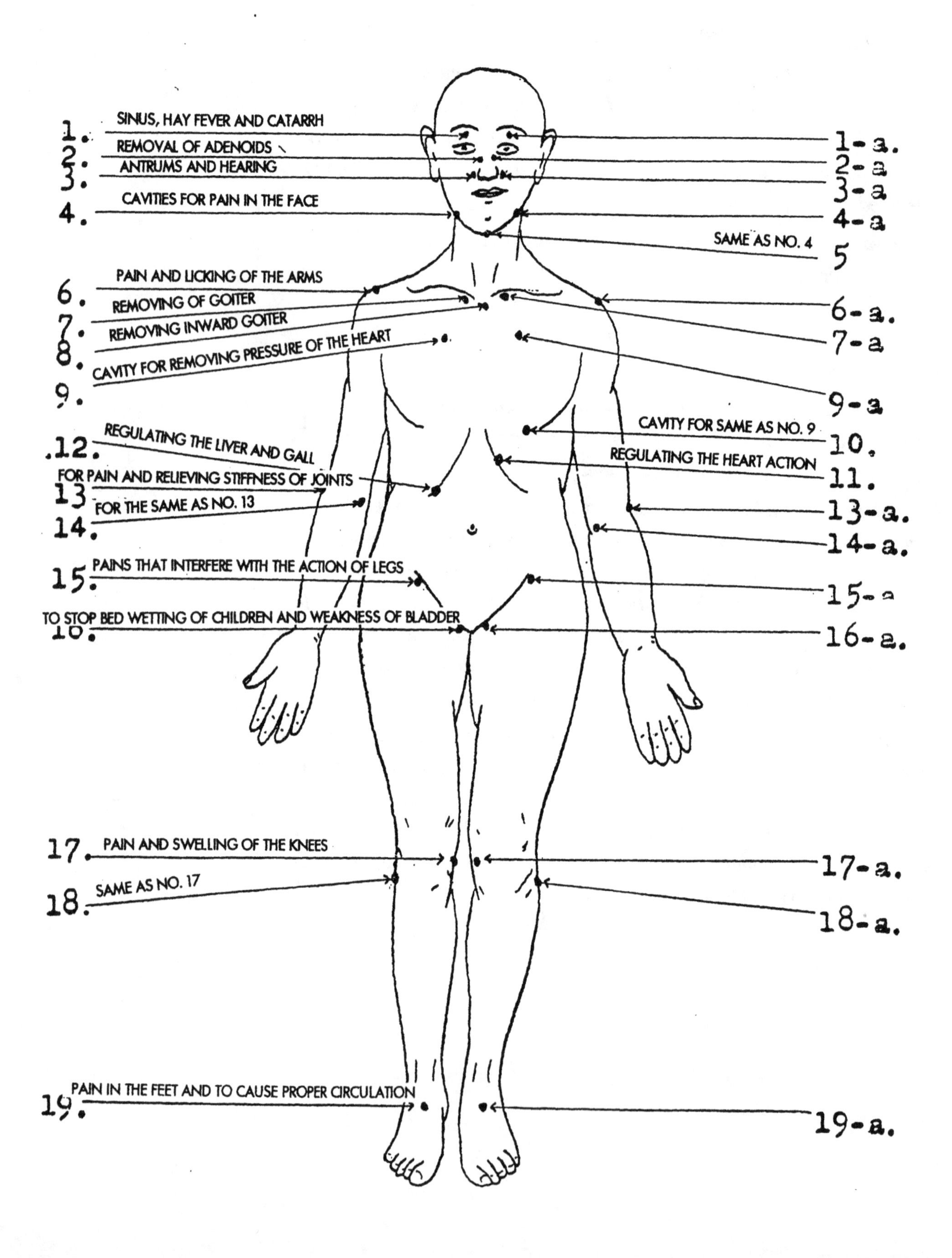
1.
SINUS, HAY FEVER AND CATARRH
1-a.
2.
REMOVAL OF ADENOIDS
2-a
3.
ANTRUMS AND HEARING
3-a
4.
CAVITIES FOR PAIN IN THE FACE
4-a
SAME AS NO. 4
5
6.
PAIN AND LICKING OF THE ARMS
6-a.
7.
REMOVING OF GOITER
7-a
8.
REMOVING INWARD GOITER
9.
CAVITY FOR REMOVING PRESSURE OF THE HEART
9-a
CAVITY FOR SAME AS NO. 9
10.
.12.
REGULATING THE LIVER AND GALL
REGULATING THE HEART ACTION
11.
FOR PAIN AND RELIEVING STIFFNESS OF JOINTS
13
13-a.
FOR THE SAME AS NO. 13
14.
14-a.
15.
PAINS THAT INTERFERE WITH THE ACTION OF LEGS
15-a
TO STOP BED WETTING OF CHILDREN AND WEAKNESS OF BLADDER
16.
16-a.
17.
PAIN AND SWELLING OF THE KNEES
17-a.
18.
SAME AS NO. 17
18-a.
19.
PAIN IN THE FEET AND TO CAUSE PROPER CIRCULATION
19-a.

Back

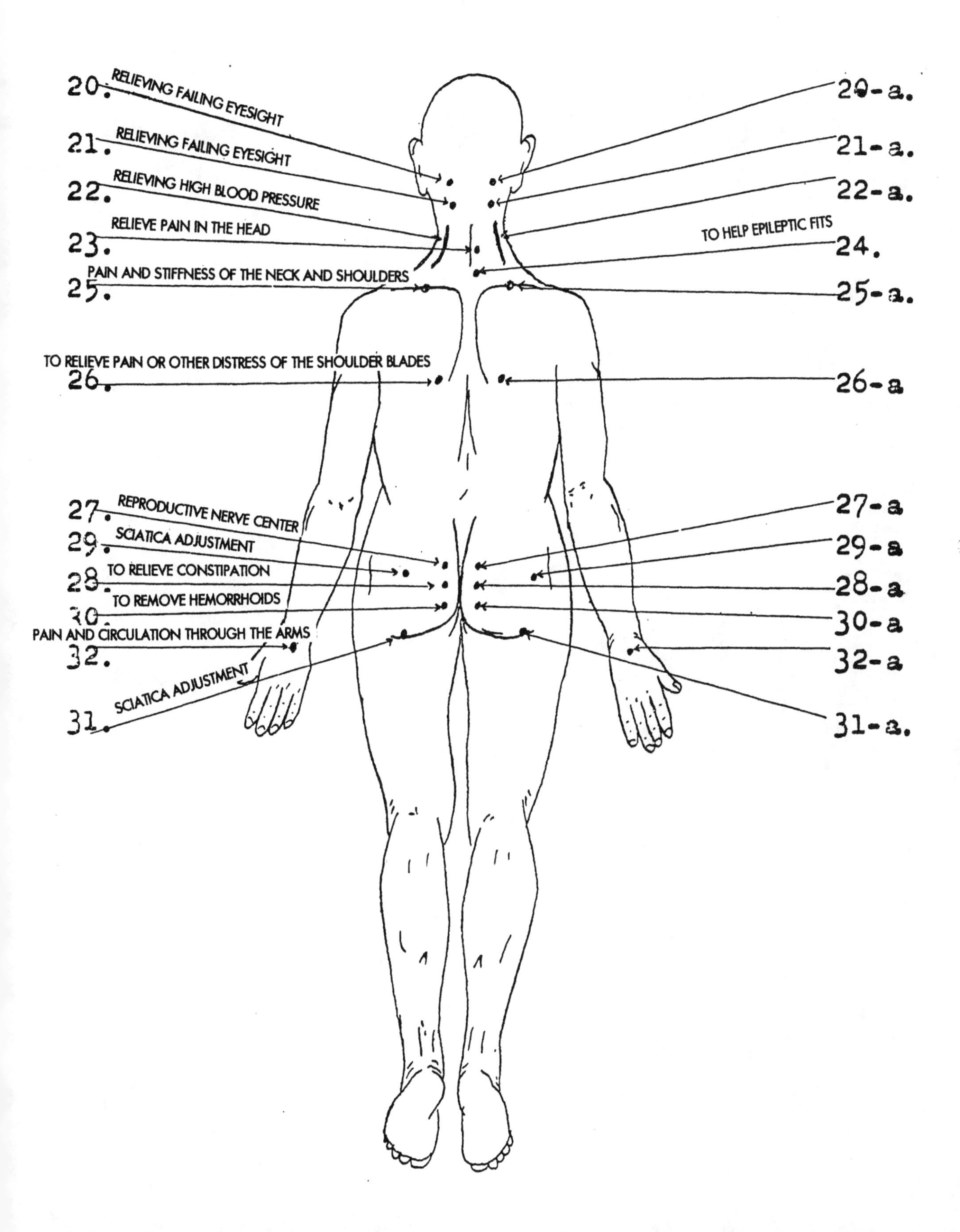

20. RELIEVING FAILING EYESIGHT
21. RELIEVING FAILING EYESIGHT
22. RELIEVING HIGH BLOOD PRESSURE
23. RELIEVE PAIN IN THE HEAD
25. PAIN AND STIFFNESS OF THE NECK AND SHOULDERS
26. TO RELIEVE PAIN OR OTHER DISTRESS OF THE SHOULDER BLADES
27. REPRODUCTIVE NERVE CENTER
29. SCIATICA ADJUSTMENT
28. TO RELIEVE CONSTIPATION
30. TO REMOVE HEMORRHOIDS
32. PAIN AND CIRCULATION THROUGH THE ARMS
31. SCIATICA ADJUSTMENT
20-a.
21-a.
22-a.
24. TO HELP EPILEPTIC FITS
25-a.
26-a
27-a
29-a
28-a
30-a
32-a
31-a.

Chapter 2 ♦ Head and Neck

Understanding and Care of the Head and Neck

We use our heads to think about everything, but we seldom think about taking care of the head itself until it begins to hurt. We can live without an arm or leg and even some of our organs. However, the head and neck are the central control for the body and the conduit into it; they keep all body systems working properly.

Mr. Stephenson said that our body is assembled in such a way that nerve impulses in the brain activate corresponding nerve endings throughout the body, causing a finger, leg or any other part of the body to move. This explanation gives us insight into Mr. Stephenson's understanding of body functions and is the basis for his unique and successful treatments: we must discover the obstructions between an affected region of the body and the corresponding nerve impulses in the head. He also believed that drainage from the body above the stomach descends from the head into the stomach by way of various channels.

We know that blood circulates constantly into the head; Mr. Stephenson warned us of illness caused by cooling of the blood stream through chilling of the head and neck. He advised that wearing a hat and/or a scarf was especially important for those with difficulties stemming from poor function of the head or neck.

Mr. Stephenson also warned about weather changes when ground moisture, evaporating into the air, creates a chill zone stretching 10 to 12 feet up from the ground. He cautioned against changing to summer clothes too quickly at the first warm days in spring, at a break in the winter cold, or during the first days after a rainy period. After two or three days of warm weather have dissipated this moisture, it is safe to wear lighter clothes and keep the body at normal temperature.

The back of the neck plays a vital and delicate role in the proper functioning of the body, and obstructions in this area have varied and far-reaching consequences. The back of the neck may be compared to the back of a telephone exchange board in which thousands of wires and interconnected circuits interweave. Proper work on the back of the neck needn't attempt to differentiate as to which specific "wire" or "circuit" causes trouble in the body. "Undifferentiated downward work on the back of the neck can put thousands of things in place and none out of place," Mr. Stephenson said. There are only three exceptions to the rule of working in the downward direction on the back of the neck: treatments for pigeon toes, polio, and shaking palsy, and all three have to do with nerve endings in the head.

Upper Respiratory Treatments

Sinus and Hay Fever

The complete treatment for these ailments takes only a few minutes, but you must remember that you are only setting the healing process in motion. Nature is equipped to do her own healing: your duty is to start the process.

The germs that come to life in all of these cases are self-contained along with many other organisms in the area of the forehead. Certain conditions will bring them to life.

Mr. Stephenson explained that the sinusitis germ works in shifts. It may start at 7 am and begin to bore up into the arch of the brow, giving much pain. It will eat away for two or three hours then fall asleep and not come to life again for 24 hours. The patient will be aware that the extreme pain of sinusitis is not continuous like other sinus headaches.

Position

Patient sits on a firm, level surface or bench. Creative Healer stands behind so the patient may comfortably rest the head against Creative Healer's chest without the head or body being drawn backward.

Vacuum stroke

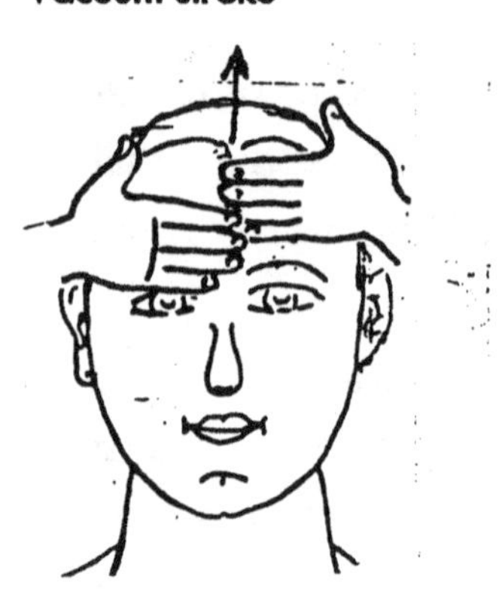

➧ **Step 1: Vacuum stroke.** Use the index and middle fingers of both hands to stroke upward from the bridge of the nose over the forehead to the hairline. The stroke is quick and light but smooth. The fingers of one hand follow the fingers of the other, the middle finger behind the index finger in a single line. Rest your thumbs on the side of the patient's head as you stroke only along the center line and only in the upward direction for 30 to 60 seconds. This encourages drainage from the upper sinus into the nasal cavity and draws the germs upward to the little cavities (nerve centers) found under each eyebrow. The vacuum (one hand following the other) is called a double vacuum. It is used when the material to be moved is thick and difficult to drain.

➧ **Step 2: Pressure application at the nerve centers.** Rest the thumbs on the forehead above the brows. Place the tips of the curled index fingers under the frontal bone, near the nose. Move the bony tips of the index fingers away from the nose along the underside of the frontal bone to locate small notches out about 3/4 of an inch. In these notches, quickly press the fingertips while moving them slightly from side to side, to reach the center of the notch. Direct the pressure upward and angled slightly backward. Release immediately. Be careful not to put pressure on the eyeball. The pressure in the notches is directed to nerve centers that help regulate circulation to heal the mucous-lined, honeycombed structure of the sinuses that is so difficult to reach.

Pressure at notches

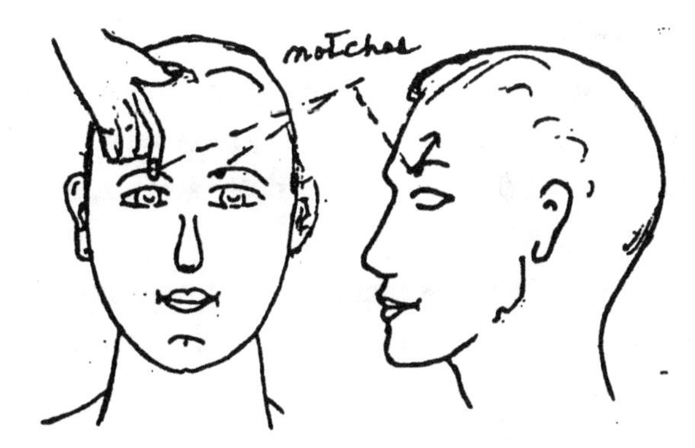

Repeat steps 1 and 2 two more times, increasing the pressure in the notches from one time to the next. The strength of the pressure should be adapted to the case at hand: with children it is necessary to start with a very light pressure and to increase it gradually.

➤➤➤CAUTION: In cases of long-standing sinus infection, if a blue cast or line is seen on the forehead, do not use the pressure in the notches because the bony structure might collapse under pressure. The stroking, however, may alone give relief.

➧ **Step 3: Remove heat.** If there is heat in the forehead after completing step 2, stroke with well-oiled palms from the center of the forehead toward the temples until the heat is withdrawn. Place one palm lightly on the center of the forehead and the other palm lightly on top of the first hand. Slowly and simultaneously draw the hands to the sides of the forehead, the fingers of each hand finishing the stroke. Repetition will restore the area to normal temperature. Heat is always withdrawn through the palms.

Removing heat

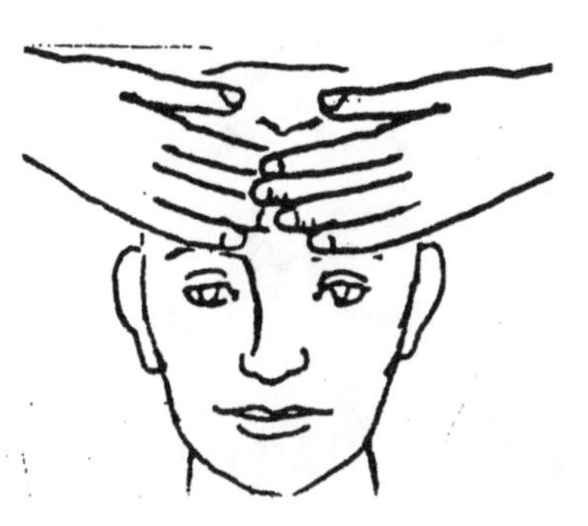

Duration

The time required may vary from a couple of minutes to 4 or 5 minutes if there is heat.

Frequency

Once a week for 3 weeks should bring relief. If results do not become apparent after 3 weeks, a deep-seated inflammation that follows the mucous membranes back over the brain may be indicated. Increase the frequency to twice a week and decrease the pressure in the notches to one half.

These treatments may be self-administered. If you have fever however, you cannot remove heat from yourself or from a patient.

Hay Fever and Catarrh

The hay fever germ is different from the sinus germ but it is in the same region and the treatment method is the same. The hay fever germ may be brought to life by many things, such as flowers, weeds, dust, aromas, etc., when the internal conditions of the body and mind are receptive.

Catarrh, an inflammation of mucous membranes of nose and throat with a post-nasal drip, is brought on by a draft. Catarrh and post-nasal drip will respond to the treatment described for sinus problems.

The Nose

Flattened Nostrils

Occasionally the openings of the nostrils become extended and flattened to such a degree that breathing, inhalation in particular, is impaired. This occurs most frequently in men.

To remold the nose to its natural shape:

➧ **Step 1:** Press straight back on the cartilage at the median line.

➧ **Step 2:** Massage upward on the sides until the nostrils appear more expanded.

Deviated Septum

If the cartilage of the nose is out of position to one side or the other, do the following:

➧ **Step 1:** Grasp the nose securely between the thumb and index finger.

➧ **Step 2:** Draw down, moving the cartilage and resetting it to the center.

➧ **Step 3:** Hold with a slight upward pressure to firm its position.

Nosebleed

For repeated bleeding apply the high blood pressure treatment, page 2–37.

Sneezing

➧ **Step 1:** Administer the adenoid treatment; see next page.

➧ **Step 2:** Center cartilage of the nose (see above, *Deviated Septum*).

In obstinate cases place a small amount of ground cinnamon up each nostril. Use a small portion at a time. An alternative is to use a Q-tip dipped in olive oil. Very carefully blot the oil high up against the walls of the nostrils. It may also be helpful to combine the cinnamon and oil methods.

Adenoids

The adenoid glands are part of the body's first line of defense. They constantly expel a secretion to combat foreign elements that are breathed in through the nose, the natural inhaling channel. When the secretion becomes excessive, breathing is obstructed. The surplus secretion is removed by the adenoid treatment.

Adenoid trouble gives the nose a flattened, puffed up appearance. Though adenoid trouble occurs most frequently in children, this treatment can help anyone to breathe more easily.

Adenoids are treated by pressure applied in two spots, one on each side of the nose, midway between the bridge and the tip. These spots are detectable as depressions and feel spongier than the surrounding tissue. They are usually found on the bony part of the nose but occasionally on the cartilaginous part.

Position

Patient is seated. Creative Healer stands beside the patient.

Thumb and finger position

➧ **Step 1: Hand placement.** To treat the left adenoid spot, stand to the right side of the seated patient. Hold the head against your chest with your left hand. To position the fingers of the right hand, rest the last joint of the index finger against the thumb and rest the thumb on the bridge of the patient's nose. This position of the thumb acts as a depth gauge, preventing the finger from sliding too far toward the patient's face. Take care not to place the finger too high to prevent pinching facial tissues of the tear ducts of the eye.

Area of adenoids

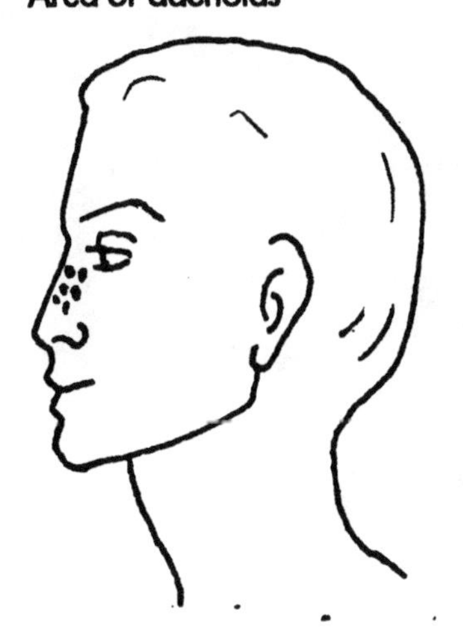

➧ **Step 2: Pressure application.** With the tip of the right index finger exert a firm pressure on the adenoid spot only once. There will be a visible depression where the pressure is applied. Hold the pressure for a few moments and remove your finger slowly.

➧ **Step 3: Treat the right side.** To treat the right side, reverse right and left in the preceding description.

Frequency

Treat once a week for 6 or 7 weeks or until breathing is no longer obstructed and appearance is normal.

From the writings of Joseph B. Stephenson

On duty as usual, but felt I wanted to rest a little, so walked into my office, looked around, and there was a mother sitting on the davenport with a baby like a skeleton. I asked the mother what was wrong with her, and here is what she told me.

"I have just come from the hospital. My child was born six weeks ago. She weighed eight and one-half pounds. She is now only six and a half pounds. All of the medical doctors in the hospital have examined her and they cannot find anything. As soon as she tries to take milk from the bottle she strangles and goes into spasms."

By this time I had seen the cause of all the trouble, so I said to her, "Give me your baby. You may hear her cry, but I won't hurt her." I took the baby into my treating room, pinched her nose, squeezed the surplus secretion out of her adenoids, then brought her back to her mother.

I asked my secretary if we had a baby bottle in the house and to go and make it up for the baby. She brought it up, and I handed it to the mother.

I said, "Give that to your baby—try her."

The little thing grabbed the nipple and drank it down, not stopping until the bottle was half empty. The mother sat there, the tears streaming down her cheeks.

"Now take her home and when she cries give her more milk until she is filled up. She has been starving."

In a month that child gained all its weight back.

Three months later as I was coming out of the bank I met a doctor. He stopped me and said, "Stephenson, what did you do to that child we sent over to you?"

"Oh, I just pinched its nose to clear its breathing channel."

He said, "Well, I'll be damned."

"Try to eat with a clothespin on your nose or drink out of a bottle and you will understand why that child could not take milk out of a bottle."

Foul Breath, Chronic Indigestion, and Sick Stomach Due to Post-Nasal Drip from Brain

With advancing age, people often develop a post-nasal mucous drip. Mr. Stephenson said that this does not come from the head sinuses but from the brain and is caused by the weakening or deterioration of the gelatinous substance that keeps the brain firm. If a person lives long enough, this weakening or deterioration, together with the ensuing drip, will inevitably develop, according to Mr. Stephenson.

While mucous from the head sinuses can be handled by the digestive system, this discharge from the brain cannot. It is indigestible. It coats the walls of the stomach and small intestine and interferes with proper digestion. Food becomes embedded in it and for want of being digested, putrefies. The symptoms are chronic indigestion, a sick stomach and foul breath.

Older persons are cautioned never to swallow this mucous when it drips down during their waking hours. It must be drawn down from the nasal passage, coughed forward and spit out. The detrimental effect of the drip during sleep still remains and there is no way of preventing it. However, *Eno* fruit salts taken as described below will gradually loosen the coatings in the stomach and intestines.

To 1/2 glass of lukewarm water, add 1/4 teaspoon of *Eno*. Drink it either while it still fizzes or when the fizzing is completed. Drink the mixture in the morning 1/2 hour before eating anything; continue each morning for 2 or 3 weeks, stop for 2 weeks, and repeat if necessary. The effect is nullified if greater amounts are taken in an attempt to accelerate its action. In this weak solution, the coatings crumble away. An indication that this is taking place is an accentuated foul odor of the stools, which becomes noticeable in a few days.

In a case of heavy coating, after the patient has taken the *Eno* for a while and it has had its crumbling effect on the walls of the stomach, induced vomiting would bring up the loosened material. Vomiting may be induced at a spot about 1 inch or more below the feeding spot for the spleen; see page 5–13. Reach into the soft tissue with the first two fingers and gently push up. Mr. Stephenson felt that such accumulations from the brain could lead to a certain kind of cancer of the stomach and even to death.

Ear Treatments

Hearing and Antrums

Unless the eardrums have been tampered with and injured with a sharp or irritating instrument, they seldom cause deafness.

When hearing loss begins to occur it is sometimes caused by the closing or collapsing of the channels that carry air to the ear. Two interior channels supply air to the ear. The lower channel is the eustachian tube from the tonsil region; the upper channel begins just above the eyeteeth, on the outside of the nostril and passes below the cheekbones to the front of the ears. Congestion in either of these channels may be brought on by swimming, diving, extremely loud noises, excitement, or after high fever. To restore this type of hearing loss, the channels must be cleared to allow the passage of air to the ears.

Near the end of the roots of the eye teeth are depressions under the skin known as antrums (antrum means cavity), one on each side of the face, next to the base of the nose. These antrums spots play a double role: they promote drainage from the maxillary sinus and supply air to the ear. To relieve congestion of the sinus openings in the upper jawbone area and restore reduced hearing, do the following.

Position

Patient is seated. Creative Healer stands behind.

➧ **Step 1: General treatment, page 1–8.** As you give the general treatment, pay particular attention to the area behind the ears.

➧ **Step 2:** Ask the patient to remove any upper denture and to breathe through the mouth, keeping the mouth open during the treatment. This is important to the success of the treatment; your little fingers are in a perfect position to check the mouth from time to time to be sure it is open.

Antrum spots

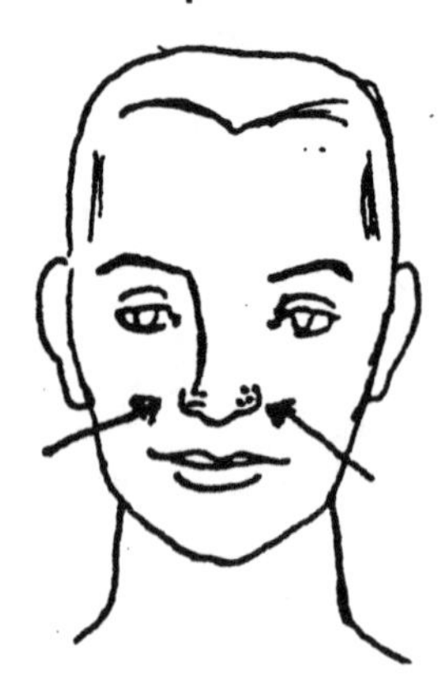

➧ **Step 3: Clear the antrums.** Stand behind the patient and rest the head against your chest. If need be, lean forward so that the patient's head remains vertical; don't make the patient tilt backward. Place the tips of your oiled index fingers on the antrum spots. With a circular motion, imagine you are gathering substance and at the end of each circle press it lightly inward toward the back of the head. (Example: the action is similar to that of feeding putty into a hole in a board.) This gentle massage opens a passage so that air can enter the sinuses and promote their natural drainage. **Repeat this movement 6 to 8 times.**

Create a vacuum

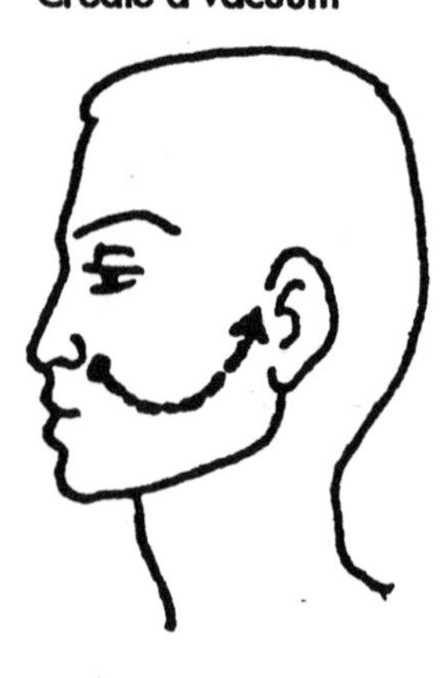

➧ **Step 4: Create a vacuum from antrums to ears.** Place the middle finger of each hand on both antrum spots. From there, gently draw the full length of the fingers along the deepest natural channel beneath the contour of the cheek bones up to a hollow in front of the ears. Visualize this movement creating a delicate vacuum on the tube along this path. This vacuum clears the tube for supplying air to the ear. The vacuum will also draw out mucous discharged into the back of the throat (pharynx). Keep the length of the fingers on the face until the movement ends; do not use just the tips of the fingers. **Repeat this vacuum movement 6 to 8 times.** If the tissues close to the ear have become congested, use a gentle massage with the fingertips in front, below and around the back of the ear to soften these tissues. If the lower passage is also congested, place your hands in the same position as for the draining movement for tonsillitis, page 2–12. The fingers create a vacuum and channel for air, from under the lower jaw to the front of the ear. When both upper and lower air channels to the ears are open, and air can pass through to the ears, proceed to the next step.

Final position before moving the hands straight out

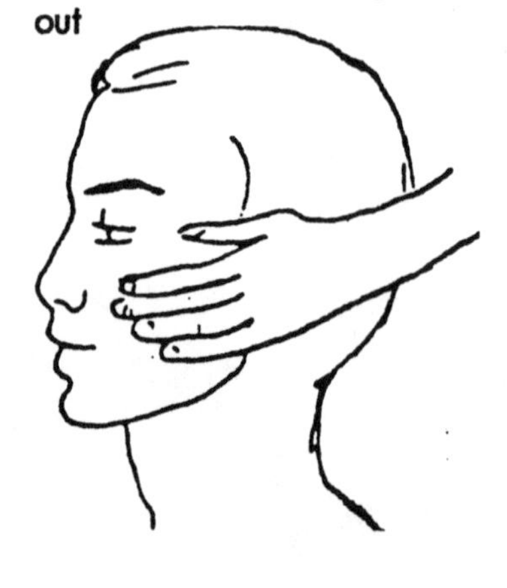

➧ **Step 5: Clear the ears, vacuum treatment.** This part of the treatment is intended to equalize air pressure on both sides of the eardrum. If the vacuum does not develop, or the person feels pain, stop the treatment because the eardrum has become porous and air is being drawn through it. The patient must breathe through the mouth during this treatment and the hair must be cleared away from the ears so that it does not break the vacuum.

Place well-oiled palms, fingers pointing forward, a little below the center of the patient's ears. Rotate palms firmly upward until they are centered over the ear openings and press slightly to create a seal. Fingers are now pointing slightly downward. Pull the palms off the ears quickly, at right angles to the ears and away from the head; this movement makes a pursed lips kiss sound. Begin gently at first, increasing the intensity of the movement as it is **repeated 6 or 8 times.**

Release of pressure by the oiled palms creates a vacuum on the outside of the eardrum. The suction created when the pressure is released draws air through the antrums described in step 3 and allows the eardrum to assume its natural shape.

Frequency

Repeat once a week until the condition is eliminated. This treatment may be self administered.

Self-administered vacuum treatment

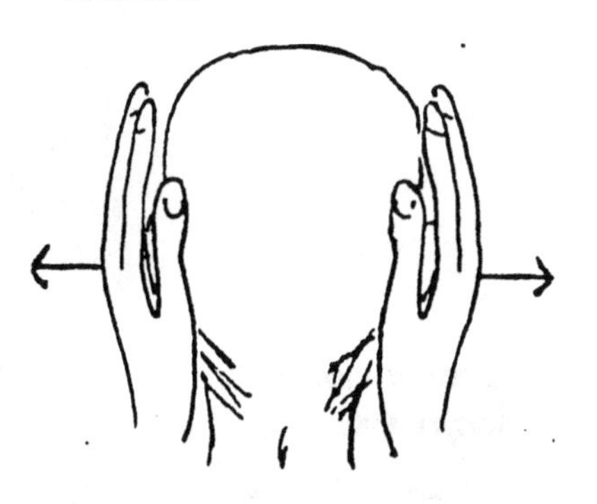

Other Uses

Steps 3 to 5 may be administered very gently on infants and children to relieve stuffy noses and open mouth breathing.

The vacuum treatment in step 5 is also helpful for dizziness, loss of equilibrium, and ears that don't "pop open" on an airplane ride.

Example from a Creative Healer

A person with a sinus problem was treated by a drug that eliminated her sense of smell. The hearing and antrums treatment cleared the maxillary sinus and restored her sense of smell.

Earache

➧ **Step 1:** Perform the drainage part of the tonsil treatment, page 2–12. If taut cord is found, do the drainage treatment until gone.

➧ **Step 2:** Do the sinus and hay fever treatment, page 2–2.

➧ **Step 3:** Complete with the hearing and antrums treatment, page 2–7.

Other Ear Problems

Hearing Loss Caused by Wax Buildup

The eardrum is kept flexible and non-porous by ear wax secreted within the ear. If this secretion slows down or becomes too firm, the eardrum loses its flexibility and hearing deteriorates. One drop of warmed olive oil inserted at the edge of the cavity once a week will often help this condition; the oil will creep in on its own. More than one drop may dissolve too much wax; this could allow the eardrum to become porous, allowing cold air to enter the ear and cause pain.

Fungus Growth in Ear

A drop of olive oil may help to cleanse the ear from certain fungus growths.

Ear Problems on Airplanes

Problem may be relieved by vacuuming the ears for relief. (See hearing and antrums treatment, step 5, page 2–7.) This has been used successfully on small children.

Labyrinthitis

Labyrinthitis is an inflammation of the inner ear where the balance of the body is maintained. It causes dizziness, sometimes nausea, and loss of balance.

These are the steps to take to relieve the condition:

➧ **Step 1:** Open the back of the neck with the general treatment, page 1–8.

➧ **Step 2:** Reposition the cartilage in the cervicals of the neck as in headache treatment, page 2–39.

➧ **Step 3:** Open the triangular areas at the base of the skull with a gentle, circular breaking up treatment with the index finger. See triangular area treatment, page 2–31.

➧ **Step 4:** Drain as in the treatment for tonsillitis, page 2–12, especially firm around the jaw bone.

Circular motions for labyrinthitis

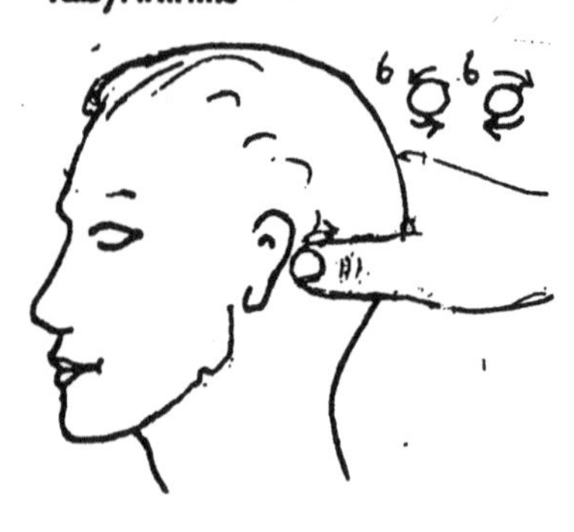

➧ **Step 5:** Stretch the hand and place the thumb on one side of the head, the middle finger on the other side at the depressed area on the mastoid bone behind each ear to administer the treatment on both sides simultaneously. As in the withdrawal treatment for the eyes, create a vacuum with 6 withdrawing circles then in direct reversal, perform 6 feeding circles as in feeding the eyes. Repeat, alternating these circular motions for withdrawing and feeding as long as needed, perhaps as much as 15 minutes. The circular motions are light and gentle so as not to collapse the vessels and stop the flow.

➧ **Step 6:** Press firmly as you roll the fingers along the scalp on each side of the temple (in the hair line) in front as in the neuralgia treatment, page 2–35.

➧ **Step 7:** Do step 2 of the hearing and antrums treatment, page 2–7, to create a vacuum from antrums to ears.

➧ **Step 8:** Do the breaking up massage behind the ears.

Many conditions, deep inside the cranium, which seem inaccessible, may be reached by alternating the withdrawing and feeding treatment as described in Step 5.

Mastoid Trouble

The mastoid is a portion of the temporal bone located behind the ear. Inflammation of the mastoid can be critical and cause great suffering. The area may be so hot, inflamed, and painful that it cannot be touched directly. Even a close approach to it may make the person recoil. Yet, the most critical mastoid conditions become manageable if treated as follows:

➧ **Step 1: Apply a cooling treatment.** Without touching, stroke from the head down over the neck and shoulder one hand following the other, to draw out the inflammation and pull heat off the body.

➧ **Step 2: Administer the general treatment.** When heat subsides, gently and with much oil on the hands, start from the outside edge of the shoulder filter area and clear the entire filters. With the same gentleness, open up the back of the neck. See page 1–8 for the general treatment.

➧ **Step 3: Base of skull.** Make circular breaking-up movements along the base of the skull.

➧ **Step 4: Create a vacuum.** Create a vacuum at the mastoid foramen (the upper portion of the bone behind the ear that has lace-like openings inside) on both sides at once using the soft pads of the finger and thumb. The contact used must be very delicate so as not to stop the withdrawing action. This vacuum is like the withdrawing treatment for the eyes. Applied to the mastoid foramen, which develops a little differently in each person—some have a groove in the bone, it decongests and drains from deep within the mastoid. Use a tiny, local circular motion to apply the vacuum action on the downward and backward stroke (clockwise over the right mastoid foramen and counterclockwise over the left). The crisis should be over in one treatment.

Duration

After 20 or 25 minutes of treatment, the area should be at normal temperature, and nature can complete the healing. Hot and cold devices must be avoided.

Frequency

The Creative Healer may need to see the patient every day to confirm that the restoration remains stable.

Throat Treatments

About the Throat

In treating the throat, the Adam's apple is the line of demarcation—for treating above the Adam's apple stroking is directed upward, and for below the Adam's apple it is directed downward. The reason for upward stroking is because in tonsillitis and quinsy, congestive material is mostly trapped in folds or pouches that form the natural partitions of the throat, which do not drain by themselves but need help to direct their drainage up into the throat. Mr. Stephenson said that if, contrary to its actual form, the human body were so formed that the chin pointed straight up, these folds and pouches would drain by gravity. The drainage is thus directed to spill into the throat by the upward stroking and from there it is either expelled or channeled into the stomach by way of the esophagus.

The primary reason for the downward stroking in the laryngitis treatment is to use a vacuum to get the natural secretions to "wet" the dry spots of the mucous membrane of the larynx and the vocal chords.

Tonsillitis

Mr. Stephenson taught that a germ cannot grow in the normal temperature of the human body. The treatments for the throat easily demonstrate the truth of this statement. When the throat is brought to normal temperature, self healing begins and is evident to the patient almost immediately.

There are three types of sore throat, recognized by where the heat and pain are located, and each is treated in a different way. Two Creative Healing principles are used: bringing the body to normal temperature by removing heat, and creating a vacuum to drain unwanted material.

In tonsillitis, the fever is concentrated at hot spots high on both sides of the throat, just below the jaw. The treatment removes the heat and drains congested material out of the region in one gentle and continuous movement of the hands.

Position

Patient sits. Creative Healer stands behind.

Remove heat and drain

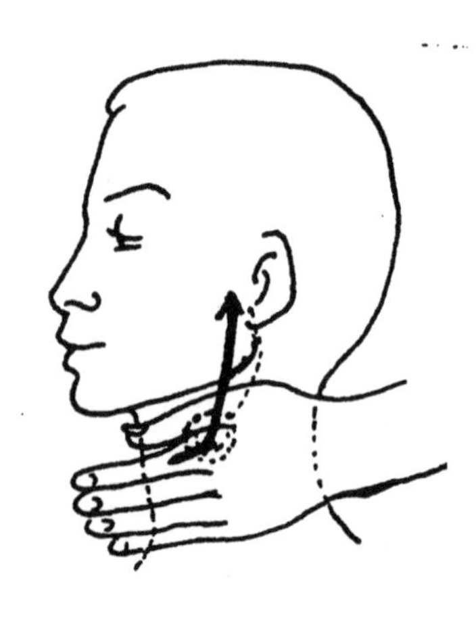

➧ **Step 1: Remove heat with palms.** Support the patient's head against your chest. Place your well-oiled palms on the hot spots with the fingers extended along and just below the jaw. Draw the palms back behind the angle of the jaw and then upward. Keep the fingers together, pointed out in front of the body, and do not cup them around the throat. As the palms follow the angle of the jaw they are lifted from the face and the fingers complete the stroke. The pressure is light for removal of heat.

➧ **Step 2: Drain with fingers.** The fingers (the middle one in particular) continue the stroke up the side of the cheek to a small hollow space in front of the ear opening. At the end of each stroke, pause briefly. The palms remove the heat while the action of the fingers creates a vacuum that drains the congestion from this region of the throat. The middle finger naturally completes the stroke. Keep the full length of the finger on the face around the angle of the jaw until the tip of the finger reaches the hollow in the front of the ear; keep the fingers pointing down.

Duration

Repeat the entire action until the hands feel that all the heat in the tonsil region is gone. This may take as few as 6 or 7 strokes or as long as 20 minutes. When the heat is gone the body heals itself.

Frequency

If heat returns the treatment should be repeated. Otherwise, 3 treatments, one every other day, is enough to be sure it will not return.

Strep Throat (Quinsy)

Strep throat symptoms include a very sore throat and difficulty swallowing. Hot spots will be found in the mid-region of the throat. Congestive material in tonsillitis and strep throat is mostly trapped in the folds and pouches that form natural partitions of the throat. The folds, by their configuration, do not drain easily when in trouble, but need help to direct their drainage to the throat.

Position

Patient sits. Creative Healer stands behind.

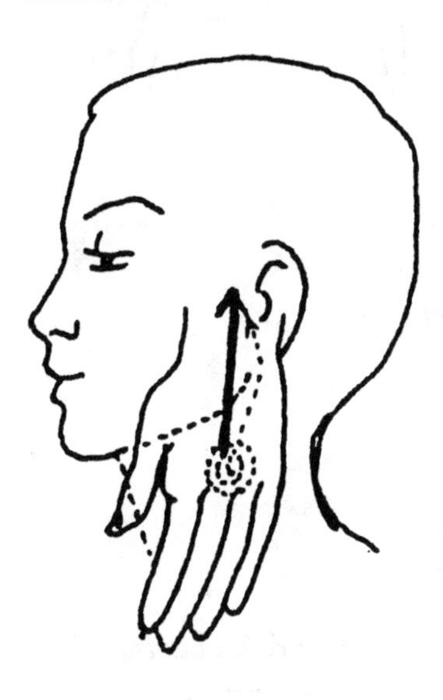

Strep throat; heat is in mid throat

Step 1: Remove heat and drain. Place your well-oiled palms on the hot spots at the mid-region of the throat. Fingers will point downward and contact will be very gentle, almost non-existent, because of the soreness. Move your hands vertically upward, to remove the heat. Continue this finger movement to the same drainage spots in front of the ears as for tonsillitis. At the top of the stroke, the fingers pause briefly before repeating the movement. The palm collects the heat and the pressure is light for removing heat. The finger movements drain and this gradual drainage prevents the formation of an abscess. When this part of the throat is again at normal temperature, stop the treatment.

Step 2: Test. After the throat has been brought to normal temperature, check to see if the patient can drink a small glass of room temperature water without discomfort. If not, let the patient rest for 20 minutes and repeat the treatment. Do not leave the patient until water can be drunk as described. If unable to drink after several repetitions of the treatment, refer the patient to a physician.

➤➤➤CAUTION: Treat every day for 4 days. Make an agreement with the patient that this schedule will be kept; sometimes patients will be so improved after the first or second treatment, they will consider themselves cured. Unfortunately, if the work is not completed, the problem returns within a week or two, stronger than before.

When the patient is free of fever but full of mucous, repeat the above treatment with more firmness on the drainage part of the treatment.

Laryngitis

In laryngitis, congestion and heat are found below the voice box. Laryngitis is usually accompanied by loss of voice because the vocal chords in the voice box (larynx) have dried out from the heat and cannot function normally.

In treating the throat, the Adam's apple is the line of demarcation. For the treatment of tonsillitis and strep throat the strokes are directed upward, but for laryngitis the stroking is downward.

Downward stroking for laryngitis creates a vacuum to start the natural secretions to "wet" the dry spots of the mucous membrane and the vocal chords.

Laryngitis

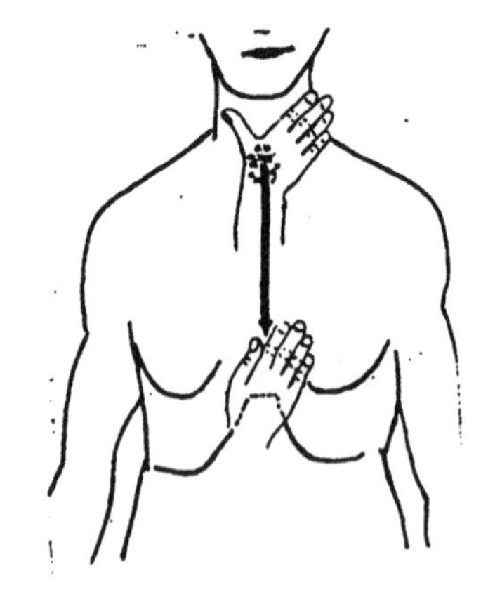

Position

Patient sits. Creative Healer sits facing and to the right of the patient.

➧ **Step 1: Positioning.** Place your left hand on the patient's back, near the base of the neck, for support. Place your well-oiled right palm on the hot area just under the Adam's apple. The thumb will be to the right and the fingers to the left of the larynx. The patient should keep the chin in a normal position to relax the tissue and should resist the temptation to raise the chin.

➧ **Step 2: Remove heat and drain.** Move your hand downward with the palm following the center line of the body. The thumb unites with the fingers just below the voice box in a gentle, flowing movement. Continue the stroke down to the change in chest curvature. The light-pressured palm removes the heat while the fingers create a vacuum for drainage, which brings the natural secretions down to wet the vocal chords and restore normal function.

Duration

The treatment is continued until all heat is removed. This may take 15 or 20 minutes because of heat in the bony structure of the chest.

Frequency

Usually, 1 treatment will be enough. If not, treat every day until the result is achieved.

Loss of Voice Without Heat or Soreness

Centering ring of cartilage

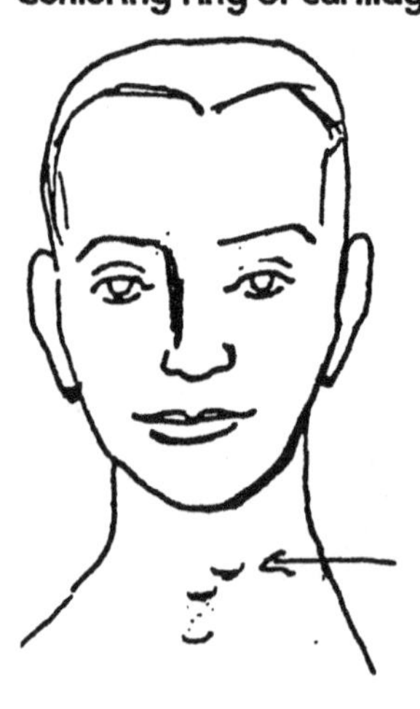

Loss of voice may be caused by shouting, singing or straining the voice in some way. These activities can displace a ring of cartilage found above the voice box and will prevent the proper functioning of the vocal chords.

➧ **Step 1: Replace cartilage.** Between the thumb and forefinger of the right hand, clasp the ring of cartilage that is protruding to the right or left. By applying gentle pressure on the protruding side, the ring will slip back into place, sometimes making a clicking sound as it does so.

Piercing Pain when Swallowing

A patient with a sore throat may complain of pain when swallowing that begins behind the angle of the jaw and pierces through to the ear. Check around the soft part of the throat under the angle of the jaw for a string or cord-like formation in the painful area.

➧ **Step 1: Remove heat from the throat, as in tonsillitis.** See page 2–12.

➧ **Step 2: Administer the general treatment.** See page 1–8.

➧ **Step 3:** If a cord-like formation is detected when the drainage movement is performed, use the fingers in the upward rather than downward movement around the ends of the jawbone; this will create a vacuum draining upward to the hollow spot in front of the ear (as in tonsillitis, page 2–12). Apply a stronger contact over the cord as the fingers move upward to dissolve it and drain the congestion into the throat.

Scratchy Dry Throat

A scratchy, dry throat that persists while all other aspects of sore throat are healed can be caused by dry spots of mucous membrane in the throat. This is especially true if the person breathes through the mouth while sleeping. White *Karo* syrup will wet dry spots in the throat and the patient can self-administer by following these directions:

- Lie on your back within reach of a small quantity of *Karo* syrup in a saucer.
- Swallow your saliva as completely as possible so that you can refrain from swallowing as long as possible.
- Place a tiny drop of *Karo* on your tongue. By natural action, the *Karo* will spread, creep, and climb, wetting all dry spots. This will continue as long as you do not swallow.

The procedure can be repeated, if necessary, but avoid swallowing a spoonful as that will not serve the need.

Persistent, Unproductive Cough

- **Step 1: Have the patient self-administer as for scratchy, dry throat, above.**
- **Step 2:** When there is a dry throat and no fever apply the laryngitis treatment, page 2–13 with more pressure to draw out secretions.
- **Step 3:** For a persistent, unproductive cough after chest congestion is healed, apply the treatment for dislodging mucous under the breast bone as detailed in esophageal hernia, step 2, page 4–15.

Swelling on Right Side of Throat

In Mr. Stephenson's view of the body, there is a tube leading from the liver to the bladder through which the liver disposes of wastes.

When a swelling is found on the right side of the throat, above the collarbone, it may be caused by a blocked condition of this drainage tube that leads from the liver into the bladder. It will not yield to local treatment where the swelling is located, but it can prove fatal if not taken care of. The pancreas feeding movement (page 5–11) will clear this tube, and the swelling will disappear.

Clearing treatment

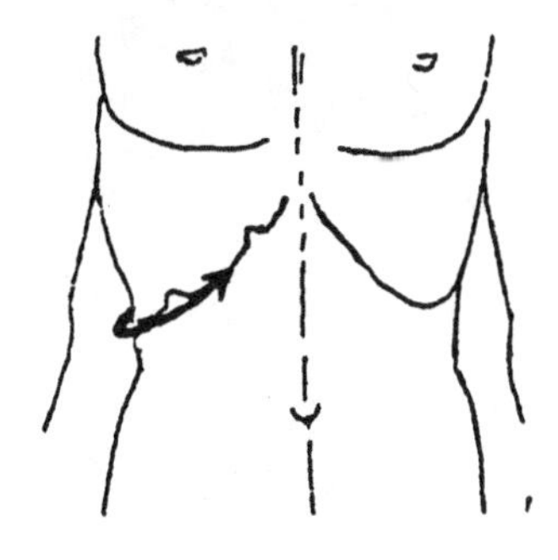

Position

Patient lies on the back. Creative Healer sits at the patient's right.

➧ **Step 1: Locate hand operation.** With the tip of the right thumb pointing toward the patient's right side, use the pad of the thumb to trace along the lower edge of the ribs from where they touch the bed to mid-way between the liver and gall bladder notches.

➧ **Step 2: Thumb movement.** Move the thumb lengthwise along this path in the flesh of the abdomen in a feeding pressure, which is a more positive pressure than a vacuum stroke, but still it is never heavy. This stroke is repeated as necessary, perhaps as much as 8 minutes.

➧ **Step 3: Give the Liver Treatment, page 5–5.**

Inward Goiter

Inward goiter trouble occurs most frequently in women. Its cause may lie in repeated chilling of the upper chest, due to open-necked clothing. The patient needs to understand that this region must be protected by keeping it at normal temperature to prevent recurrence of the trouble.

Mr. Stephenson saw three ducts, or channels, issue from the thyroid gland: two from its outer portion and one from the interior of the thyroid. His concept of this gland and its function differs from the accepted idea of the thyroid as a ductless gland.

The secretion from the interior of the thyroid is a fluid that acts as an oil to "lubricate" the heart. It is channeled toward the heart by the interior duct. Inward goiter trouble arises when this duct fails to function, and the secretion dams up and accumulates. This causes the gland to swell and the muscles behind the eyes to be fed too much secretion. These muscles, in turn, swell and displace the eyes forward. It also causes the heart to be affected, making it speed up and become irregular, because of the lack of lubrication.

The secretion from the interior of the thyroid congeals when the duct dams up, but the accumulated material will yield to the drainage treatment, enabling the gland to return to its normal size and function. Also, the surplus secretion fed to the muscles behind the eyes will respond to the withdrawing action of the eye vacuum movement. The muscles will resume their normal size returning to their natural position in the head.

The goal of the work on the front of the neck is to reopen the duct from the thyroid to the heart. This allows the accumulated secretion to be drained off and the normal flow to the heart is reestablished.

The inward goiter treatment on the front of the body may be used in other cases. For example, it is used in cases of heart murmur. It is also used for extremely nervous people who have a sense of agitation, without apparent cause.

This three-part treatment begins on the back, the second part is on the front of the body and the third part is for the eyes.

Part 1: Back of the Body

➧ **Step 1: Orientation.** The patient sits on a bench. The Creative Healer sits behind. An inward goiter patient usually is extremely nervous. The heart beats may rise so high (120 to 140 a minute) and be so irregular (because of added vibrations) that they are hard to count. The patient may have breathing and swallowing difficulties and be in a state of general anxiety.

Before starting the treatment, quietly place your hands on the patient's shoulders. This will be soothing and the patient will feel less anxious.

Place the fingers of the left hand flat and parallel to the collarbone on the front of the shoulder. You will, especially with the middle finger, feel the "wild" pulse beat. Keep the left hand in this position throughout the second and third steps of the treatment. This will allow you to keep track of the pulse beat and have a continued calming affect on the patient.

Inward goiter heart spot

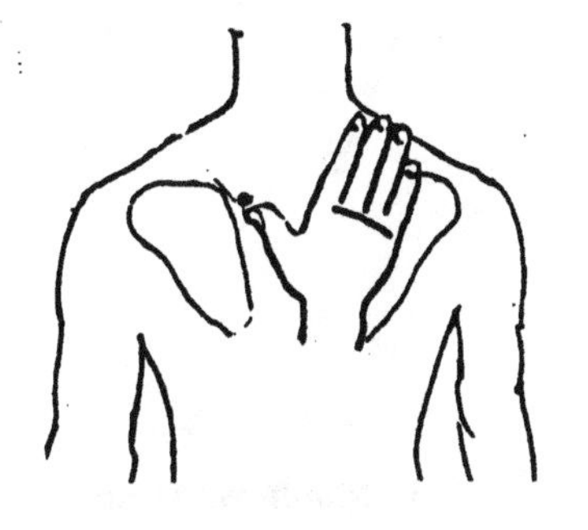

➧ **Step 2: Locate the heart and circulation spot on the back.** A very important and very delicate spot, connected with the heart, and vital for the circulation on the left side of the body, is located on the back. It is on the back near the inner side of the left shoulder blade toward the spine but slightly below the top of the blade. The first step of the treatment for inward goiter concerns this spot, called the #1 spot for inward goiter.

As you sit behind the patient, place the palm of your right hand between the spine and the left shoulder blade. The cushion of your first or second finger will locate the spot by its high temperature, congestion and sensitivity. Let the patient's reaction be your guide to the exact location of the spot.

When this spot is obstructed, scratch marks from the patient's fingernails will frequently be found just above the spot. Usually, the scratching will have been done unconsciously, in sleep. It testifies to the fact that the patient is, in some way, aware of the trouble at the spot and is making an effort to free it.

Stroking up and down to disperse substance

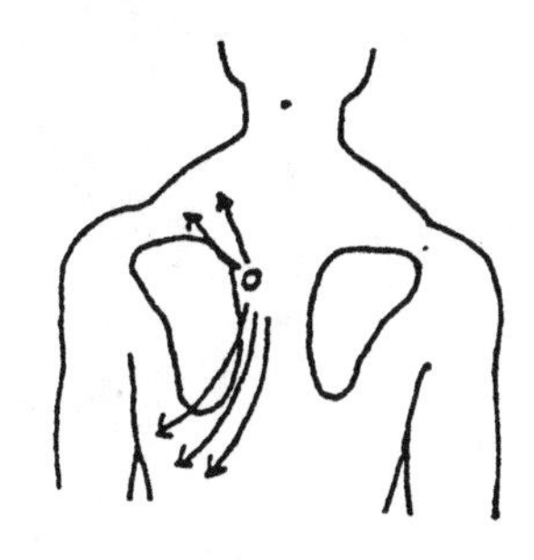

➧ **Step 3: Break up congestion.** Remove the congestion with a clockwise circular breaking up movement with the cushion of your right thumb. Dirrct it to an area no larger than the eraser on a lead pencil. Your thumb should not be too heavily oiled, but cling to the skin, taking the surface tissue with it. Continue 3 or 4 minutes or until you notice with the left hand that the heart has slowed, the nervous vibrations have disappeared and the pulse beat has returned to nearly normal. Never press on the spot as this might collapse the circulation. The spot is vital for the circulation specific to the left side of the body.

➧ **Step 4: Stroking up.** Stroke alternatively with both hands, fingers leading, from just above the spot, *being careful not to touch it again*, up over the patient's left shoulder, to distribute into the circulation that which has been broken up below. Include some counter-clockwise circular motion in the left filter area at the the base of the neck.

➧ **Step 5: Stroking down.** Then, starting just below the spot and again being careful not to touch it, stroke downward and forward beneath the shoulder blade, hands alternating, the fingers pointing toward the left side of the patient. Carry this movement around the front of the body toward the #5 heart spot.

The purpose of the up and down stroking movements following the actual breaking up treatment at the spot is to stimulate the circulation to carry off that which has been broken up. Red blotches may appear along the course of the downward stroke. Break them up individually, by the circular breaking up movement, and then finish cleaning them out by stroking over them with the thumb toward the heart.

The treatment of the #1 spot for inward goiter is always required in the case of inward goiter. It is also used in work aimed at restoring normal function to the heart, for conditions that have nothing to do with inward goiter trouble. See, for example, fast heart and erratic heartbeat pages 4–28 and 4–31.

➤➤➤ CAUTION: Never massage the spot when it is congested, except in the manner described above. When it is not congested, feel free to massage over it in any direction, but always follow the above instructions when it is obstructed. In inward goiter cases, follow the additional rule not to touch the spot again during the same treatment session.

Part 2: Front of the Body

Double vacuum with loose wrist

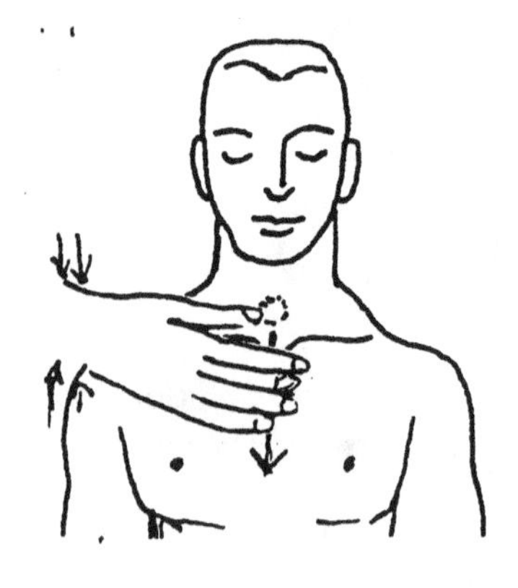

➧ **Step 6: Double vacuuming at the throat.** The fingers must be well oiled to begin the treatment, since the vacuum strokes must be performed with light pressure and rapidly, at the rate of about 200 strokes a minute and continued for 7 minutes. For men with hairy chests, use a double amount of oil.

Standing to the right of the patient, let your left hand rest on the nape of the neck.

Extend the first and third fingers of the right hand supported by the middle finger, which lies in lengthwise contact behind them. This spacing of the first and third fingers provides the double vacuum as downward stroking is performed with the cushions of these two fingers.

The hand is horizontal as the fingers create a double vacuum from just beneath the larynx downward along the center line of the throat to where the breast bone begins to change shape, about 4 to 5 inches. The intention of the vacuum movement is to stimulate downward drainage. The fingers may remain in contact with the skin on the upward stroke but this contact must be very light with no trace of pressure. Continue the double vacuum stroking for 7 minutes.

To perform the 7-minute vacuum with greater ease, hold your hand so that your fingers stay in position but keep your wrist loose and free so that it amplifies the motion of the forearm by providing its own motion. Performing the vacuum in this manner will be much less strenuous than doing so with a locked wrist.

➧ **Step 7: Circle #1 heart spot (see heart treatment, page 4–22).** During the 7-minute vacuum, allow your fingers to glide laterally downward into the #1 heart spot 3 or 4 times. Each time use the middle finger to make clockwise circles at the heart spot. Return immediately to the vacuum stroking. Draining off the excess secretion toward the heart explains why inward goiter patients sometimes feel a discomfort on the left side, in the region of the lower ribs, in front. If this occurs, have the patient lie down and give the vacuum stroking treatment as indicated in step 1 of the basic heart treatment, page 4–21. This will disburse the excess fluid.

Clockwise circle to the right

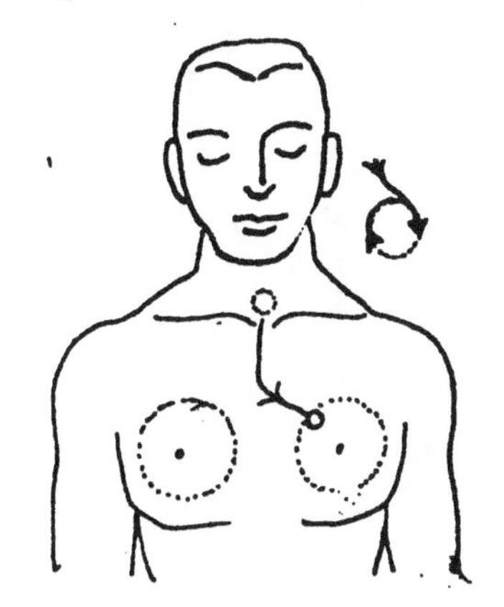

Part 3: The Eyes

➧ **Step 8: Withdrawing.** An inward goiter patient will usually have an awareness of pressure behind the eyes. The eyes may protrude, depending on the duration and severity of the trouble. Patients who have had the inward goiter removed surgically may still have protruding eyes.

To remove the pressure and return the eyes to their normal position, apply the treatment for withdrawing from the eyes, page 2–23. In cases of extreme protrusion, it may be necessary to apply this treatment for as long as 15 minutes at any session.

Frequency

The entire three-part treatment should be performed once a week for 3 or 4 weeks, in succession. By the third or fourth week, the patient will usually have come through the whole week without the heart racing. The interval between treatments should then be extended to 2 weeks and finally to 3 weeks.

In general, 7 treatments should restore normal function, except possibly for the eyes. In cases in which the eyes protrude greatly, continue the withdrawing treatment for the eyes once a month, for as long as 6 months or until the eyes are fully normal. Try to complete the rest of the treatment in 7 applications.

Outward (Pendulous) Goiter

The cause for outward and inward goiter lies in the repeated chilling of that region of the body. Again, this trouble occurs most frequently in women. The same caution to the patient applies as in other cases: keep the neck and upper chest at normal temperature.

The outer part of the thyroid gland secretes a fluid that acts as a lubricant for the lungs. This lubricating fluid is channeled toward the lungs by two ducts that issue from the outer part of the gland. If the lubricant is dammed up, it will partially solidify. Unlike the inward goiter, the secretion from the outer ducts of the thyroid gland back up and eventually harden to produce an outward goiter.

In an outward goiter, there will be swelling on one or both sides of the lower neck in the region of the larynx. These swellings occur when the ducts fail to function. The treatment opens the congested ducts and breaks up the swelling. The solids are reduced to a fluid state and drained off. The gland can then resume its normal size and function.

The ducts leading from the thyroid gland to the lungs lie in the junction of the collarbone (clavicle) and the breastbone (sternum), on each side.

Position

Patient sits. Creative Healer is to the right of the patient facing the shoulder, first standing then sitting.

➧ **Step 1: Double vacuum.** Stand to the right of the patient. Place your left hand behind the shoulder at the base of the neck for support. Use the right hand, the first and third fingers separated and backed up by the middle finger, as directed in step 6 of inward goiter, above. Begin the stroke at the base of the swelling. The double vacuum relieves the congestion in these ducts.

The position of the fingers and the hand, and the rate at which the strokes are performed, are the same as for inward goiter treatment except the strokes pass through the junction of the collarbone and breastbone, parallel to, not on the center line of the body, and the strokes are only 2 to 3 inches long. Alternate this vacuum movement with the movements described in steps 2 and 3, below; they are designed to break up and reduce to a fluid state the solid part of the swellings.

➧ **Step 2: Breaking up.** Sit at the right side of the patient. Continue to support the back of the neck and shoulder with your left hand. The aim of step 2 is to break up the remaining obstructive material. To be removed, it must be converted from a solid to a liquid state, so that it can be drained off. A circular breaking up movement around the periphery of the swollen area (especially the lower edge) will do this. Depending on the size of the goiter, use one or more fingers or the thumb. Also use the breaking up movement with the web of the thumb and fingers at the lower margin of swelling.

Work repeatedly with these movements on the outer portion of the swollen area and the swelling will diminish. The hardened portions will be reduced to the fluid state and this fluid, in turn, will be drained off by the vacuum actions of steps 1 and 3.

Double vacuuming after breaking up

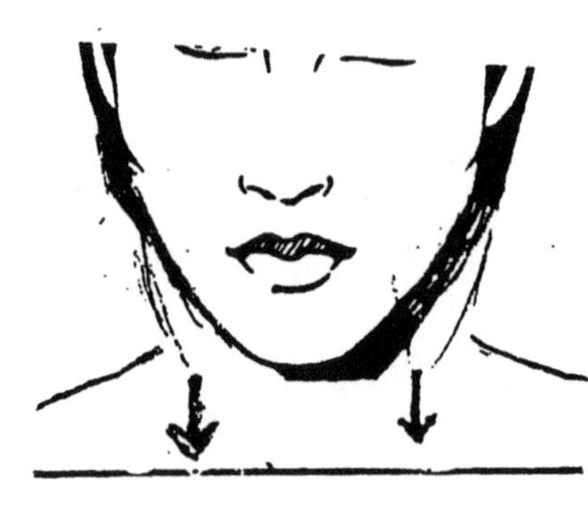

➧ **Step 3: Final vacuuming.** Continue to support the back of the patient's shoulders at the base of the neck with your left hand. Hold your right hand in the same way as in the draining movement for laryngitis, page 2–13. The movement of the hand is downward from the center of the swelling to the sides drawing the fluid material down.

Duration

Perform the 3 steps alternately, for about 15 minutes in all.

Frequency

The outward goiter treatment will make rapid progress at first, with considerable reduction in the swelling. This occurs when the congestion in the ducts leading to the lungs is removed, and the accumulated fluid drains off. After that, progress is very slow, especially in long-standing cases where there has been much hardening. If the lungs are long deprived of their lubricant, they may become caked and hardened.

The breaking up of the solid part of the swelling is a laborious and tedious task. It is discouraging to both the patient and Creative Healer. After the first reduction, Mr. Stephenson often advised his patients to have what remained of the swelling removed surgically.

Eye Treatments

Enhancing Distance Vision

Mr. Stephenson believed that every part of the body that has not been properly nourished will show weakness. When the eyes begin to dim prematurely and one is not able to see clearly at a distance, sufficient blood is not being delivered to keep the eyes in their natural state. Lack of circulation to the eyes may be the beginning of a cataract condition. If the eyes are properly nourished, they will be strengthened and return to normal.

We can nourish our own eyes or someone else's through two oval shaped grooves on the back of the head. These feeding spots are crossed with the eyes, the right side feeding the left eye and the left feeding the right. The treatment is a powerful one and should never be done more than 15 minutes in one week; 2 minutes a day is sufficient if you are doing the treatment for yourself. The results will begin to be apparent within a month.

Before feeding or withdrawing from the eyes, give the General Treatment, page 1–8.

Position

The patient sits. The Creative Healer stands.

➧ **Step 1: Locate spots.** Support the patient's head with one hand on the forehead. Place the thumb and middle finger of the other hand in the grooves, which are easily detected as depressions at the back of the head. Locate by drawing a line from the corner of the eye to just below the tip of the ear lobe to the depressions that are about an inch from the ear. Even if badly obstructed, the spots may still be recognized because they feel spongier than the surrounding tissues.

If you are giving your own treatment, place a thumb in each groove and let your fingers and palm surround your head for support, leaving the thumbs free to move.

Step 2: Nourish (feed) the eyes. Perform a circular massage upward and toward the eyes. Move your hand forward toward the eyes and upward. The pressure may be quite firm on the forward and upward movement as the tissue moves along with the fingers. The movement is continuous as a slow, rhythmic, circular motion, without pressure on the downward side of the circle.

The thumbs are able to do this same circular motion quite easily if you wish to enhance your own vision.

Enhancing distant vision

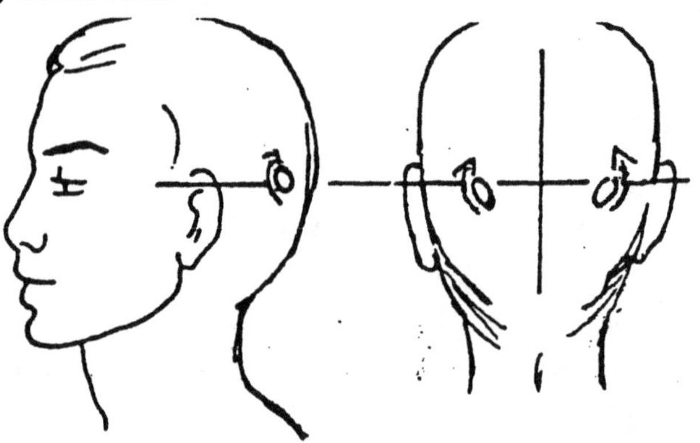

Duration

Never feed the eyes more than 15 minutes a week. This may be done once weekly or twice a week for 7 1/2 minutes each.

Frequency

Perform this treatment at the duration above until desired results are reached.

In addition this treatment may also be used for cataract, astigmatism, double vision (hold pressure for a few seconds firmly on the feeding spots periodically), and detached retina.

From the writings of Joseph B. Stephenson

Eyesight Regained

I was called to supper. When I got down into the waiting room there was a man who seemed to be very uneasy.

He said, "I am next. How long will I have to wait?"

"I will be fifteen minutes."

When I returned I called him upstairs and asked his trouble. He said he was losing his eyesight. He had been to lots of specialists but they could give him no hope.

"But," he said, "maybe I am in the wrong place. Do you heal by faith?"

I said, "No, only by common sense. Take your collar and tie off and I will soon tell you yes or no."

I started to treat him and after I had been treating him about five minutes he began to get nervous.

I said, "What is the matter with you?"

"Why," he said, "I can see those houses across the street."

"Well, didn't you come to get your eyesight helped?"

"Yes, but I never thought it would come that soon."

I was through in fifteen minutes and he took two one-dollar bills out of his pocketbook to pay me.

"My God," he said, "I haven't seen the one on a dollar bill for two years."

He gave me the money, put his tie and collar in his pocket, then made it for the stairs without his glasses. I let him get halfway downstairs when I told him he better come back and get his glasses. He did. But I said, "You will not be able to wear them; they will make you dizzy."

He tried them on, said "My God" and started home.

Cataracts: Raw Milk Compresses

Mr. Stephenson found that many kinds of eye trouble are helped by placing pads soaked in raw milk, at room temperature, on the closed lids for 15 minutes, several times a day, while the person is reclining. Cataracts respond very well to raw milk compresses.

Mr. Stephenson describes a cataract as a compensatory mechanism that acts to protect the delicate sensitivity of the eye from too much or too strong light. Such a cataract condition is always caused by the eyes having been deprived of their natural nourishment. To correct this deficiency, the eyes should be fed by the distance vision enhancing treatment, step 2, page 2–22, and the application of raw milk compresses.

The feeding treatment (enhancing vision) is done 15 minutes a week or 7 1/2 minutes twice a week.

Inflamed or Bulging Eyes

(Withdrawing Treatment)

Feeding the eyes is never done for inflamed eyes or when the eyelids are red or granulated with a feeling like there might be sand in the eyes. When eyes bulge as in a goiter condition, feeding is not the solution. In these cases it is important to give the general treatment as a preliminary to the withdrawing treatment.

The withdrawing treatment is given when one or both eyes are severely congested to withdraw congestion or stagnant circulatory fluid from the eyes, to relieve pressure or for simple eye strain. Congestion is indicated when the eyes are bloodshot and sore to the touch or when they cannot tolerate normally bright light. This treatment is effective for glaucoma and for protruding eyes associated with thyroid disease.

➧ **Step 1: Give the general treatment, page 1–8.**

➧ **Step 2: Locate the spots.** In an adult the spots are 1/2 inch below the depressions for feeding the eyes (see step 1 in enhancing vision treatment, page 2–21).

Eyes, withdrawing treatment

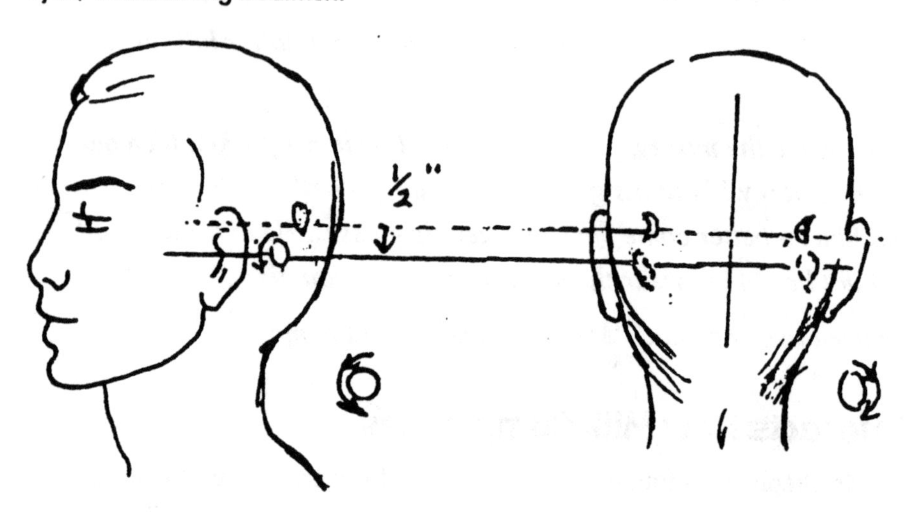

➧ **Step 3: Withdraw congestion.** With the thumb on one side and the middle finger on the other side of the head, locate the spots and circle with the whole hand downward and backward away from the eyes. With this repeated motion you are creating a vacuum through which the congestion may be encouraged to drain. The withdrawing vacuum movement is much lighter than the feeding pressure and more rapid. During a 10- to 15-minute treatment, reorient yourself in relation to the feeding spots because it is easy to move off them. The withdrawing spots are not crossed with the eyes as are the feeding spots so that work on the right spot withdraws from the right eye and work on the left spot withdraws from the left eye.

Duration

The treatment may take 10 or 15 minutes when one or both eyes are severely congested.

Frequency

Treat as needed until desired results are reached.

If eyes are overfed and become bloodshot the withdrawing treatment is used immediately. This is the only time you would withdraw and feed in the same treatment.

Note: After glaucoma pressure is gone, if vision is not good, do the feeding treatment.

Any vision distortion is helped by the rolling motion on the scalp above the ears (at side of head) using the finger pads. (See neuralgia treatment, page 2–35.)

From the writings of Joseph B. Stephenson

An Eye Specialist from Somerset

I called "next" and a man and woman came upstairs. I could tell that it was the lady who needed my help, and I could see that the man was a doctor of some kind. I took them into the room, and the man said, "Stephenson, I am an eye specialist, and my wife has something wrong with her eyes that I don't understand. A Dr. Smith from Alto Hospital was up visiting us last week and advised me to bring my wife down to see you. He'd said, 'that man knows everything' so if you can do anything for my wife, I will be very grateful."

I said I would look at her eyes. The tears were dripping all the time and around the eye was all red and swollen caused by continuous wiping. After I looked them over for a few seconds, I said, "Yes, I can heal your wife's eyes, but you will have to answer a few questions. Did you take a long trip sometime and were her eyes sore before you took that trip? I believe you went to Japan."

"Why yes, but how did you know that?"

"Because this eye trouble can come only from Japan, and you must have brought the very thing back with you that started this trouble. You did bring a plant that gives off an aroma and has a beautiful flower with it."

Then he stopped me and said, "Stephenson, this is uncanny. You seem to know everything."

"Yes, it's this plant that keeps her eyes agitated, so take it out of the house. I will give her a treatment to take the inflammation out; then as soon as you get home carry the plant out, burn some rags in the house before you let her go in and you will find that in a day or two she will start to feel better. Bring her next week; she needs another treatment."

So they came in a week and her eyes were 85% better. He again questioned me how I knew he had been in Japan. I told him that the only country where that plant grows was Japan, so that was easy.

"Have you had eyes with the same thing before?"

I said, "Doctor, there is only one disease I have not had before and I have not had one yet, and that is leprosy. Outside of that there is nothing I haven't seen before."

"Do I have to bring her for more treatments?"

I said, "No."

But in about three weeks they came back again and she was just as bad as ever.

Then I turned to him and gave him a bawling out for doing such a dirty trick on his wife. Then he confessed he brought the plant into the house again to test my theory. After he did and he was satisfied that I knew my business he put out and destroyed it then buried it once and for all. I gave her another treatment.

"Stephenson, you will have our deepest gratitude for life. I do love my dear wife."

Strained or Tired Eyes

To refresh strained and tired eyes, perform the following treatment.

Position

Patient sits. Creative Healer stands at patient's right side.

➧ **Step 1:** Place your left hand on the back of patient's head. Place the thumb and middle finger of the right hand behind and below the outer corners of the eyes within the soft part of the temple.

➧ **Step 2:** Perform a circular massage, moving the tissue upward and forward, continuing to a point just above the outer end of the eyebrow. Relax the contact, return to the initial position and repeat. Do this for 3 to 5 minutes. The whole massage is carried out very gently, within the soft part of the temple.

Instead of rubbing tired eyes, teach yourself this treatment: Locate the small grooves at the outward corners of the eyes in the soft area. Place a forefinger on each groove and gently massage toward the eye and upward. This will stimulate the secretion to the eyes and they will feel as if they have been bathed.

It is quite possible to administer all the treatments for the ears and eyes to oneself.

Blocked Tear Duct

Blocked tear duct: use tip of little finger

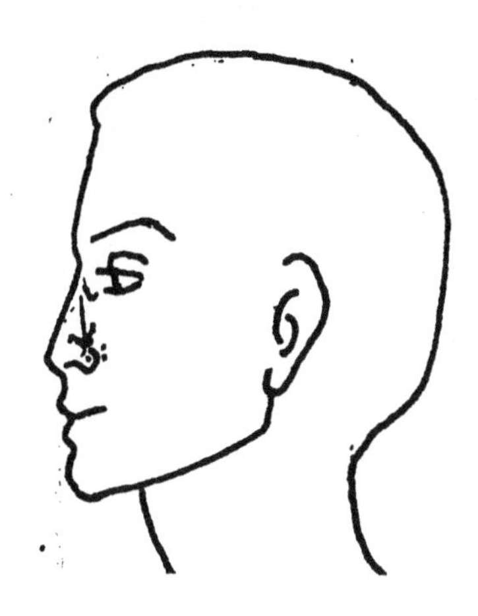

When the tear duct is obstructed, drainage may be restored by creating a vacuum with the tip of the little finger. Begin as high up under the "eaves" of the nasal bone as possible and draw the little finger straight downward toward the antrum spots mentioned in hearing and antrums treatment, page 2–7. (They are located on each side of the face, next to the base of the nose, near the roots of the eye teeth).

The vacuum strokes may cause considerable discomfort, feeling as though a razor blade or a piece of glass is in the channel over which the strokes are passing; sometimes liquid will flow from the eyes, like tears. Continue the vacuum massage for 3 to 4 minutes. At the end, all discomfort will have disappeared and the tear duct will open.

Twitching Eyelid

A twitching eyelid is a disturbance that usually occurs only in one eye and is involuntary. Such an uncontrollable movement is caused by the displacement of one or two fine nerves that lie in bony notches where the eyelids meet at the inner or outer edge of the eye.

With the tip of the index or little finger reposition the nerve in its notch with delicate up and down movements. Repeat the movements so that the nerve is centered by being brought to lie on the extension of an imaginary line drawn through the junctures of the eyelids.

If the twitching lid draws to the outside, work at the junction of the eyelids at the outer edge of the eye. If the twitching is toward the inside, work at the inner meeting of the lids. Here, the little finger will be the appropriate tool. If the twitching is more general, center both nerves.

In some cases, the twitching eyelid is felt by the person but little or no movement is perceptible to the observer. To treat this condition use the edge of the last joint of the forefinger to scrape upward and then outward along the lower edge of the frontal bone from the bridge of the nose to the notch referred to in the treatment for upper sinus, page 2–2. Here, hold for several moments with a firm pressure and then release gradually. The object of this treatment is to carry dislocated nerves back into position.

Involuntary Blinking

Involuntary blinking is a contraction of the eyelids that may be accompanied by nodding and thrusting with the head and chin. It occurs mostly with boys, usually in their teens, sometimes in their twenties. The head and chin motions are the body's attempt to release the contraction in an area located on the back.

The critical area lies from the inner edge of the left shoulder blade (scapula) to the spine. The area extends from an imaginary horizontal line even with the top of the scapula to an inch or more below that line. This space is located approximately two vertebrae above the spot for pain between the shoulders.

➧ **Step 1: Quarter twist.** Perform the quarter twist (see page 3–3) between the vertebrae in the described area on the left side. Work firmly with the thumb in short downward strokes. Make some strokes inward toward the front of the body.

➧ **Step 2: Soften tight muscles.** Use breaking up movements to the muscles in the area interspersed with the replacing of substance between the vertebrae with the quarter twist.

➧ **Step 3: Increase circulation.** Stroke down over the back, one hand following the other to bring circulation into the area.

Diligent work here will eliminate the annoying affliction.

Sty

A sty is caused by a maggot-like organism, according to Mr. Stephenson. Touch a gold ring that is at room temperature to the sty, gently passing it over the area. The coolness of the metal reduces the temperature so that the organism either dies or goes to sleep.

Repeated occurrence of a sty points to the necessity of attending to the hygiene of the eyes. For example, do not rub the eyes with the hands or any other object that could be contaminating, especially when eyes are teary or reddened.

From the writings of Joseph B. Stephenson

This case came before me in 1923 in Johnstown, Pennsylvania before I made this town my home. I was going to Johnstown to treat a few people three nights a week, then on Saturday about five hours. If I missed the last train home, I used to go and stay all night with one of my patients. This Saturday night I could have caught my train but I thought I would stay in town all night. I was tired. When I got to my friend's home there was another man visiting. He had been a big man in business but had retired. I asked him why he had retired so young. He then told me this story.

"I am losing my eyesight. One eye is gone and the other is getting weaker all the time. You see, my grandfather went blind when he was 65, my father went blind when he was 62. Now I am just past 60 and I have already lost one eye and the other is going too."

"Have you seen many eye doctors?"

"Yes, at least ten or twelve of them, but all they tell me is it is in the family. Just be prepared for it. Don't worry; that will make it quicker."

By the time he had finished talking, I had made up my mind I was going to break this hereditary business. So I said to him, "Well, here is what I want to do. I want to give you ten treatments—one every Saturday night, here for ten weeks. But money must never be mentioned in this deal and I will restore your eyesight. And when I do, I will give you a written guarantee if you wish, that you will see as long as you live."

"Does that mean that I have not long to live?"

I said, "Well, if I give you 20 years will that be enough? And when you do pass on, you will pass on seeing your people around you."

"Well, what more can a man ask for. What do you want me to do?"

"Just take off your collar and tie. It is just a fifteen-minute treatment.

So I started. Now, this was my first case of this kind, yet I was positive of myself. On the third treatment he could see more out of his good eye and light was coming back into his blind eye. In ten weeks he could read without glasses.

Then one day I met him on the street and he insisted I eat a meal with him. While we sat at the table he pulled out his checkbook and said, "Stephenson, if I gave you the 1000th part of what my eyes are worth, I would not have a damn cent left. But I will write you a check to double any month's wage you have earned."

I said, "You don't know what you are saying so better just put your checkbook away and pay for this meal. I will never need the money you want to give me."

This man went into business for 16 more years, died at the age of 81 and saw until the last day of his life.

Head Treatments

Fainting During Treatment Session

1. Sudden release of nerve life. Faintness or fainting should never be an alarming situation. While working on the neck or spine, there may be a sudden release of nerve life. If the flow of nerve life had been severely blocked, a sudden release brings a momentary void or gap in the energy flow, causing faintness. This surge will continue until the dammed up flow catches up with the normal flow and equilibrium is reestablished.

The Creative Healer can often be warned of oncoming faintness by a sudden change in the feel of the patient's skin. Cold sweating may set in or the person may display a slight unsteadiness or weaving to and fro. In such a case, the patient will usually want to lie down, and may feel nauseated. Fainting can then be averted because the horizontal position enhances the flow of energy.

2. Blackout due to a displaced nerve. If a person blacks out instantly when subjected to pressure or even a light contact over regions of the shoulders and back, the cause is a nerve that is too close to the surface. This nerve is located at the center line between the vertebrae below the base of the neck, high up in the thoracic region. This is corrected by burying the nerve deep within, using the edge of the thumb, in one positive quarter twist, not by massaging.

3. Brain tumor. See explanation under CAUTION in high blood pressure Treatment, page 2–39.

Fainting Outside Treatment Sessions

If a person has a tendency toward faintness outside the treatment sessions, it is usually because of inadequate blood circulation to the head. There are various causes:

1. Most often there is an obstruction in the neck that impairs the return flow of blood to the heart, diminishing the heart's capacity to deliver sufficient blood to the head. Give the general treatment, page 1–8.
2. A dysfunction of the heart will directly affect blood flow to the head. The heart function may be impaired by faulty valves or erratic heart beat. Give appropriate heart treatment, page 4–21 to 4–33.
3. A dysfunction of the liver. Give the liver treatment, page 5–5.
4. Lack of proper nutrition. Give the digestive tuneup, page 5–14.
5. Anemia. Give the spleen feeding, page 5–13 and the five point heart treatment, page 4–21.
6. The effect of medicines. Give kidney and liver treatments, pages 5–5 , 5–42.
7. The result of sitting too long in one position. Unconsciousness may occur to restore the body to equilibrium.
8. A dysfunction of the semilunar canal of the inner ear, usually the result of obstruction in the neck or other causes such as those enumerated above rather than a problem with the inner ear canals themselves. Give the labyrinthitis treatments, page 2–10.
9. The use of a hair dryer causes too rapid evaporation of moisture and chills the neck causing pressure and headaches. The neck should be protected by a towel and in serious cases, the patient should refrain from using a hair dryer.
10. Loss of balance after walking fast. A person may complain of having to take a step backward to maintain balance when coming to a sudden halt, especially after running or walking fast. Use the thumb to bury the nerve at the center line between the vertebrae below the base of the neck.

Because the neck will play an important role in many of these cases, it is important to explore the neck and remove any obstructions. The general treatment is of great importance to every patient.

Triangular Areas at the Base of the Skull

The triangular areas extend from the center line at the base of the skull, outward toward the ears approximately 1 to 1 1/2 inches, then proceed diagonally upward to the protuberance at the center line again, and from there, return to the starting point at the base of the skull. Symptoms of problems in the triangular area are a stiff neck in the daytime and waking at night with a headache on one side of the head, and soreness where the head connects to the neck. If touched, the area will feel swollen on the headache side when compared to the opposite side.

In this area on both sides, the tendons of the muscles holding the head upright and controlling its movements enter into the skull. Long-standing tension and unrelieved stress in these muscles and tendons will prevent nourishment flow, leading to congestion beneath the tendons near their points of insertion. Even after the neck has been treated, this area can still be extremely painful.

Movement for breaking up congestion

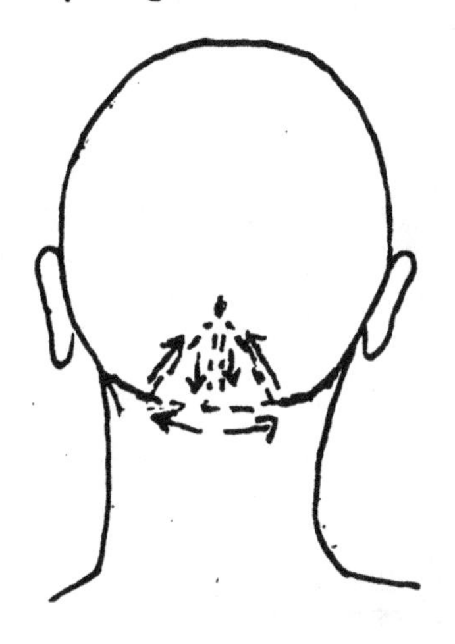

➧ **Step 1: Breaking up massage**. Perform very tiny breaking up circles with the fingertip to relieve the congestion. Start at any point on the triangle with a firm pressure and the positive thought of breaking up the congestion there. After treating a spot for 30 to 50 seconds, let it rest and treat the next one, moving slowly toward the center line, then upward to the slight protuberance, then down the side of the triangle and back to the starting place. A half hour later or at the next treatment, the spots will be much less sensitive and swelling will decrease. The area should be free of sensitivity within a few days of treatment but it may return if the head happens to assume the causative position during sleep.

Draw finger to center line

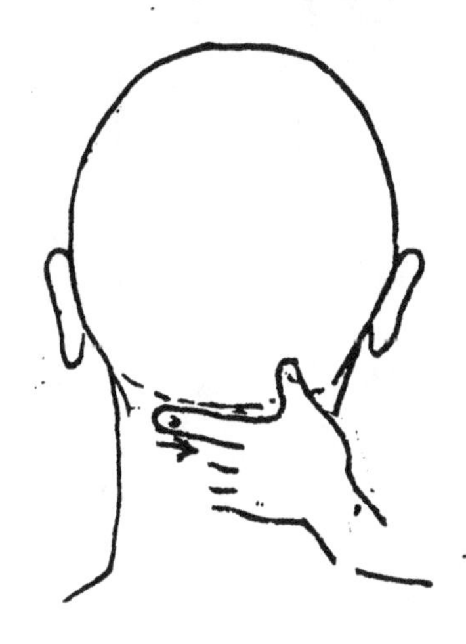

➧ **Step 2: Replace tendons.** Sometimes the congestion will have caused swelling and lateral displacement of the tendons resulting in a very stiff neck. After giving the breaking up massage to the triangular area, it will be necessary to draw the tendons from their unnatural lateral displacement to their more natural central position near the median line. Use the thumb side of the index finger to gently move the tendons toward the center line. They may escape the finger when they reach their natural position, which is the desired outcome. Usually only one side needs a treatment.

This treatment can be self-administered.

Example from Creative Healers

After sitting in a dentist's chair time after time for the capping of eight teeth and a new bridge, with my head turned to the right and up, I began to wake up in the night with this area on the right side of the back of my head so painful and swollen, I would have to get up to give myself some relief and the treatment just described. This continued long after the dental work was done and if I sleep a certain way it still happens.

When it happened to my daughter-in-law she was quite frightened by it and called to see what might be the cause and treatment. I could help her with both. She and her husband had gone on a sight-seeing train trip that required them to look up to see the sights out the window. With her head cocked to the left and drawn back for the better of several hours, her night pains were on the left side. The treatment brought relief from the pain and released her from the fear that something terrible and unknown was happening to her neck and head.

Pain Spots at the Base of the Skull

Several spots located at the base of the skull are significant to the flow of circulation and nerve life. When they are heavily obstructed and they are not cleared, serious consequences may result; for example, the clearing of these spots is vital in any stroke case.

These spots, and they are truly spots, not areas, are located on both sides of the head at the joining of the neck and the base of the skull, at the uppermost point of the vacuum for high blood pressure, close to the back of the ear.

Upon pressure, particularly combined with a slight breaking up movement these spots will register strong sensitivity or even severe pain when involved. The intensity of the reaction reveals the magnitude of the obstruction and even the extent to which the body is affected.

Breaking up circles and clearing the channels

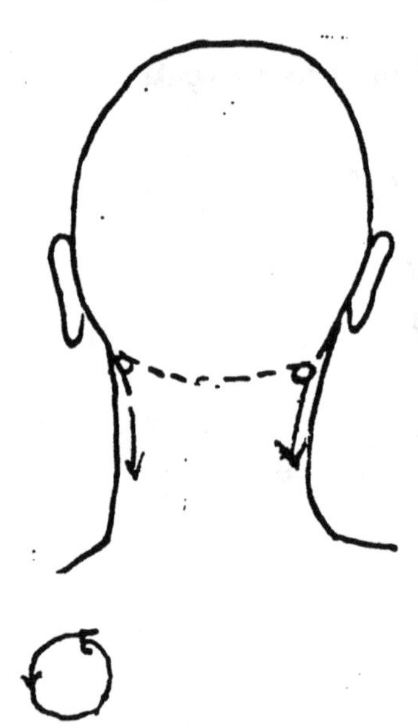

➧ **Step 1: Give the general treatment.** Clear the channels in the back of the neck with the vacuum portion of the general treatment; see page 1–8.

➧ **Step 2: Breaking up circles.** Use a breaking up circular movement. Then expand it to include a vacuum within the breaking up circle by stressing the downward part of the circle.

➧ **Step 3: Clear the channels.** Again clear the broken up material with the vacuum treatment on the channels of the neck.

If, after having once been cleared, the spots again become obstructed, repeat the treatment. Make sure by regular checking that they remain clear.

Head Problems

Head Injury

If a lump can be felt on the outside of the head, Mr. Stephenson said there would be a lump the same size on the inside of the head, pressing on the brain. This treatment is done to prevent a tumor from forming.

Use the fingertips in a very gentle breaking up movement all around the edges of the lump until gradually the lump becomes smaller and disappears. Do not go to the middle of the lump: just reduce the size by going around the edges.

If there is no lump with the head injury, work around the edges of the soreness in the same gentle manner until all the soreness is gone. This may take several sessions.

Loss of a Sense of Smell

There are many instances when a combination of treatments resolve a problem.

Example from Creative Healers

The sense of smell was lost when medicine was given to heal a sinus problem. The Creative Healing treatment for sinus was given with the Adenoid treatment. This opened the passageway and stimulated the olfactory nerve and the patient could smell again.

Mouth Ulcers and Dental Infections

For conditions of red and white ulcers in the mouth, denture soreness, general soreness, inflammation of the gums and mucous membrane of the mouth (gingivitis), red port wine used as a mouthwash is an effective healing agent.

Swish the wine around for 3 or 4 minutes and then spit it out. The wine will draw the poison from the tissues. Often this will appear in the form of curdled masses of dark material. If the tissues are too sensitive, the port wine may be diluted with water as much as 50% at first. Gradually work up to full strength. Apply the mouthwash several times a day for 3 days for complete healing.

Abscessed Tooth

Pinch gums around the tooth and "milk" around it away from the gums to help it drain. Then use red port wine as in mouth ulcers, above, to help it heal.

Dislocated Jaw

The lower jawbone is connected to the head bone through a soft cartilage hinge that may become displaced on either or both sides of the face. Such displacement may be caused by prolonged dental work, by unsymmetric chewing, or by poorly fitting dentures that do not produce the right spacing between the jaws. It may also be due to mismolding of the cartilage during sleep or by an accident, if the jaw is pressed out of position. Such a dislocation of the jaw may eventually cause hearing trouble.

This simple treatment, which can be self-administered, will reposition the cartilage and the pain will stop.

If pain or clicking sounds are felt on the left side, the cartilage will be out of place on the right, and vice versa.

Fingertips on jaw hinge

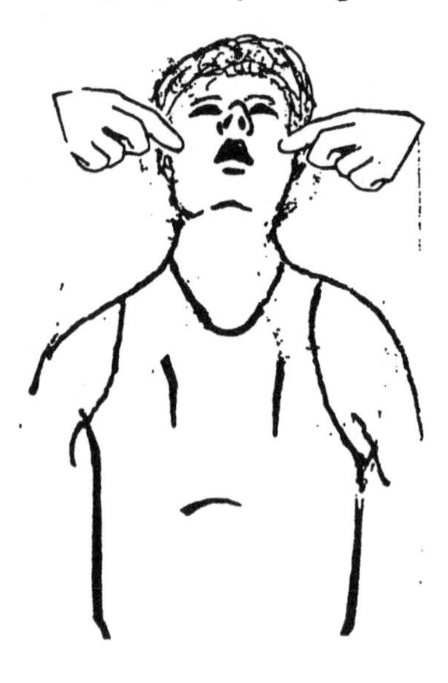

➧ **Step 1:** Stand behind the seated patient with patient's head leaning against your chest and with mouth wide open.

➧ **Step 2:** While the patients's jaw is extended and the mouth is wide open, place the tips of your index fingers on both sides at the jaw hinge points (the highest protruding cartilage).

➧ **Step 3:** Sustain a gentle increasing pressure as the patient slowly closes the jaws and draws the teeth to a clenched position. The sustained pressure becomes firm enough to center up the cartilage as the jaws close.

Lockjaw

According to Mr. Stephenson, lockjaw is the result of a "stalemate" occurring between the nerve control within the brain and the corresponding nerves that lie within the muscles of the parts affected. Mr. Stephenson suggested this lock could be broken by bending one of the patient's big toes sharply downward. The patient exclaims "Ouch!" and the jaw opens with the exclamation.

Night Sweating

Beneath two spots on the head are nerve centers of the brain, which, when agitated, press against the skull causing excessive sweating, often in the form of night sweats. When night sweating or other excessive sweating is caused by the agitated nerve centers, the following treatment will bring relief. If the sweating has other causes, such as overloaded kidneys, this treatment will yield no results but it will not interfere with any body functions. It may also not be helpful in menopausal night sweats.

➧ **Step 1: Locate depressions**. Imagine two plane surfaces, one horizontal on the top of the head and the other vertical against the back of the head. On the part of the head that lies between these two surfaces and about 4 inches apart in adults, are two detectable depressions.

Night sweating: locate depressions

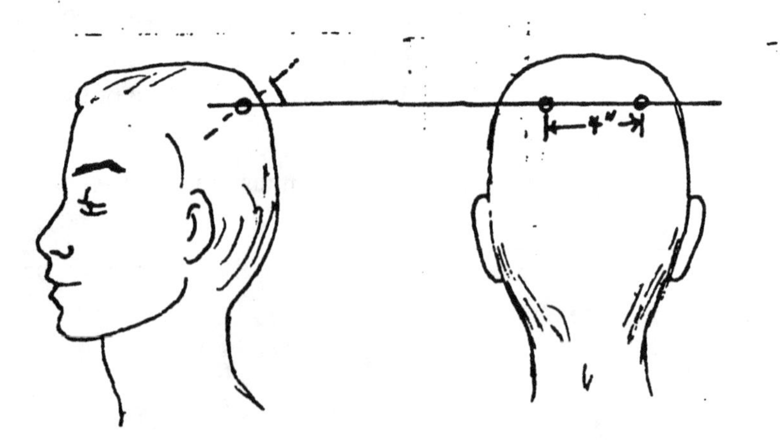

➧ **Step 2: Apply firm pressure.** To treat these nerve centers, stand to the left side of the patient, support the forehead with the left hand and exert a firm pressure on both spots at once with the thumb and middle finger of the right hand. Elbows should be slightly raised. Direct the pressure in and up keeping the thumb and finger on the spots; one time is enough.

Frequency

Repeat once a week until results are obtained. Usually one treatment will be enough. In extreme cases of continuous excessive perspiration, apply pressure once every hour until perspiration ceases.

Treatments for the other causes of night sweating could be the kidney and pancreas treatments, pages 5–42 and 5–11.

Neuralgia

Neuralgia may occur along any nerve path in the body but occurs most frequently in the head. Neuralgia is caused by obstructions along nerve paths caused when the head is chilled by a sudden and repeated loss of body heat. An overheated condition followed by a sudden cooling off, can affect circulation and cause obstructions that interfere with the flow of life along the nerve path. A less frequent cause might be a compressive force such as a hat band or headgear that is too tight.

Neuralgia expresses itself as a sharp, streaking pain. It is an intermittent pain and the streaking nature and sharpness of the pain make it alarming and appear to be related to the brain. Neuralgia designates nerve pain as opposed to neuritis which designates nerve inflammation.

Neuralgia in the head is the only form discussed here but the principles discussed apply to all types of neuralgia. The pain seems to travel along three sets of paths.

1. The most frequently obstructed path lies within a channel about 1/2 inch behind the temples, the lower edge 1/2 to 1 inch above the attachment of the ear extending in a horizontal direction 1 inch wide, to the back of the head.
2. A second path lies along a line from the center of the hairline at the forehead over the top of the head.
3. The third path lies in one of 2 channels above the orbits of the eyes, approximately the width of these orbits, extending upward and backward with a slight degree of convergence (without meeting) to the crown of the head.

The neuralgia spots can be recognized by a spongy feel and may be very sensitive. These spongy spots are scattered along the path. The intention of the treatment is to remove these obstructions in the nerve paths.

Neuralgia: roll index finger

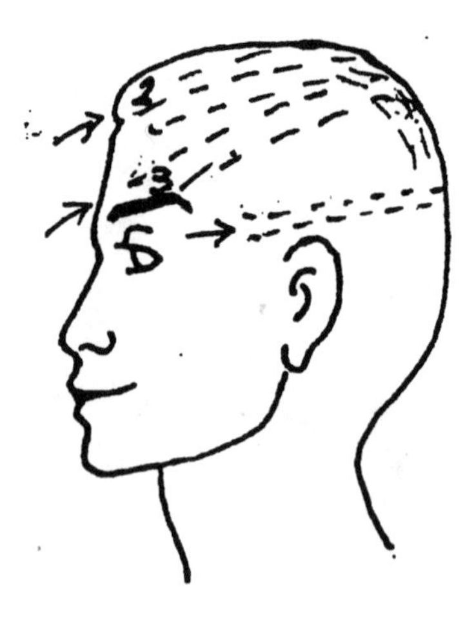

➧ **Step 1:** Roll the tip of your index finger over the spongy and sensitive spot until the finger tip comes to rest on its other side; use a firm, positive pressure that follows the direction of the path from front to back. The finger covers the spot in one direction only: no rolling back and forth.

➧ **Step 2:** Treat the spots on the top of the head with the rolling movement and with direct pressure downward toward the center of the head.

➧ **Step 3:** For any spots on the back of the head the direction is downward. Do not dwell on any individual spot but return to it once or twice later during the treatment.

Frequency

In 3 or 4 sessions even a bad neuralgia case should be cleared up.

It is the responsibility of the person to protect the head from sudden loss of body heat by wearing a hat. The hat, discarded by fashion, should be reinstated by common sense.

Baldness

Only men are subject to slick, shiny baldness through an inherited characteristic. The following treatments do not apply to this type of baldness.

Spotty baldness is the type that frequently occurs in women. It is caused by circulatory disturbances and may be helped by the treatment for neuralgia, above.

Complete absence of hair on the head, including the eyebrows and eyelashes, arises from any extreme fever in the head for men or women. Such baldness is corrected mainly by attention to the back of the neck under the eaves of the skull.

➧ **Step 1:** Do a circular breaking up treatment at the base of the skull from ear to ear.

➧ **Step 2:** Give the treatment for neuralgia, above.

➧ **Step 3:** Loosen the scalp from the skull with massage so that it has free motion.

➧ **Step 4:** After the scalp is thoroughly loosened, apply the following movements: With the hands widespread from the thumb to middle fingertip, place one hand at the forehead and the other at the base of the skull. Press with the thumb and middle finger on each hand from the perimeter of the scalp toward the crown with firm, slow moving, nourishing strokes. Engage as broad a line of contact as possible. Then, let the hands begin the same strokes with the thumbs and middle fingers from the sides of the head at the temporal regions toward the crown of the head. Do each direction once.

➧ **Step 5:** Give a thorough general treatment, page 1–8.

➧ **Step 6:** Do step 8 of the inward goiter treatment, vacuuming for 7 minutes as applicable.

High Blood Pressure

Mr. Stephenson had a unique view of blood pressure. He said that there is no universal standard of blood pressure and he compared the human body to a train engine. If the engine is on a level track, it needs an even amount of pressure, but if it has to climb a mountain, it is common sense to know that the pressure must be increased.

High blood pressure is not causatively connected with the heart, but is frequently brought on by repeated chilling of the neck, which can create a coating of the blood vessels and impair circulation. This congestion slows the flow of blood returning from the head to the heart. Dizziness or slight pains or noises in the head can be cause for concern.

Congestion occurs in the triangular filter areas bounded by the ridge of the shoulder, the base of the neck and the collarbone. These filters, by regulating and restoring blood to normal consistency, are an automatic safeguard protecting the heart or other vital areas from blood clots. A filter area acts like an oil filter in a car. Thickened blood will accumulate behind the filter until it is sufficiently broken down to pass through it. In cases of very high blood pressure, the filter areas may look and feel puffed up. Congestion in the filter areas backs into the channels leading up to the region just below the mastoid bone.

Note: There are two more major sets of filter areas, one on the wrists and one on the ankles.

The use of a hair dryer causes too rapid an evaporation and a chilling of the neck. To prevent this, the neck should be protected by a towel. In serious cases, the patient should avoid using a hair dryer.

Filter areas

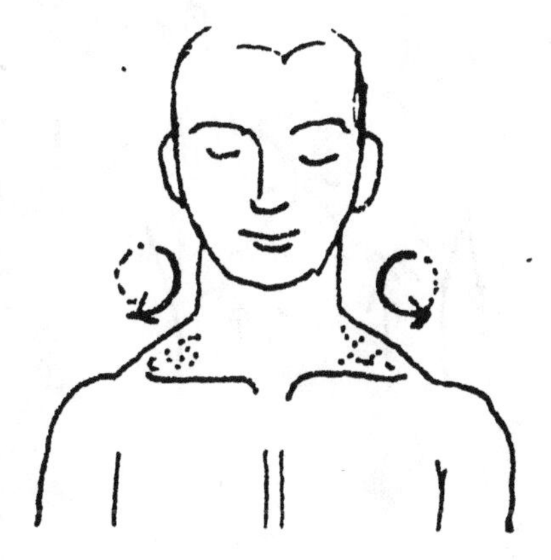

The treatment for high blood pressure is effective whenever the patient has symptoms of this disorder, even without actually suffering from it. Symptoms such as dizziness and pressure in the head are often caused by an obstruction in the neck. In any high blood pressure or stroke condition avoid exercise on a slant board (where head is lower than the rest of the body) until the back of the neck is completely free of congestion.

If blood pressure is normal or low, it will remain totally unaffected by this treatment, no matter how long it is performed. It will lower the blood pressure only when it is too high.

Position

Patient sits. Creative Healer stands behind for steps 1 and 2.

Clear the filters

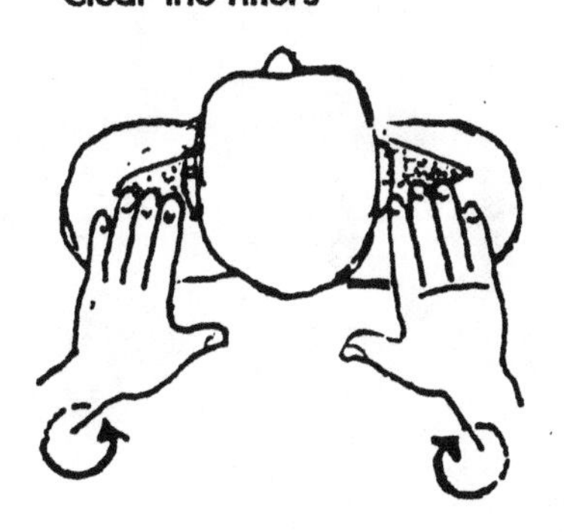

➧ **Step 1: Clear the filters.** To clear the neck filters, place 3 fingers of each hand on the filter areas. The palms rest lightly on the patient's shoulders and the thumbs touch at the back of the neck. With the flats of the fingers in lengthwise contact with the skin, make circular breaking up movements over the entire filter areas. Only the surface tissue moves with the fingers. This movement, as seen by the Creative Healer, is clockwise on the right and counterclockwise on the left. A very light pressure is applied downward (toward the heart) carefully staying within the soft tissue below the base of the neck.

Vacuum downward

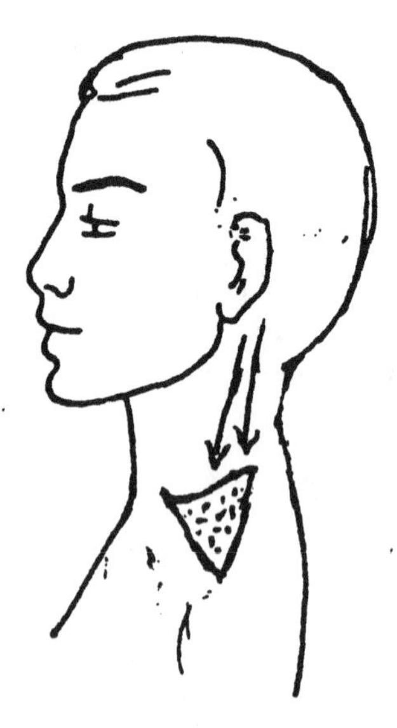

Step 2: Vacuum the channels. When the congestion in the filter areas is relieved, begin the decongestion of the channel areas. The channels run from the mastoid to the filters. The two sides of the neck are now to be treated separately. To treat the right side, support the patient's head gently with the left hand. With the fingers of the right hand, create a vacuum down the right side of the neck by gently stroking along the channeling area, from the base of the skull to the filter area. Hold the middle finger slightly forward of the other two and continue the stroking for 1 or 2 minutes, downward only. It may be performed rapidly. Treat the left side with the left hand and then, lightly and briefly, clean out the filter areas again.

It is important to create the vacuum to the two sides of the neck separately at first. Treating both sides simultaneously could, in serious cases, cause the patient to faint. When the filter beds are well cleared and the vacuum has been created on each side several times, then perform the stroking on both sides at the same time with the thumb on one side and fingers on the other. This allows for comparison of the channels to detect any differences that need more attention.

Relax shoulder and back muscles

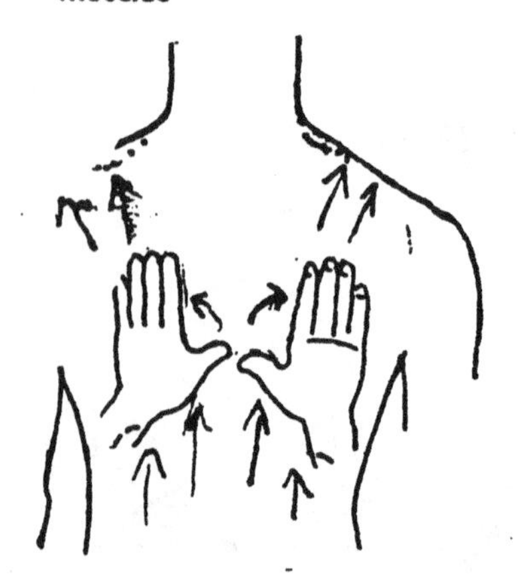

Step 3: Loosen up the back. Sit behind the patient. The third step of the treatment relaxes the muscles of the upper back from the bottom of the shoulder blades to the shoulders and over the trapezius muscle, thus increasing the circulation. To achieve this loosening, place the palms on the back, below the shoulder blades, and work up very gently, in a circular motion with the whole of the hands. At the same time, with a kneading motion, move the thumb in lengthwise contact toward the base of the fingers. Be sure to maintain the palms in contact with the tissue throughout. This combined movement is designed by its rhythm to suggest a gentle jiggling motion of the palms and thumbs. Do this from the base of the scapula to the shoulder ridge.

Step 4: Further decongesting movement. As you're performing steps 1 to 3, explore thoroughly the entire area on the back and sides of the neck and the base of the skull. Use your thumb and fingers in a breaking up movement to locate and gently remove any obstruction or congestion in these tissues of the neck. If the patient feels faint and wants to lie down, encourage this and check heart and breathing. If within a few minutes he is not feeling all right, be alert to the heart spot on the back (found in Inward Goiter treatment). Ask the patient to sit up, clear that spot and return to the vacuum movement.

Duration

Repeat, alternating in sequence, the four parts of the treatment for 20 minutes.

Frequency

Treat once a week for 7 weeks. Between treatments the blood pressure may go up but not as high. As it continues to stay a little lower each week any medicinal treatment will need to be adjusted by the patient's physician.

The high blood pressure treatment is also applied for repeated nose bleed.

➤➤➤CAUTION: Brain Tumor. If, while creating a vacuum downward on the back of the neck, the patient's skin suddenly starts to feel cold, wet or clammy to the touch, or if the patient suddenly feels faint, stop the treatment. This may be an indication that there is heavy obstruction of circulation within, to, or from the head, or an indication that the patient will soon feel very ill. In that case, stop the treatment at once because this reaction may indicate a brain tumor. A brain tumor contains the vilest poisons the body can harbor and if they are suddenly released in quantity, death could ensue when they reach the heart. One may actually treat this formation under the skull by working short periods at a time directly over the channels that are in contact with the tumor. One can drain the tumor without the patient feeling sick at any time. The complete guide to success is to never allow the point to be reached at which the patient feels in the least sick. With this treatment, the patient's health is never in jeopardy.

Common Headache

According to Mr. Stephenson, the immediate cause of every headache is stagnant blood on the brain. This may be due to too much blood, unequalized circulation, or poor condition of the blood. Therefore a few minutes of general treatment, which could in itself be adequate, should be given with each headache treatment. If the general treatment is not adequate, look to further possible obstructions in the neck. When there is a good, wholesome blood supply to the head with proper drainage out of the head, directed by nerve life that is not subjected to interference, there can be no headache.

In addition, be alert to conditions of the blood stream, taking into consideration the possibility of a sluggish liver or bowel or even inadequate heart action. Do not forget sinus congestion or congestion of the scalp, and be sure to see that the body and head are kept at normal temperature.

Often the cause of common headache is trouble in the neck. Between any two consecutive vertebrae in the spinal column, the substances involved (cartilage, nerve, ligament, muscle, connective tissue, etc.) are normally smoothly embedded. If the substances become displaced backward and/or to one side or the other, trouble arises.

For common headache, the displacement is often near the middle of the neck, but can be in any of the spaces between two consecutive cervical vertebrae.

Position

Patient sits. Creative Healer stands behind.

Hand position

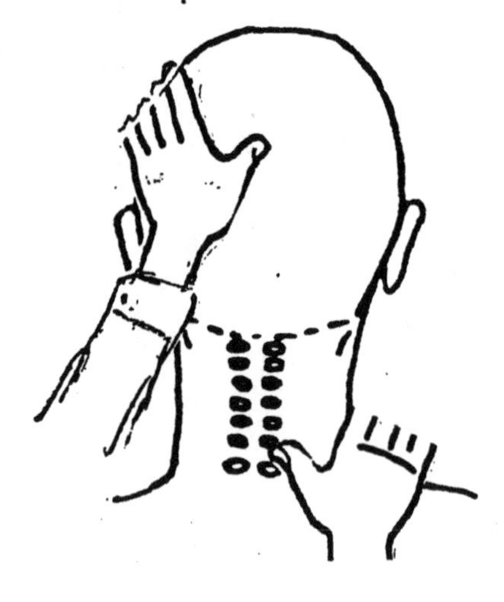

➧ **Step 1: Hand and thumb placement.** Rest the fingertips of your left hand lightly on the top of the patient's head. Ask to be allowed to guide the movement of the head as the treatment proceeds. To replace substance that has been displaced to the right, place the right thumb so that its left edge is to the right of the center line of the neck. The hand rests on the patient's lower right neck and shoulder.

➧ **Step 2: Press and circumduct.** Apply a light thumb pressure to the displaced substance, on a space between and on the side of the cervical vertebra near the middle of the neck. As pressure is applied, gently move the patient's head with your left hand downward and to the left. Then move it to the right until you reach the center line of the body and return it to the upright position. Thumb pressure is applied from slightly to right of the center line and directed to the left, in and up.

Circumduct the head

The principle of the treatment is easily recognized: movement of the patient's head, brought about by the Creative Healer's left hand, opens the space between the two vertebrae. Under pressure of the right thumb, the displaced substance slips back into place. Pressure exerted is just enough for the Creative Healer to feel the substance yield, as it moves into place.

➧ **Step 3: Repeat on the left, if necessary.** For displacement of substance on the left, use either the right or left thumb to apply gentle pressure, and move the patient's head down and to the right to open the space as wide as possible. This time, direct pressure slightly to the right, in and up. Bring the head back smoothly to the left and then to the upright position.

Explore thoroughly the area around the back of the neck and next to the skull. Use the thumb and fingers of the right hand to break up any obstructions.

Eno for Headache

Mr. Stephenson recommended for headache a preparation obtainable in some drugstores under the brand name of *Eno*. This product remains available in England and Canada today and an approximate, if not equivalent, product is sold under the brand name of *Brioschi*. Mr. Stephenson never recommended the use of anything that could be classed as a medicine, and *Eno* conforms to this principle. The only active ingredients are bicarbonate of soda and cream of tartar, staples common in almost any kitchen although we do not know the proportions. Mr. Stephenson was familiar with *Eno* from his boyhood in England, where the preparation was known as *Eno's Fruit Salts.* It had been in common use for decades, and often formed the sole contents of the poor man's remedy shelf.

To reach the effectiveness that Mr. Stephenson achieved with it, *Eno* must be used not according to the directions on the label but according to his instructions.

Add to 1/2 glass of lukewarm water, 1/2 to 1 teaspoon of the powder and drink it while it fizzes. It has a pleasant, lemony flavor. It will usually cause belching: an action that facilitates the healing process.

A dull, persistent headache that will not yield to any headache treatment may be due to a condition in the blood stream that relates to the quality of the blood (see common headache, above).

Migraine

Migraine headache is characterized by a violent pain at the top of the head that makes the patient feel as though the brain is swollen (which it actually is) and as though the top of the head is about to "blow off."

There is a certain nerve center on the back of the neck that controls the sense of smell. When this nerve center becomes agitated it causes a swelling in a section of the brain until it is rubbing against the skull. This creates great friction and results in the violent pain.

Thumb on obstruction

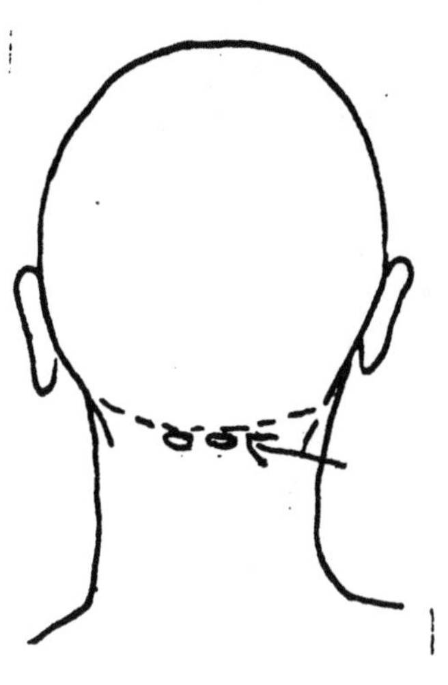

Recurrent migraine headache may be traced to a constant, daily exposure to smells that agitate the olfactory nerves such as gas fumes, explosives, perfumes, paint, makeup, or any odor that is penetrating and pungent. Persistent exposure could be a possible cause for the formation of a brain tumor. Each person must assume responsibility to determine and eliminate aggravating odors (even a change of work might be advisable). Migraines might also be caused by prolonged looking upward, with the head bent far back.

Even though the pain is felt at the top of the head the cause of migraine is usually the displacement of a nerve center located between the head and the first cervical vertebra (the "atlas"). The treatment is very similar to that of common headache. For migraine the nerve center is most frequently displaced to the right.

Circumduct head away from obstruction

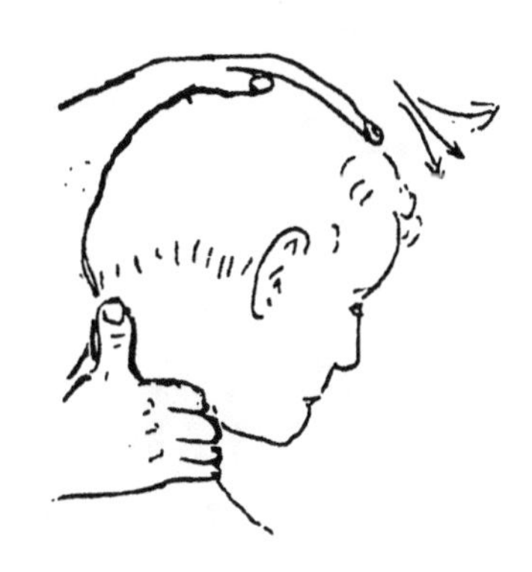

➧ **Step 1: Hand and thumb placement**. Stand behind the patient, rest the tips of the fingers of the left hand lightly on the top of the head and place the edge of the right hand on his right shoulder. Place the right thumb so that its left edge is just to the right of the center line of his neck, at the base of the skull.

➧ **Step 2: Press and rotate head**. Press gently on that spot with the thumb. At the same time (with the left hand) move the patient's head downward toward the front and to the left, and then bring it back it toward the right until reaching the center of the body, then returning it to the upright position. Ask to be allowed to guide the movement of the head as the treatment proceeds. Pressure of the thumb is applied from the right of the center line of the neck and is directed slightly to the left, in and up.

The principle of the treatment is easily recognized: moving the patient's head with your left hand opens up the space between the atlas and the head so that, under pressure of your right thumb, the displaced substance may go back into place. Hold the thumb steady but not rigidly on the spot, in such a manner as to respond to the movement of the head during the circumduction. The pressure exerted is just enough for you to feel the substance yield, as it moves into place.

If the displaced substance is to the left, use the hands essentially as before, but this time, the pressure of the right or left thumb should be applied from the left of the center line of the neck, and should be directed to the right, in and up. Move the patient's head downward, toward the front as before, and to the right to open the space between the head and the atlas. Then bring the head back to the central upright position.

Step 3: General treatment. Give the general treatment, page 1–8, for whatever length of time seems indicated. When giving the General Treatment, be sure to perform the vacuum movement on the two sides of the neck separately, at first. When the filter beds are cleared and the vacuum has been created on the two separate sides several times, you may perform the stroking on both sides, together. This is done with the right hand, the thumb on the left side of the person's neck and the fingers, the middle finger predominating, on the right side. Stand to the left of the patient and support the head with your left hand. Use a moderate pressure at first and never increase beyond what is considered a vacuum.

From the writings of Joseph B. Stephenson

Migraine Headache

Even as you read this, the doctors will not have found the cause of migraine headaches, nor will they know what to do for it. I will give you a brief case that came to me.

This patient had been in the hospital. First, they diagnosed it as migraine, then they changed their minds; they thought it might be spinal meningitis. They put a needle into his spine, six inches long and drew the liquid from his spine, which caused double pain, more that he could stand. They fed him morphine to keep him quiet then they put him through another test. They came to the conclusion it was TB of the spine. They then sent him home to die.

His wife came to see me and asked me to go see him. I said I would but only by the doctor's permission with a note saying that he prescribed my treatment. Soon she was back with a note from the doctor so I told her I would go up in the morning and would be there at 10 o'clock. When I got there all the relatives were there. The doctor had told them he would not live through the day.

His wife took me to his room and I put my hand on his brow. He had no temperature—that told me there was no danger so I got him out of bed, gave him a treatment on his migraine nerve, then massaged down the side of his neck. In less than 10 minutes, his pain was gone. In 20 minutes I had him walking around the room. All dizziness had disappeared. I went downstairs.

At 6 o'clock that Sunday night the doctor got there to see him. When he walked into the home there was his patient whom he had told on Saturday that he would not live over Sunday, and he was eating a chicken dinner at the kitchen table. Questions were asked quick and fast, then when he got home he called me on the phone, asked me this man's trouble.

I said, "You know, doctor, I am not allowed to diagnose a case."

"Yes, but I gave you a note to go there. You could at least tell me what it is, tell me the cause of his trouble.

"I will tell you that he got it from smelling too many gas fumes from auto exhaust. For instance, the same thing happens to painters, to men who clean sewers, and to men who use lots of dynamite in the mines. When these aromas become chronic, they cause agitation to the membrane of smell then it gets inflamed and swells until it rubs against the skull. If let go long enough it can develop into a tumor. Then if the doctors cannot do it any good, it finally ends up with the patient going into a crazed state of mind until the poison reaches the heart and delivers him from pain.

Epilepsy

Nerves that control and/or feed various organs or areas of our human body are normally embedded smoothly between two consecutive vertebrae of the spinal column. In epilepsy the nerve center at the base of the neck (where it joins the shoulders) is displaced to either side of the vertebrae. If the patient falls forward during seizures, the center is displaced to the right; if the patient falls backward, the center is displaced to the left. Some children are born with this nerve center out of place. Sometimes it is brought on by a twist or a fall or even by turning the child upside down during play. The treatment is similar to that of migraine and common headache.

Epilepsy: hand placement

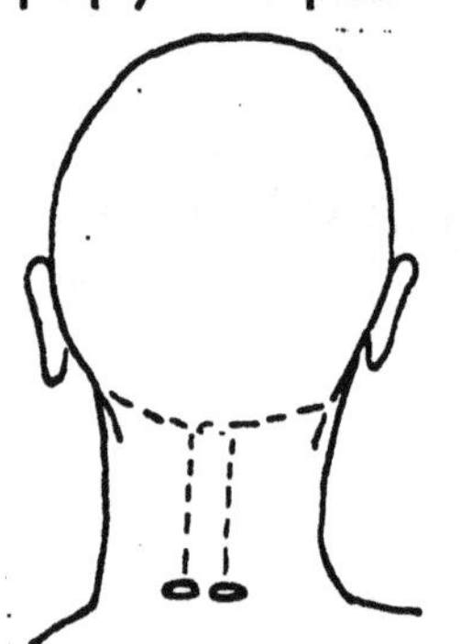

Circumduct the head

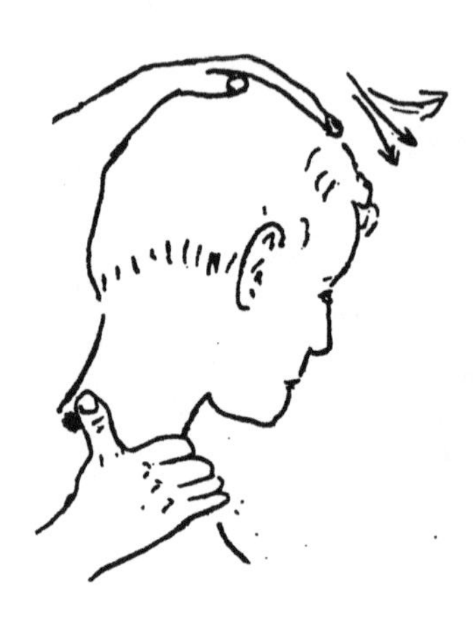

Position

Patient sits. Creative Healer stands behind.

➧ **Step 1: Hand and thumb placement.** Rest the tips of the fingers of the left hand lightly on patient's head. Rest the right palm on the shoulder. The entire length of the last phalange of the thumb is placed at the base of the neck with the tip at the displaced nerve center.

➧ **Step 2: Press and circumduct.** To treat for a displacement to the right, place the right thumb to the right of the center line of the neck then move the head forward and to the left, to open the space between the vertebrae. Bring back the head to the right and return it to the center and upright position. Exert strong pressure along the entire length of the last phalange of the thumb as this is harder to replace than the headache displacement.

To treat for a displacement to the left reverse the above instructions.

➧ **Step 3: Give the general treatment, page 1–8.** Give the general treatment for whatever length of time seems indicated, being certain to take the precaution of treating each side of the neck separately when first creating the vacuum down the sides of the neck.

Face Pain

Facial muscles as a whole do not develop with use as do other muscles and the tissues of the face are different from all other tissues of the body. In treating the face, never knead, tug or pull the tissues; gently mold them into shape as though molding clay. Any stroking of the face should be gentle and always upwards. This refers to washing and drying the face and to applying creams and lotions.

A prolonged extension of the jaw as for dental work or sometimes a sleeping position will bring about the disarrangement of a nerve center. The resulting obstruction of the life force channeled to the tissues may cause excruciating pain on one side of the face.

Small nerves and tissues that feed the face may have moved from their normal position in a cavity in the bone of the lower jawbone. This displacement most frequently occurs at the notches located on the underside of the jawbone near the angle of the jaw. The nerves in these two side grooves can be detected with light finger pressure and a pulse beat can be felt there.

Position

Patient sits. Creative Healer stands behind, resting patient's head against the chest, while holding head upright.

Replace nerves from front and side

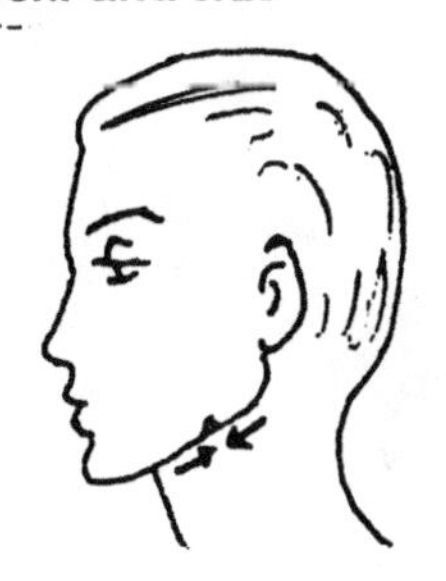

➧ **Step 1: Replace nerves from front into notches.** Use both index fingers and treat both sides at the same time. Place the edge of the second bone of the index fingers 3/4 of an inch forward of the notches. Draw the fingers along the edge of the jawbone, gently carrying the tissues beneath the surface toward and into the notches on each side and release.

➧ **Step 2: Replace nerves from sides.** Contact again behind the notch but forward of the angle of the jaw with the index fingers. Press the tissues forward but this time the fingers do not enter the notches as this could cause a renewed dislocation.

Both movements may be repeated if necessary.

When the entire front of the face and the head is involved and painful, the nerve is out of place at the center of the chin just above the lower edge of the bone. The nerve belonging to the chin can be felt only when it is out of place as it will be swollen.

Replace nerve in center of chin

➧ **Step 3: Replace nerve on chin.** Stand to the right side of the patient and hold the head firmly with your left hand keeping the head straight while using the edge of your right index finger to draw the nerve from either side to the exact center of the notch. It will probably be swollen. Do not cross the notch.

Lift face tissues

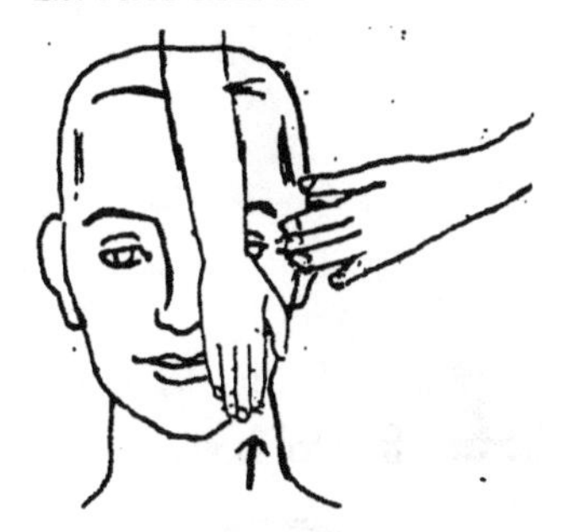

➧ **Step 4: Lift the tissues of the face (for both problems).** In extreme cases of pain in the face, it is necessary to lift the tissues of the face to permit nerve life to enter more quickly and fully. To lift the right side of the face, stand behind the patient and rest the head against your chest. With a well-oiled right palm, fingers pointing toward the floor, start a gentle stroke slowly upward from below the jaw. The tissues of the skin are lifted by the gentle suction of the palm. The touch is so gentle it is as though the oil and the patient's face were the only things in contact.

Continue the stroke beyond the temple. Slip the first 3 fingers of your left hand horizontally under the right hand to hold the place at the temple to bridge the time until the right hand again starts upward from the jaw.

To lift the left side, interchange right and left.

Duration

Work without agitating the face until free of pain.

Frequency

Treat as needed.

These treatments are also used for conditions referred to as tic douloureux, trifacial or trigeminal neuralgia and Bell's palsy or for sagging of facial tissue from a stroke.

Face Lift

The face lift massage is very gentle and with a positive intent, and is interesting for the person to watch in a mirror as someone else does the lifting.

Lift one side of the face at a time using the palms of both hands one following another in an upward movement to the temple. A little oil and a light, barely touching movement will lift the facial tissues allowing blood and nerve life to rush in and regenerate the skin and permit the life force to enter more quickly and fully.

Bell's Palsy

The face, in Bell's palsy, will often appear paralyzed and sagged on one side. The corner of the mouth may droop; the tongue may come out in a curl when extended; the lower eyelid may be badly drooped and the eyebrow sagged over the eye. However, there is usually no pain associated with Bell's palsy. Because of the appearance of the face, Bell's palsy is mistakenly considered the result of stroke but it actually has nothing to do with stroke. While all these features are common to stroke, they are due to different causes.

The causes that bring on Bell's palsy are of two kinds:

1. Repeated or severe chilling by exposure to a cold wind or air conditioning.
2. The face pressed to pillow or bed, so that life force and circulation are disrupted and the face "goes to sleep" while the person, being asleep, cannot realize it. When awakening and looking in the mirror, the person sees the alarming symptoms of Bell's palsy.

➧ **Steps 1–4:** Give the complete treatment (four steps) for face pain, page 2–44.

Scrape frontal bone

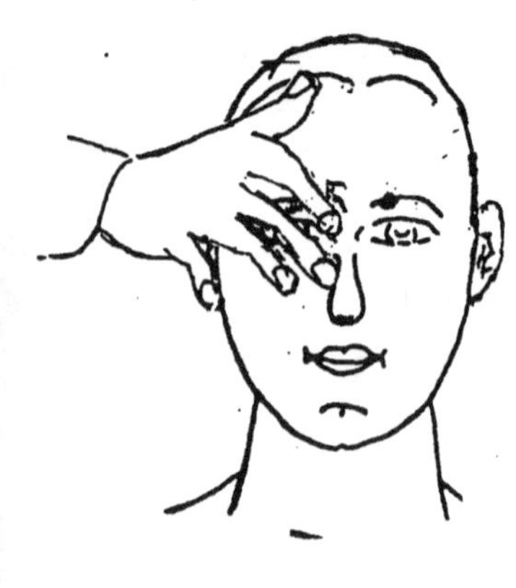

➧ **Step 5: Scrape the frontal bone.** Use the edge of the last joint of the index fingers to scrape the under edge of the frontal bone from the bridge of the nose to the notches (supra orbital notches) found on the under side of the frontal bone about 3/4 of an inch from the nose. Scrape upward and outward and hold for several moments with a firm pressure in the notch, then release gradually. The object of this treatment is to carry dislocated nerves into position. (See sinus treatment, page 2–2.)

Frequency

If the patient can be treated the same day the condition is suffered, the face can be brought back to its normal state within a few hours. Treat briefly every 20 to 30 minutes, in this case. If the condition occurred 6 months previous or more, it may take several months to bring the face back to normal. Treatments should then be given several times a week before the interval between treatments can be lengthened. The patient can be taught to do the necessary lifting with the palm and the scraping beneath the brow.

Shaking Palsy—Parkinson's Disease

Shaking palsy is the same as *paralysis agitans*, Parkinson's disease, or just plain palsy. Mr. Stephenson found that if the condition had only developed to the point that one or both hands of the patient shook but not the whole body, it was, in general, possible to correct this condition within 6 months, with treatments once or twice a week.

The cause for the disturbance is not in the limbs, but in a special condition that has developed in the brain. It is an incipient shedding of the substance of the brain. This substance, which Mr. Stephenson called a "gelatin," keeps the brain firm and steadies the nerve endings by giving them support. In the normal state, the nerve endings have full control over the limbs. When this support begins to give way, the nerve endings are left in an unsteady, shaking and trembling state. This results in shaking and trembling limbs.

As Mr. Stephenson saw the body, it was so put together that moving a finger was the result of nerve endings in the opposite side of the brain that were brought into action by thought. Although he did not attempt to describe the exact size and shape of these nerve endings, he knew that they were there and that each segment of a finger corresponded to a segment of nerve endings in the brain. When the brain segment moved, so did the finger segment, the two moving in unison. He said this same principle applied to all motions of the body. The reason for the feet to turn in as in pigeon toes, for example, was that the last segments, the tips of the corresponding nerve endings were too weak and tended to "fall inward."

This treatment for palsy is one of only three treatments in the Creative Healing work in which the treatment is an upward movement on the back of the neck: pigeon toes, polio, and palsy.

Position

Patient sits. Creative Healer stands in front of and facing the patient.

➧ **Step 1: Position.** Have patient lean forward so that the head rests, for support, against your abdomen. You will work on the pathways to the arms; these channels are located about 1 1/2 inch on either side of the median line of the neck and are probably sensitive to the touch. The work is done on one side by your index and middle fingers and on the other side by the thumb.

Upward movement

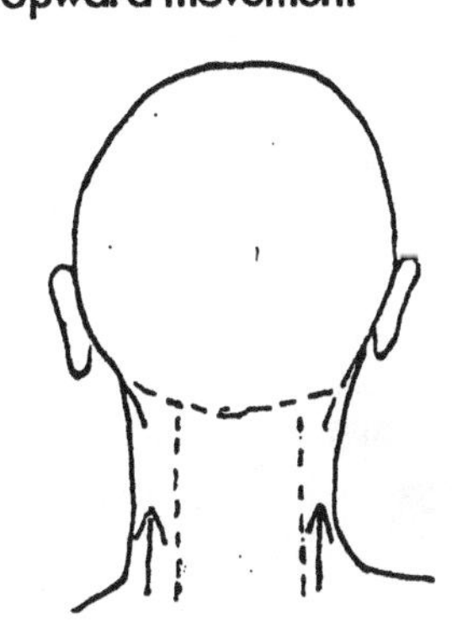

➧ **Step 2: Upward movement.** Perform firm strokes that start at the base of the neck and continue until they are stopped at the base of the skull.

In addition, check all vertebrae of the spine for the need to replace substance and, of course, any other part of the body in distress must be treated.

Duration

Continue for 15 minutes.

Frequency

Work on the patient at least once a week. The hand and arm will often become steady during the treatment. The aim is to have them remain steady and it should be possible to achieve this within 6 months.

Painter's Palsy

Painter's palsy is often contracted by older men for whom the continued "frictional drag" of working with a brush leads to over exertion. The over exertion may be caused by competing with younger colleagues. Nerves from the hand to the opposite hemisphere of the brain are pulled downward. They sag and begin to appear within the body much like a thread pulled through a piece of cloth. The nerves are held in this "puckered" condition because the recovery periods are out of balance with the periods of work.

The painting should, at least temporarily, be discontinued. If it is not, the condition may progress to that of shaking palsy. With treatment, the painter may be able to resume work, assuming an adequate balance between work and rest.

Painter's palsy is easy to overcome if the painting is relinquished. The main task is to open up the back of the neck so that strength may once again flow through into the limbs. Begin by applying the lift as in shaking palsy. Combine parts of the treatments for high blood pressure, page 2–37 and stroke, below, as needed.

As in the case of stroke, there must not be actual pulling down on the nerves. For example, to relieve a painful point in the shoulder or upper arm, there must not be a downward stroking as described in the pain in the arm treatment; the release must always be effected with the thought of restoring the sagging nerves to their natural state and getting the "pucker" out.

Stroke

Strokes may be caused by low or high blood pressure. Blood vessels may break on the top of the head because of high or low blood pressure. They may break also at the back of the neck. At all places, the vessel breakdown may cause the paralyzing symptoms of stroke.

Mr. Stephenson said a child could have a stroke going into a tantrum or a young person using his or her resources beyond capacity. However, mostly older people have strokes because as the years go by the arteries change: some sag and some tighten and retard the flow of blood but do not regulate the action of the heart. The heart pumps out the same amount of blood to the head as it did before any obstruction in the blood stream. This causes dizziness, loss of eyesight for a moment, and a continuous ringing noise in the ears; all are warning signs.

Part I: Top of Head–High Blood Pressure

A stroke caused by high blood pressure never occurs without a warning: a sharp, pinpointed pain on the top of the head. The pain is either to the right or to the left, at the place where the actual breakdown will occur if the warning is not heeded. The pain is like that of a pinprick, or that caused by the pulling of a hair, locally well defined. (This pain must not be confused with the streaking or shooting neuralgia pain that is caused by an obstruction in the scalp.) If the pain is on the left side of the top of the head, the right side of the body is threatened with paralysis. If the pain is on the right, a stroke will affect the left side of the body and the heart will be affected.

If the warning is misunderstood or ignored, the breakdown occurs in the artery that gave the signals. The vessel that breaks is as fine as a human hair, or even finer. As blood flows out, coagulating and forming a clot, the nerve endings and nerves, so vital to motion, become bound down and immobilized at that spot. The corresponding areas of the body, controlled by these nerves, will be paralyzed. The true trouble at this stage is not in the limbs but in the head. The nerves are inoperative, and the muscles are not told what to do. Massage any pinpoint pain with finger tips and in a few seconds the pinpoint pain stops and you have broken that clot.

Then be sure the back of the neck is immediately cleaned out; the paralyzing effects of the stroke may be averted.

Nature will attempt to heal the damage in the head; if the back of the neck is obstructed, a hard spot will be produced to cover the area in the head, like a bandage. Nature's healing of any damage to tissue directly fed by the vascular system is well under way within the first 5 days after the damage has occurred. Nature will have to apply the "bandage" much as one would if given the task of repairing a crack in a water pipe with the pressure still on: a large bandage. In order to prevent the "bandage" from becoming a large, hardened area, it is important to clean out the back of the neck within the first 5 days, the sooner the better, to effect a true healing.

In every case of stroke, thoroughly open up the back of the person's neck with the high blood pressure treatment page 2–37. By this work, conditions become favorable for healing the damaged area within the head. This healing may be so complete and the area so strengthened that the person will never again experience a stroke at that same spot. On the other hand, every day that elapses without treatment beyond the 5-day period, reduces the possibility of complete healing because of the bandage situation.

This bandage of nature will most likely lead to a succession of strokes, due to the breaking of the hardened spot at its edges, and ultimately lead up to the last stroke. This does not mean that, if treatment is impossible within the first 5 days, none should be applied. One should still go ahead, even at a later time, but the results are apt to be less satisfactory and less permanent.

Part II: Top of Head—Low Blood Pressure

Low blood pressure, leading to the collapse of an artery, can also produce a stroke. However, in low blood pressure there will be no warning. After the stroke occurs, conditions will be much the same. A clot will form with the same consequences. Again, it is of utmost importance to clean out the neck because low blood pressure cannot be further lowered by giving the high blood pressure treatment; it should be used to clear the neck channels; see page 2–37.

If the patient reports that feelings of cloudiness, dizziness, faintness or fuzziness are relieved by the treatment, this would be a good indication that favorable conditions for healing are being established. This is especially true if the treatment is applied within the first 5 days.

In addition to treating the back of the neck, the appropriate treatments for whatever has caused the low blood pressure must be given. Some of these causes are: insufficiency of blood in quantity and volume, the heart resting too long between beats or skipping beats, and inadequate digestion. All these conditions may be worsened by extreme fatigue. The patient can tell that not enough blood is getting to the head, and must understand that during feelings of weakness or faintness, it is important to rest until strength is regained. This is especially pertinent when skipped heart beats or other erratic heart function is involved.

The symptoms described might also be a warning of a threatening stroke that might be averted if timely treatment is given. The treatments that apply are the digestive tuneup, page 5–14, the basic heart treatment, page 4–21 and the spleen treatment, page 5–13.

Part III: Back of Neck—High or Low Blood Pressure

A stroke caused by high or low blood pressure can also occur in the back of the neck, including the area beneath the base of the skull. The breakdown of a vessel on the right side of the neck affects the right side of the face and body while a stroke on the left side of the neck affects the left side of the body and face. Clearing out the back of the neck remains as important as for the other types of stroke. The indicative spots at the base of the skull must be treated in any event of stroke.

Part IV: Pain Spots at the Base of the Skull

Pain spots at base of skull

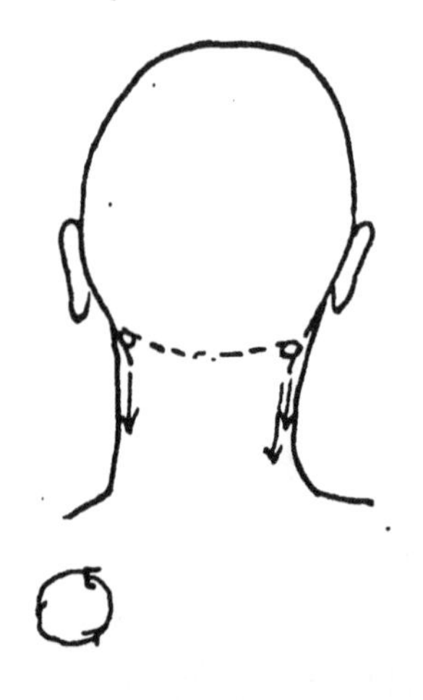

Several spots located at the base of the skull are important to the flow of circulation and nerve life. When they are heavily obstructed and are not cleared, serious consequences such as a stroke can happen. The degree of involvement is revealed by their degree of sensitivity.

These spots, and they are truly spots, not areas, are located on both sides of the head where the neck joins the base of the skull at the uppermost point of the vacuum for High Blood Pressure, close to the back of the ear. If pressure is applied, particularly when combined with a slight breaking up movement, these spots will register, if involved, strong sensitivity or even severe pain. The intensity of this reaction reveals the magnitude of the obstruction and even the extent to which the body is affected.

After clearing the back of the neck as described in the high blood pressure treatment, page 2–37, always be sure to clear these spots, using a breaking up movement. Expand the movement to include a vacuum movement on the downward side, causing the obstructing material to move down the back of the neck. Both of these movements are done within the breaking up circle itself by stressing the downward part and the actual downward stroking.

If after having been cleared the spots again become obstructed, repeat the treatment. Make sure, by regular checking, that they remain clear. The clearing of these spots is vital in any stroke case.

Part V: After Stroke–Treatment of Affected Regions

Although the real trouble is in the head or neck and the treatment there has been described, the paralyzed limbs must also receive adequate care.

Because there is no control of the stricken limbs from the brain by way of the nervous system, these limbs hang inert. Gravity can pull them badly out of position with reference to the trunk, particularly at the shoulder and hip joints and these limbs may lose their proper alignment. A finger placed on the shoulder above the ball of the arm might rest within the region of the socket if the arm sags badly. The sag is further compounded and the damage increased because the circulation is deranged. The muscles can be seen and felt to hang with dead weight. It almost appears as though there is something more than gravity pulling and causing the sag.

The treatment must counter the sag and must therefore be exclusively directed upward. In counteracting the sag, the treatment will preserve circulation and minimize deterioration.

➧ **Step 1:** With oil on the hands, apply a gentle lifting upward stroking. Use your whole hand, gently curved to cradle the tissues. Hold your fingers as a unit and extend your thumb. Lift only the tissues of the skin, with no pressure so as not to collapse them, and as though the oil and the skin are the only things in contact as in the lift of face treatment, page 2–45. This allows the circulation to flow in underneath the surface tissue and toward the extremity as strongly as possible. Perform this lifting and molding with the feeling that the flow of circulation is freed beneath the contact of the hand. It should be done daily. If done correctly, without pressure, it cannot be done too frequently.

➧ **Step 2:** Keep the limbs in position by keeping the balls of the joints opposite their sockets. Support a sagging arm with a sling fastened over the opposite shoulder that holds up the forearm. Such a sling might be a triangular type in order to have a broad contact with the forearm. A narrow contact would cut into the tissue and impede circulation. The sling might extend to support the wrist and hand. If needed, further support may be given by tying the upper arm to the trunk of the body. This should be done with a broad band, applied just tightly enough to hold the ball in the socket.

➧ **Step 3:** If a leg is stricken, lift it and press the ball into the socket at the hip joint. Support the leg in this position by placing a large sandbag against the foot. A broad band extending from the hip over the thigh and fastened around the other leg may also be helpful. Such a band could be made out of sheeting that is more than 1 foot wide.

Treat the limbs in this way so that as soon as recovery in the head takes place (or neck, depending on the source of the stroke) the limbs are ready to respond. Otherwise, when the limbs have been left to sag badly, it seems as though the rest of the body abandons these stricken limbs to shift for themselves. The Creative Healer will understand the condition and will work, at whatever stage it may be, to recover what is possible. If the face has been affected by the stroke, treat as for pain in the face, page 2–44.

➧ **Step 4:** A person in bed because of stroke or illness is often propped up with so many pillows that the neck, chest, and abdomen are cramped. This distorted position of the body sets up stresses through the back and the neck that may reach even into the brain. It is vital that such stresses be relieved. Many people will not permit the excess pillows to be taken away abruptly and this should certainly not be done. Work in a gradual manner, keeping stresses neutralized at every stage, so that the body can eventually extend and lie reasonably flat in a natural manner.

Pigeon Toes

Movement upward from base of neck to base of skull

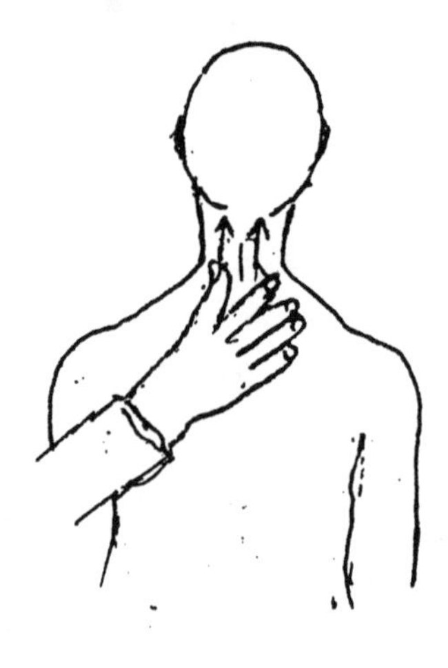

The conventional treatment for pigeon toes is to apply casts. However, because Mr. Stephenson saw the cause of the problem in the head, he believed that it could be treated. He believed that nerve endings in the brain direct actions in corresponding nerve endings in the whole body. The reason the feet turn in is that the tips of the nerve endings that correspond to the last segments of the toes are too weak and tend to "fall inward." Thus, treatment for pigeon toes is done on the back of the neck to feed the nerve endings so they have the strength to fully extend.

While standing behind the seated patient, use the thumb on one side and one or two fingers on the other side about 1 inch from the center line (pathways to the legs), to stroke upward. The strokes start at the base of the neck and extend to the base of the skull and are continued for 15 minutes. This is the same as for Shaking palsy except the pathways to the legs are closer to the center than those leading to the arms. Five or more treatments may be needed.

From the writings of Joseph B. Stephenson

In Johnstown, Pennsylvania, a physician brought his 17-year-old grandson to Mr. Stephenson to get help for his severely pigeon-toed condition. Several attempts with casts had failed but when Mr. Stephenson began to work on the back of the boy's neck and continued for 15 minutes, the grandfather exploded saying it was ridiculous to try to straighten feet by massaging the neck and left with his grandson. Mr. Stephenson refused payment from the grandfather but told the boy to return in 3 days. When he returned he reported that he had better control of his feet. He received 5 treatments at 3-day intervals. On the Sunday after the fifth treatment, the grandfather, sitting on his porch, saw his grandson coming up the street with his feet straight. He immediately went to Mr. Stephenson to apologize and to pay his bill.

Mr. Stephenson said that if the nerves did not cross at the back of the skull, man could not be smoothly balanced in walking, but would hop like a frog or a kangaroo in overcoming gravity. This view of the body's functioning makes one more aware of the connections between obstructions anywhere in the body and corresponding nerve endings in the head.

Chapter 3 ♦ The Back

About the Back

The spine is created to withstand much abuse and be extremely flexible but it is also subject to many problems. Mr. Stephenson would say that the Creator knew this and made the spine so that it could be fixed from the outside. Severe back injuries happen as a result of great trauma, such as a high fall or automobile accident. In such an injury the bone and ligamentous tissue may be broken, commonly called a broken back. A person with a broken back is usually not able to move his body below the break and will not be able to walk. If a person is able to walk, even though with pain, Creative Healing treatments may relieve and resolve the trouble, and may be applied with confidence. In several instances, however, the person may have lost the use of the legs without the back being broken. An example of this is a person with a "soft vertebra" (see soft vertebra treatment, page 3–7). The Creative Healer can work on any condition as long as the back is not broken.

Spinal Column. At the center line of a person's back, the spinal column, comprised of bony projections separated by hollows, is the most visible part. In side view, the normal spine proceeds from the bottom to the top along a curve consisting of three distinct arcs. The sacrum (lower part) has a very slight inward curve that extends through the lumbar area and blends smoothly into an outward curve over the chest or thoracic region and finally (except for a slight protrusion at the 7th cervical) blends into an inward or concave curve along the cervicals of the neck. If any of these curves are disturbed, the others will compensate for it.

A Flexible Column. The vertebrae (bones) of this column are stacked approximately 2 feet high with a movable filling between each bone and a heart shaped hole down the middle. The whole stack is heavily coated, surrounded and reinforced with bands of tough fibrous tissue. The side toward the front of the body is reinforced with a massive ligamentous structure strong enough to protect the spinal cord that runs through the center. The substance between the vertebrae is mostly cartilage containing a disc, which is itself tough cartilage that provides a cushion between the bones. The discs with their tissues and fluids determine the spacing of the vertebrae, their relationship to each other and their positioning front to back or sideways. The important thing is that the substance between two vertebrae reacts as a unit and no part of the intervertebral substance can move without all other parts also moving. For the purpose of understanding the Creative Healing treatments, the picture of the spine must be that of a flexible column of substance.

All units of substance between the vertebrae are held together by the ligamentous structure that provides the major vertical alignment of the body. This structure is flexible because the joints of the spine act as hinges. A joint is defined as "the unit formed by two contiguous bones (in this case, vertebrae) including the substance between them" and we know joints can move! During treatments, the Creative Healer's full attention is concentrated on the substance that provides a cushion between the vertebrae and not on the individual vertebra.

Substance. In Creative Healing a key word is substance. Mr. Stephenson used the word substance to include all the tissues, cartilage, ligaments, tendons, muscles, connective, nerve and synovial tissues, spinal fluid, etc., that contain, support, surround, join, and protect the vertebrae: our backbones. Aches and pains along the spine are almost always because of a displacement of substance, which may move out of position toward the back or toward either side and it may swell, be painful and/or affect the efficiency of other organs. One may recognize that vertebrae are out of place but the bones are never touched. It is the substance between the vertebrae, mostly cartilage, that the Creative Healer concentrates on moving and molding and repositioning to its proper place in the envisioned column. The bones will move with it as a unit.

Remolding Cartilage. Remolding cartilage permits the treatment to have effect, for cartilage can be molded like very firm clay. Cartilage is formable in that it not only yields to a formative force, but (in contrast to other tissue) it retains the form imparted to it. The cartilage contained in the substance between two consecutive vertebrae gives it body and makes it moldable. From a distorted form that may be due to displacement, the substance can be remolded into its natural shape as it is repositioned. It will retain this shape if adequately supported by the ligamentous structure.

Because this intervertebral substance holds together when it is displaced, a Creative Healer can remold and replace it in its natural position, removing any wedge effect and relieving the pain. If the substance is protruding it may be swollen and warmer than the surrounding tissue, but because of the moldable nature that the cartilage gives the entire substance, replacement or repositioning can be done.

Successive Remolding. This remolding may need to be done in successive treatments because the ligamentous structure may not be strong enough to sustain its new shape in only one treatment. When the structure becomes weakened, it allows the protrusion of intervertebral substance and becomes palpable. These protrusions cut off or diminish nourishment to the nerves that nourish organs and to ligaments that hold things together.

Thus, each remolding treatment, even if it does not last permanently, enables the ligaments to be more adequately nourished because the nourishment comes down the spinal column directly to the weakened places. Eventually they become strong and able to hold the entire substance in place. Then the protrusion disappears and the weak area becomes strong.

The Use of the Quarter Twist

Many specific names are used in connection with back trouble. However, no matter how widely the names vary, their treatment does not. Creative Healing treatments are based on restoring the flow of energy through the spinal column to allow nature to heal. From this point of view, names are irrelevant.

The parts of the spine most apparent to viewing or touching are the bony projections at the median line. They are the posterior parts of the spinous processes. The spinous processes are the posterior parts of the vertebrae.

In a healthy spine with normal flexibility, a depression or hollow occurs between each two consecutive spinous processes. The hollow is easily discerned when pressed by the thumb held in a horizontal position. If there is no hollow, if the space is filled level or even protruding, there is an obvious displacement of substance. There may be displacement not only on the median line but also on one or both sides. Creative Healing treatments remold these protrusions and reposition the substance that has moved out of place. Even when the back trouble is not caused by a displacement of intervertebral substance in the sense of its forming a palpable protrusion, the trouble can still be taken care of by the remolding movement between the vertebrae. The remolding is followed with a massage down the spine to bring in circulation and nourishment to the nerves.

The tip of the thumb is the tool for repositioning protrusions between the spinous processes. The three-knobbed formation at the end of the bony tip of the thumb is an ideal instrument with which to contact the out-of-place substance and enables the Creative Healer to feel it return to the correct position.

Pure, cold-pressed olive oil is most compatible for the great variety of human skin. It allows the hands to glide smoothly even when perspiration is present and acts like invisible gloves to protect both the patient and the helper. It is also an effective medium for heat transfer, both for the detection of hot spots and for withdrawing heat from the body (as in pneumonia or kidney treatments).

Position

Patient sits on a bench. Creative Healer sits behind.

➧ **Step 1: Seated position.** To treat the back, the patient sits on a bench with a firm level surface. The buttocks are fully supported by the bench, not hanging over the bench or the spine will sag. The spaces between the vertebrae can then open to receive the displaced substance. If the person lies on the stomach these spaces will close and will close more tightly if pressure is applied. Also, in the erect position the spine is aligned with the weight of the body on it, which is the natural situation and gravity works positively in bringing the life force from the head.

➧ **Step 2: Use of quarter twist.** You will replace and remold substance by using the thumb in a gentle quarter twist movement. To do this, place the cushion of the thumb on the back, horizontal to the spine, between two vertebrae, with

Beginning and ending positions for the quarter twist

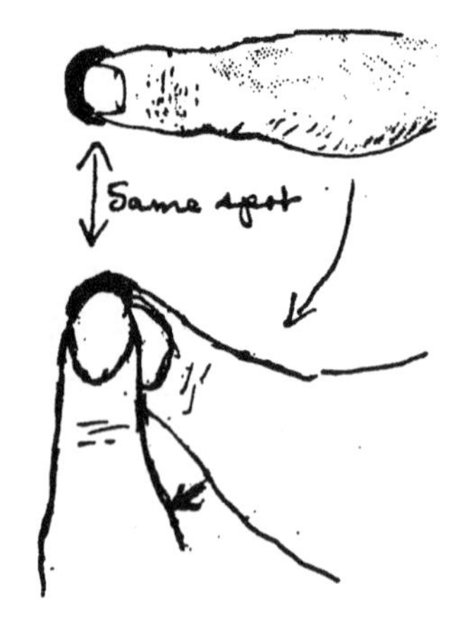

the palm and fingers lying flat. Then with a light pressure, rotate the thumb on its cushion as a pivot until it is vertical (pointing upward). The hand follows the motion of the thumb naturally. Begin at the bottom of the spine and repeat the quarter twist treatment in exactly the same way for each vertebra. Do not go beyond the quarter twist movement or the substance could be displaced again. If displacement occurs not only on the median line but also to the right or left of the spine, shift the cushion of the thumb to that side. You can use both thumbs, one to the right and one to the left: the left thumb beginning horizontally but rotating counterclockwise and just the opposite of the thumb on the right. When the displacement is to the sides, mentally direct the pressure along a line that is angled toward the median. The idea is to compact the joint by directing the substance into the spinal column where it belongs: see it in its correct place. During the entire twist the thumb stays in the depression between the two vertebrae: do not let it slide out of place.

In the lumbar region, the body of a vertebra is more forward from its spinous process than are the smaller vertebrae on up the spine, so that the direction of pressure to treat a lateral (either side) protrusion will be graduated as you move up the spine.

In treating the spine, work from the bottom to the top—each part of the spine's lower portion is the foundation for what sits above it. Attempt to have all depressions uniform; however, perfect uniformity cannot be achieved and is never observed (we are not perfect). The remolding is followed with a massage down the spine one hand following the other as far as the sacrum, to stimulate circulation. This is the kind of help family members can give each other when no specific back problems exist because it can strengthen the back.

When the substance yields and moves into place under the thumb, it is no longer palpable. The degree of pressure and speed of rotation of the thumb are governed by the time the substance needs to warm, yield and move into place. One develops a sense for using only enough pressure to feel the substance yield. Any pressure beyond this would be excessive and unnecessary. It is also better to work too slowly than too fast and to work with a gentle, healing touch.

➧ **Step 3: Check the symmetry.** Use both thumbs and fingertips to determine what condition lies just beneath the surface. Check for protruding substance, sharp contractions, asymmetry of the joints as well as the progress of the molding quarter twists. With oil on the hands, let the thumbs or fingers glide gently over the areas in question to determine what lies beneath, comparing one side with the other. Another way to check the symmetry is to use the index finger on one side of the spine and the middle fingertip of the same hand, on the other side. Glide the fingers upward, vertebra by vertebra, in short intermittent strokes, each stroke overlapping the upper portion of the last one, without removing the fingers from their firm contact with the spine. The movement is not smooth but jerky. Another valuable movement for checking and remolding work is the scissors movement ; see below.

If a patient feels faint when you are working along the spine or neck with the principle of replacing substance, let them lie down to rest before continuing. Freeing the blocked flow of nerve life allows it to speed along its path, creating a "gap" in the flow of energy until equilibrium can again be established and a feeling of faintness may be the result. This might also be a sign that a kidney treatment is needed.

➤ ➤ ➤CAUTION: If you find a reddish, bluish or mottled swelling filled with fine lines along the spine, and the swelling feels firm as though it were attached to the spine, stop any treatment to that area. It could be a blood clot and that must not be disturbed. This is the sole prohibition for using the quarter twist to reshape or relieve back pain.

Remolding of the entire spine is a treatment for strengthening the back. The following example shows the possibilities for this hands-on work:

Example from Creative Healers

I watched as an expert Creative Healer (my teacher) remolded the thoracic curve on a young woman's back to be correct and really more beautiful. He worked upward from the lower back, doing the quarter twist first on the right side in the space between each vertebra, then on the left. The thumbs moved upward together, pushing a little flesh ahead to better feel what came under the thumbs. The hands moved smoothly and gently and were never removed from the body until they reached the top.

With each quarter twist, an audible gurgle began low and deep inside her body and gurgled up the spine to the throat area. When the healer's hands reached the seventh cervical, the gurgles stopped. The change in the contour of the spine had been corrected and her posture improved so much that the woman's husband, who came in after the treatment, noticed the difference immediately.

The Scissors Movement

Another valuable movement for remolding the spine is the scissors movement, which loosens obstructions of nourishment to the spinal tracts and reestablishes the nourishment. When this treatment is followed by a light stroking (down only) with the palms, the life force is drawn down through the spinal tracts. This treatment is one of the most effective ways of evaluating the spine, to understand the conditions present and how to approach them. This is the way to check for protruding substance, for sharp contractions, for asymmetry of the joints as well as the progress of the remolding and to check on the symmetry of the spine to find the least thing that might not be in order beneath the surface.

This treatment is excellent for multiple sclerosis and other ailments of a similar nature where the life that should move through the spinal tracts has been shut down. The combined scissors and stroking treatment is also excellent for the elderly when they are stiff and their movements are difficult.

Position

The client sits upright on a bench; the Creative Healer sits behind at a comfortable height and distance to accomplish the work described. Use olive oil on the hands for protection and ease of operation.

Scissors movement

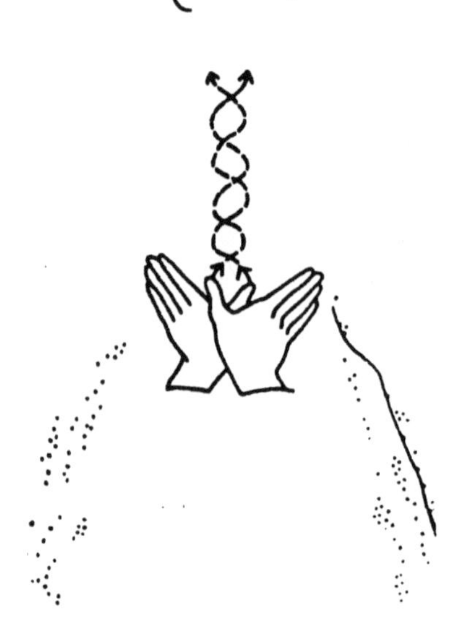

Step 1: Placement of thumbs. In the scissors movement, the thumbs act like the two blades of a pair of scissors. The important part of this concept is that the blades are of unequal length, due to the position of the hands on the person's back. Holding the fingers together as units, place the hands on each side of the spine just above the sacrum, with the thumbs crossing each other at the center line of the back. Place the left thumb in the space between the right thumb and finger unit and the pad of the left thumb at the rivet spot, the space between the fifth lumbar vertebra and the sacrum. The left thumb protrudes to the right of the middle bone of the right thumb, thus the parts of the thumbs projecting beyond their crossing are unequal in length. The spine is centered in the opening between the two thumbs.

Step 2: Action of thumbs. The thumbs are brought together toward the intervertebral spaces on the spine. The left thumb is at the lower level (L5: sacrum) and the right thumb at the higher level (L4–L5) as described. By pivoting the thumbs as the "scissors" close, the pressures are between the vertebrae but are directed by the intentional mind toward a point 1 inch or more beneath the surface at the median line. As the thumbs pivot with a partial quarter twist, a gathering and feeding movement imparts a gentle loosening and rocking motion to the vertebrae.

Detail of thumbs

ration © 1996 Valerie Randall, All rights reserved

Proceed up the entire spine to the base of the neck. Then interchange the positions of the two thumbs and begin again, this time with the right thumb at the rivet spot on the left of the spine and the left thumb between the fifth and fourth lumbar vertebrae on the right of the spine, to repeat the entire movement. These two upward movements are called a pair.

Step 3: Drawing life force into spine. Draw strength into the back by stroking down over the spine with the palms, letting one follow the other so that when the first has reached the sacrum, the other palm starts at the top. Perform 5 or 6 pairs of the scissors movement in succession then stroke down over the spine in a double vacuum, one palm following the other. Repeat as needed.

Soft Vertebrae

In a case of back problems where there is no palpable protrusion of intervertebral substance and the spinous processes cannot be felt, Mr. Stephenson called it a soft vertebra. Such a soft spot on the spine is almost always because of an injury, where nourishment to the substance between two vertebrae was severely cut off, causing the substance to collapse and shrink above and below the affected vertebra, forcing it forward. The spinous process, bony protrusions of the vertebrae that can be seen or felt, is also displaced forward. The soft spot includes the entire region between two spinous processes, with the process (bone) between them appearing to be missing. Here there will be trouble in the spine without any protrusion of intervertebral substance. The spot is soft or spongy to the touch.

If treatment is given soon after an injury, restoration may come within a few days. But if the soft spot is of long standing, the patient may have limited use of the legs, being unable to stand full weight or to walk without support. If there was further injury to the soft spot (an extremely vulnerable place) there may be paralysis of the legs. This is most likely to occur if the soft spot is located at the fifth lumbar vertebra.

Treat a soft spot by nourishing it and it will gradually again thicken, the vertebera having moved out of its tilted position and back into its natural position. Necessary remolding may be done only when the spinous process (bone) again becomes palpable.

The procedure is the same, no matter where the soft spot is located but since a soft spot occurs most frequently where the spine joins the sacrum at the fifth lumbar vertebra, the treatment is described for this place. Mr. Stephenson named it the "rivet spot."

Positions for soft vertebrae

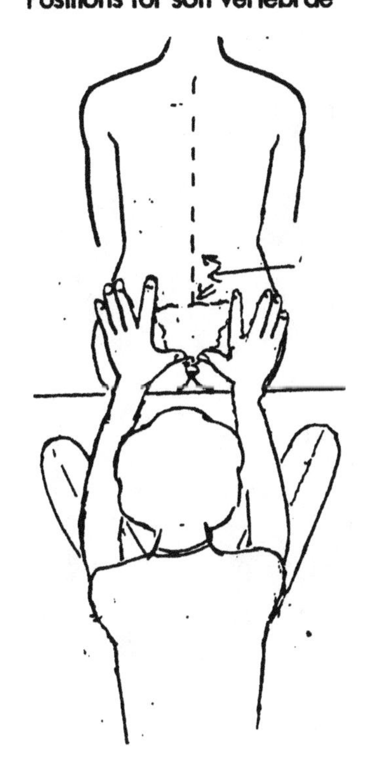

If the soft vertebra is in the thoracic region, check first on the left side of the spine for a swollen column, described under that treatment on page 3–13. This must be cleared before attempting to treat the spine.

➧ **Step 1: Positioning of patient.** If the patient has strength to be in a sitting position, even with support at the elbows or underarms, this is the position of choice. If this is not possible, the patient must lie on the stomach, draped over a mound of pillows. The back must be rounded so that the soft spot is free of any compression, and the feeding movement upwards from the sacrum may begin in this position. When the patient is strong enough to sit upright, the benefits of the feeding treatments will accrue more rapidly. Patient comfort is important. Any twisting or jerking will destroy the benefits of the delicate nourishing action. If the patient can sit on the bench, the Creative Healer sits behind.

➧ **Step 2: Positioning of Creative Healer for upward feeding.** Place your thumbs about 1 inch apart on the patient's back where the sacrum joins the tailbone in full horizontal contact on either side of the center line. Spread your fingers and rest them on the patient's buttocks. Rest your forearms on your spread-apart thighs. By moving your legs slowly together, the fingers and thumbs are pushed up the sacrum. This smooth and slow UPWARD ONLY massage strengthens that entire area of the body. As the soft spot is approached and the thumbs are about to leave the support of the sacrum in their upward glide, be careful that they continue on the same plane as that of the sacrum and glide lightly over the soft area without pressure.

➤➤➤ CAUTION: The thumbs must not dip into the soft spot!

Step 3: Diagonal feeding. For the first 3 or 4 sessions the treatment should be comprised of the upward feeding. When the patient reports feeling stronger in that area and the soft spot feels less soft as the tissues are beginning to strengthen, then you may add a diagonal movement to the straight upward movement. These gentle diagonal movements are also done with the thumb. Begin the stroke on the sacrum with the thumbs separated more than before; they are far enough apart so that when they leave the sacrum they contact the erecting muscles on either side of the spine in the lumbar region. They move diagonally toward a spot on the spine that is several inches above the soft spot and meet there.

Step 4: Side feeding ending in quarter twist. Begin the side feeding movement after several sessions with the upward and diagonal massage, after which there will be a noticeable strengthening. Side feeding movements bring the thumb tips at right angles to the spine (as earlier described) but as the thumbs approach the edges of the soft spot, perform the quarter twist with each thumb without any added molding pressure. If you were working in the thoracic region, the thumbs would follow the direction of the ribs.

➤ ➤ ➤CAUTION: Several sessions of the three combined feeding movements will be necessary when the thumbs must not dip into the soft spot.

Duration

These sessions may last 15 or 20 minutes. The length is often guided by the responses of the body. You may feel a sensation of pressures being equalized under the thumbs or fingers and occasionally you may hear gurgling. With the flow of circulation, the patient may experience a tingling feeling into the toes or a sensation of warmth radiating from the area into the legs. When the soft spot is at the fifth lumbar vertebra, strong sensations may be felt in the abdomen and sometimes all the way up the back into the head. Continue the treatment as long as these responses continue—they are desirable. Life force that had been diminished is again increasing.

Occasionally the patient may have a strong burning sensation, as of a raw cut, radiating from the soft spot to both sides. This sensation does not stem from the treatment (it is purely incidental to it) but is caused by a seepage from the capsules surrounding the tilted vertebra; it could be a seepage of synovial fluid.

In such a case, use very gentle, side-feeding movements directly over the channels where the burning sensation occurs. End the movements with a quarter twist without any pressure and with the thought of sealing off the seepage.

In very rare instances the feeding may cause a sudden release of nerve life or circulation that may be unpleasant, even painful, particularly in the legs. This reaction is not harmful but is good for the entire process of restoring correct circulation to the spine by this gentle approach. You must be careful not to apply pressure for remolding prematurely as this would be undesirable. This treatment takes time and patience.

➤➤➤ **CAUTION: If there is a reddish or bluish mottled swelling along the spine filled with fine lines that, when touched, feel firm as though attached to the spine, do not give any treatment in that area.**

Blood Clot on the Spine

A violent fall or an auto accident are largely responsible for a blood clot on the spine. Depending on the severity of the injury, the range of effects on the nerve tissue can extend from minor disturbances to complete paralysis below the level of the body where the injury occurred. Severe injuries cause high compression plus twisting along the spine and injury to or rupture of vascular tissues, causing blood to flow against or around the spinal cord and the nerves immediately emanating from that region.

The condition should be treated as soon as possible before the clot hardens and leads to further damage and deterioration by shutting off the feed to the damaged tissues and nerves. The starvation of these tissues can cause permanent paralysis. A clot is most often found between the fifth lumbar vertebra and the sacrum, with the next most probable location in the lumbar region itself, but it may be found anywhere.

If the initial condition continues to deteriorate, it can manifest as a soft vertebra, regardless of the degree of paralysis that may have ensued. From the point of view of Creative Healing, a soft vertebra is always caused by the cutting off of the feed to the tissues in the adjacent intervertebral spaces. When a soft vertebra is encountered, you can be suspicious that it may have been caused by a blood clot on the spine and the resultant deterioration. Any contact to the tissues must, especially at first, be of a very gentle, even subtle nature. No matter at what stage the condition is encountered, the treatment must be designed to break up any possible clot, thus preventing a more permanent obstructive mass from lodging in the affected area.

Position

The patient sits, with arms on arm rests if such support is necessary, or lies prone over a mound of pillows to open up the spaces between the vertebrae. Creative Healer sits behind patient in the first instance and stands in the second,

➤ **Step 1:** Apply the treatment described in soft vertebrae, page 3–7.

Step 2: In addition, intelligently apply breaking up circles and stroking feeding motions directed towards the tissues in the space or spaces between the vertebrae that have been injured. Also, apply gentle molding motions. The molding gradually replaces the supportive substance so that the restrictive pressures may be eliminated. Thus, the compression is lifted from the finer tissues between the vertebrae, and the vertebrae are ultimately returned to their proper spacing.

All this is done in order that the circulation may be reestablished, circulation being the only agent in the body that can carry in repair and carry out waste. From all that has been said it is obvious that a heavy-handed approach could never bring healing to a case of this kind.

Pain Between the Shoulders

Locating the spot

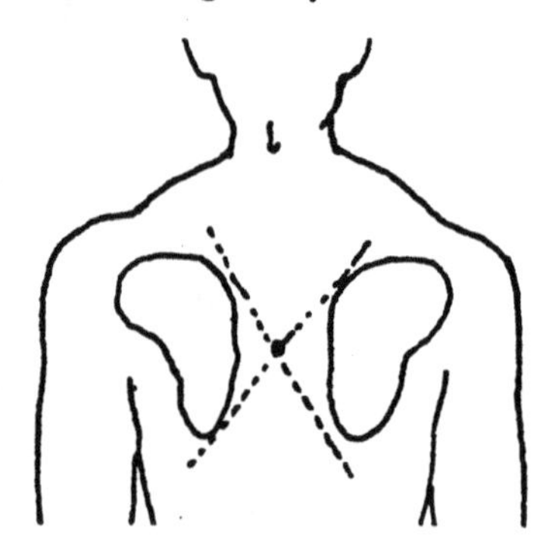

On the spine between the shoulder blades (scapulas), there is a spot that often causes pain so severe that it seems to go through to the chest and can give the impression of a serious heart disturbance.

Position

The patient sits on a bench; the Creative Healer sits behind.

Step 1: Locating the spot. To find this spot, when it is in trouble, consider the section of the spine centered between the shoulder blades. As the thumb glides down along the center line of the body, find one of the spaces between the spinous processes that is quite sensitive, or painful. It may even give off heat. If in doubt about the space selected, draw a line from the top of one shoulder blade to the bottom of the other shoulder blade and repeat on the opposite side. The spot where these lines intersect is usually the spot for this treatment. Check the spaces between the spinous processes immediately above and below the sensitive one. Because pain so often occurs here, it is called the spot for pain between the shoulders. A vital nerve and circulation center is located at this spot and the pain is caused by a displacement of substance. This displacement causes the space to feel fuller and firmer to the touch than the normal adjacent spaces.

Pressing and rotating

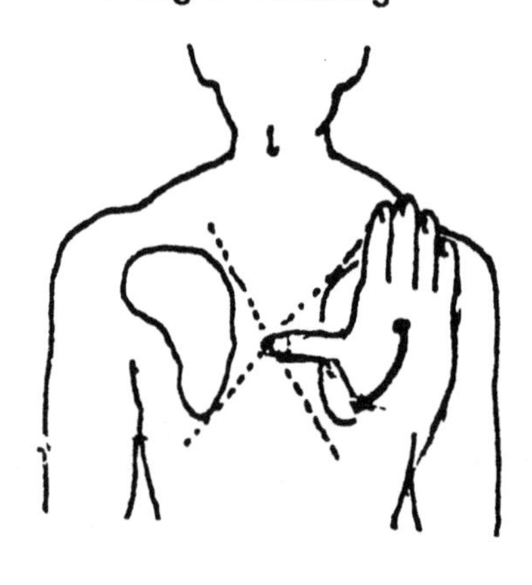

Step 2: Pressing and rotating, the quarter twist. To replace the substance, place the cushion of your right thumb on the spot on the center of the spine. The thumb is horizontal and the palm and fingers lie flat on the person's back. Press straight forward on the spot with the thumb and at the same time rotate the thumb clockwise using its cushion as a pivot. Carry the rotation through to where the thumb is vertical. The hand follows the motion of the thumb in a natural manner. The pressure, applied in this manner will push the substance into position. If the displacement is not straight back, but to the right or left of the spine (a lateral protrusion), shift the cushion of your thumb to that side. If the left hand is used, merely interchange left and right, and replace clockwise by counterclockwise, in the above description. When the displacement is straight back, the pressure is directed straight forward into the body. When the displacement is to the right of the spine, do not push straight forward, but direct

the pressure along a horizontal line that is angled slightly to the left. For a displacement to the left, direct pressure angled to the right.

Be careful, in all cases, not to carry the rotation of the thumb beyond the vertical line, through the spot. This might displace the substance anew. It is tempting to carry the rotation beyond the vertical, especially if the substance has not yielded. Do not give in to this temptation but instead, repeat the treatment, as needed, to achieve the desired result.

In severe cases where pain persists, it is helpful to coordinate the breathing as the pressure is applied. In these cases of severe pain between the shoulders, ask the patient to draw a deep breath and let it out slowly. The pressure is exerted and the quarter twist performed slowly as the patient exhales. Ask the person to simultaneously pull the shoulders back and together, as much as possible. After completing the pressure, hold the shoulders in the pulled-back position for about 30 seconds. Make sure the patient's shoulders are not pulled upward, as in a shrug.

It may be helpful to stand and place your left hand on the patient's chest opposite the painful spot to balance the pressure on the back. But you should not attempt to pull or bend the spine backward over the contact point of the thumb as you apply pressure on the chest with your left hand.

Pain between the shoulders may also occur when there is no apparent displacement of substance, but merely a contraction at and around the spot. Loosen it by first working on the muscles on both sides. Then, with the thumb placed in the same position as for the quarter twist movement pry apart the spinous processes that have drawn too close together. Use the inner edge of the thumb, while performing the quarter twist as before.

➧ **Step 3: Stroking down the spine.** In all cases, after working on the painful spot sit down again behind the patient, and stroke down over the spine with both hands, letting one follow the other. This encourages the blood and nerve life to flow freely, to complete the healing.

➤➤➤ CAUTION: Before working on contractions at and around the spot for pain between the shoulders, always check at the spine for a swelling. This is best described as a "swollen column" that runs parallel to the spine. It is most often located about 1 inch or more to the left of the spine. It will be a raised, enlarged band of tissue about 1/2 to 1 inch wide and, occasionally, a reddish color. It may feel above normal temperature to the touch. This column may be highly sensitive. It is vital that it be cleared BEFORE any work is done on the contractions at and around the spot for pain between the shoulders. (See moving the swollen column, page 3–13.)

The Flu Spot

There is a breathing nerve center that is helpful in heading off the the threat and speeding the recovery from flu. Where there is flu, this spot will be found to be sore and sensitive and a strong contraction has closed down this nerve center. In any respiratory treatment this nerve center should be repositioned and centered.

When Mr. Stephenson worked in the mines he used this treatment to restore respiration to a person who was unconscious from an electric shock and whose breathing had stopped.

Position

The patient sits on a bench; the Creative Healer sits behind.

Placement for the flu spot

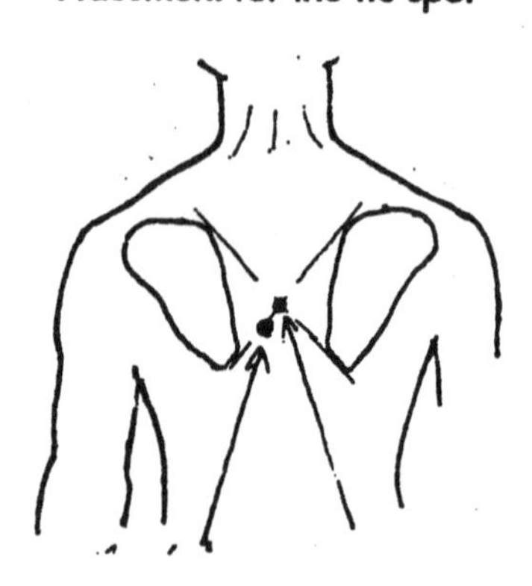

➧ **Step 1: Placement.** Find the spot for pain between the shoulders; see previous treatment. Place the tip of the thumb to the left of the first space below the spot for pain between the shoulders and hold in a horizontal position straight out from the body.

➧ **Step 2: Breaking up movement.** Keep your thumb stiff and your fingers touching the body in such a way that they support and add strength to the thumb. Then extend your arm from the shoulder and maintain this position while the thumb does a gentle, breaking up movement that breaks up the strong contraction at the nerve center in the mid-section of the body. Envision that the thumb's vibration is penetrating to the center of the chest (like a drill).

➧ **Step 3: Continue until pain is gone.** Soon the patient will complain of a pain deep in the center of the chest. This is the breaking up of the congestion that has caused the illness so the patient is congratulated and told to "tell me when it stops hurting." When the pain stops, usually within 3 or 4 minutes, the treatment is finished. The body will complete the healing by itself.

➧ **Step 4: Completion on the back.** Stroke down over the center back to bring in circulation. The flu treatment might include bringing the area to normal temperature, and doing the liver, kidney or heart treatments, as needed.

Example from Creative Healers

Three days before I was to fly to Australia to join my husband and present a workshop on Creative Healing, I became ill with flu symptoms. A friend, who was planning to take care of our home while we were gone, offered to help. I showed her on her back where to find the right spot and what to do. She complied and with the desired results, I was able to fly on schedule. NOTE: Mr. Stephenson also recommended a small glass of whiskey for relaxation of the chest area. We tried that, too.

Swollen Column

Area of swollen column

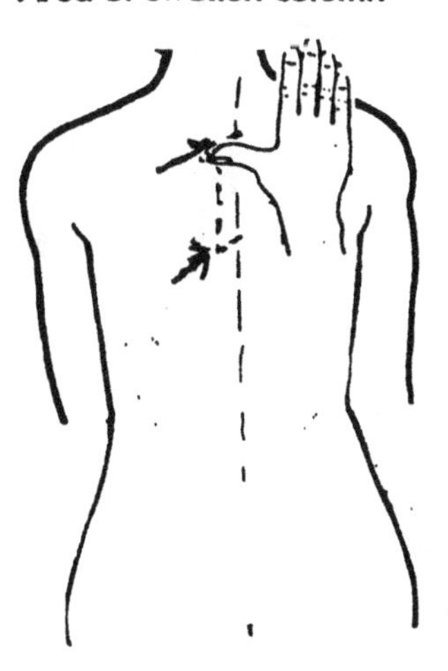

Before working on contractions at and around the Spot for Pain Between the Shoulders, always check for a swollen column that will be parallel to the spine and about 1 inch or more to the left. It will be a raised, enlarged band of tissue 1/2 to 1 inch wide and 3 to 5 inches long. It may be a reddish color and feel above normal temperature to the touch and highly sensitive.

➤➤➤ CAUTION: It may feel above normal temperature to the touch and may be highly sensitive. It is vital that it be cleared BEFORE any work is done on muscle contractions at and around the spot for pain between the shoulders.

If a reddish, bluish or mottled swelling filled with fine lines is found along the spine and feels as though it were attached to the spine, do not do any treatment in that area. See blood clot, page 3–9.

Position

The patient sits on a bench; the Creative Healer sits behind. Olive oil is used on the left thumb.

➧ **Step 1: Follow upper edge and apply quarter twist.** The thumb is used at the top of the column to follow the natural path between the ribs, which leads from the heart spot on the back to the spine. As the thumb reaches the space between the vertebrae at the left of the spine apply the quarter twist movement with the thought of embedding a nerve that lies too close to the surface.

➧ **Step 2: Work to the center of column.** Place the thumb vertically, in lengthwise contact, at the top left side of the the swollen column (the side away from the spine). Move the thumb very gently to the center of the column. Repeat this movement down the entire length of the column, displacing the hand downward each time, by the length of the last bone (top phalanges) of the thumb. This is the most effective part of the thumb for this movement.

➧ **Step 3: Follow lower edge and apply quarter twist.** As in step 1, with the thumb, follow the natural path between the ribs from the lower end of the swollen column to the spine. Again, at the space between the vertebrae, left of center, apply the quarter twist with the same thought of embedding the nerve more deeply.

➧ **Step 4: Work up and down the column and embed nerves.** With the thumb lengthwise as in step 2, work up the column moving the thumb to the center of the column. This is a gentle, breaking up movement, continued up and down the column, going over to the spine at each end of the column and embedding the nerve between the vertebrae with the quarter twist. The center of the column will often feel like a taut cord. Never force the movement through or beyond this cord until the cord has been dissolved. Where the thumb passes through the column with no feeling of passing through an obstruction, perform the quarter twist at the spine to bury the nerve more deeply. The column will grow shorter at each end until dissolved.

Duration

Sometimes there will be a marked improvement in the column at the first treatment after 10 or 15 minutes. But usually, it will take several treatments to completely break it up. Only then, proceed to work on contractions in the vicinity of the spot for pain between the shoulders.

In addition to working at the spine, there will often be obstructions and contractions in the deeper muscle tissue that lies near the spine, parallel to it. This is the tissue of the big muscles that hold the body erect in standing, walking and sitting. The rope-like character of the tissue revealing such obstructions may extend over lengths of 6 to 8 inches. Obstructions in these muscles are residual contractions that have accumulated due to exhaustion of the muscle tissues; insufficient circulation has kept them from being restored to their normal, full-toned state. Work on the muscles to remove these residual contractions until the tissue is smooth and no longer presents any ropiness or cord-like feeling to the hand. See back muscles treatment, page 3–29.

Pain or Disturbance at Heart Spot on the Back

Breaking up congestion

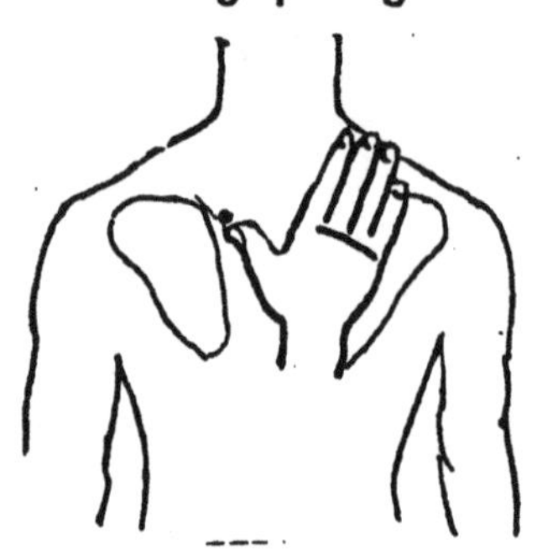

A severe chilling of the body can sometimes set up a major disturbance at the #1 spot for inward goiter: the heart spot on the back. The pain may occur right at the spot or along the channel that, following the contour of the shoulder blade, leads downward and forward passing low under the arm and continuing to the #5 heart spot on the front.

Position

The patient sits on a bench; the Creative Healer sits behind.

➧ **Step 1: Break up congestion.** The treatment consists of relieving the congestion at the sensitive spot. If this spot is severely congested, it often feels hot to the oiled palm. Perform a very gentle clockwise breaking up movement with the cushion of the thumb. The area is no larger in diameter than the eraser on a lead pencil. The thumb should not be too heavily oiled, but should cling to the skin taking the surface tissue with it. The movement is performed very gently for 3 or 4 minutes.

Stroking movements

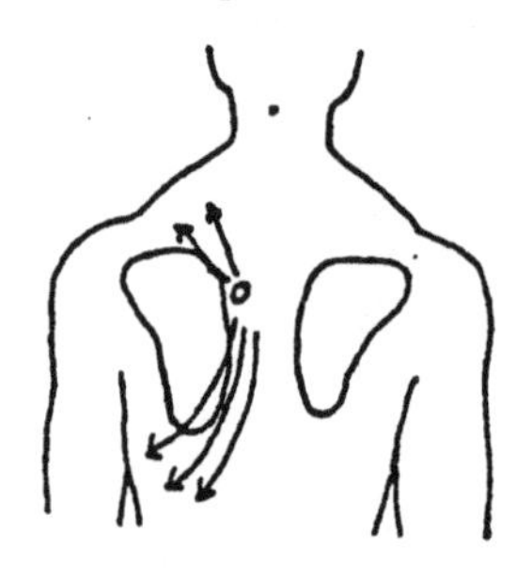

➧ **Step 2: Stroking movements.** Follow the breaking up movement with stroking movements using both hands up over the left shoulder. Alternate the hands in a fanning pattern to distribute into the circulation the substance that has been broken up below. Be careful not to touch the spot because material is fed back into the circulation. Include some circular motion to the filter area at the left side of the base of the neck. Then, starting just below the spot and again being careful not to touch it, stroke downward and forward beneath the shoulder blade. In this stroking, the fingers of the right hand lead and those of the left hand trail as the hands are again alternated. After making sure that the dispersion both above and below the spot is thoroughly carried out, feed the released material through toward the #5 heart spot. Work along the channel, downward and forward, passing low under the arm to the #5 heart spot. Red blotches may appear along the course of the strokes. Break them up individually by the circular breaking up movement. Finish cleaning them out by stroking over them with the thumb.

➧ **Step 3: Complete with patient lying down.** After completing the work on the back, ask the person to lie down. Following the remainder of the channel, continue to draw the hands forward, upward and under the breast to the #5 heart spot so that the released material reenters the circulation, both directly and through the stomach.

The idea of draining off the material toward the heart explains why a person will occasionally feel a discomfort on the left side in the region of the lower ribs, in front. If this occurs, give the stroking treatment over the heart as in step 1 of the heart treatment, see page 4–21. This will disburse the excess material as well as the discomfort.

Contraction of Muscles Under and Around the Shoulder Blade

This condition creates so many problems that the patient will be unable to pinpoint the pain. Some of the complaints are neck pain, tennis elbow, general arm pain, difficulty turning the head, numbness, tingling in the arms and hands, and inability to rest at night because of the stiffness of the muscles above the shoulder blade that affect the neck as well.

Most daily activities require the arms to be extended forward from the body. This tends to move the shoulder blade from its proper position in the back of the body to its side and the blade becomes dislocated. The situation is compounded if the person sleeps on either side with the arms extended forward or in distorted positions attempting to compensate for discomfort. Such positions will cut off circulation to the muscles in question and sleeping time is inadequate for sufficient recovery. The pain is always worse in the morning. The snapping or cracking one hears is often described as a bad joint. However, there is no joint connecting the shoulder blade with the body skeleton except by way of attachment to the collarbone (clavicle). Otherwise, the shoulder blade is completely suspended in muscle. Muscle contractions have a distorting effect on this region.

Position

The patients sits; the Creative Healer stands facing the patient's side opposite the affected shoulder.

➧ **Step 1: Placement.** Using the hand that is at the back of the patient (the leading hand) reach across the back and under the patient's armpit and place 4 fingers between the shoulder blade and the ribs. Use the other hand on the front of the ailing shoulder to assist.

Shoulder blade is moved up, then toward the spine

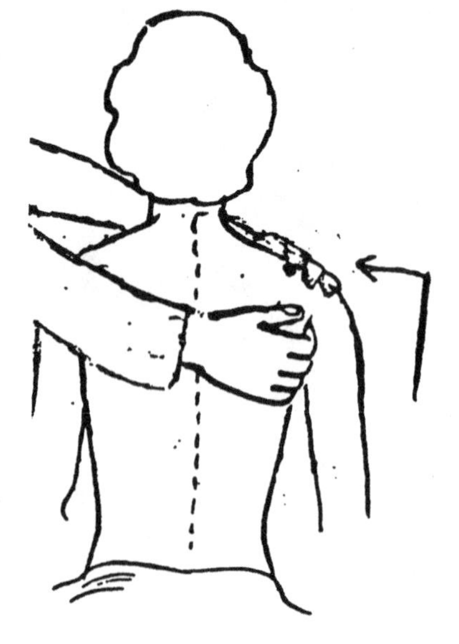

➧ **Step 2: Circumduction of the blade.** With both hands, gently but persistently move the shoulder blade in a circular motion upward towards the head then towards the spine, the fingertips of the leading hand all the while pressing inward and high up under the armpit towards the spine. This may be painful as you begin, so be brief and let the region rest so that circulation can enter. Repeat the circumduction; this time it will be much less painful. Continue until contraction subsides and cracking or popping has stopped. It is possible to achieve this in one treatment although several treatments may be needed.

If the patient is very heavily muscled, have him/her lie on the side opposite to the affected shoulder and place the arm of this affected side so that the forearm rests on the hip. Use both hands and, with the patient facing away from you, perform the circumduction. Instead of using only the 4 fingers of the leading hand you may use the thumb so that its tip rests high up towards the back of the armpit. The other hand assists in the circumduction by grasping the front of the shoulder joint with its cupped palm. This pressure plus the circumduction stretches the muscles. The heel of the leading hand may continue pressure as it glides down over the shoulder blade towards the spine. The muscles will change shape so that the shoulder blade can once again resume its natural position.

Example from Creative Healers

This is a condition I suffered for nearly six months. I went to medical doctors, chiropractors and therapists without relief. Then while collecting all the Creative Healing treatments to put into this book, I found this treatment which described my condition perfectly. My husband performed the treatment immediately and the muscles in my shoulder began to relax. By the third day, the pain and tingling in my hands was gone and I could go to bed without waking to the pain that had been increasing for six months.

Whiplash

Whiplash has become very prevalent; however, because the injury seems inaccessible from many approaches, it has the reputation of being something very difficult to treat. Recovery is often extremely slow, stringing out over weeks, months and even years, and sometimes never completed. Because of all this, whiplash cases appear to have a sinister aspect. However, this must not deter the Creative Healer who has the knowledge to resolve nearly every one of these cases and only needs to realize it. Do not be deterred from offering treatment even in the most extreme cases of whiplash or wry neck. You have the knowledge to solve the problems in a gentle, loving manner.

Position

The patient sits on a bench so that the spine carries the weight of the body; the Creative Healer sits behind.

➧ **Step 1:** Work on the spine from the bottom to the top to replace substance between vertebrae and relax muscles.

➧ **Step 2:** Give the general treatment, page 1–8; massage the neck gently and the muscles of the spine, using the palm after palm method. As these steps are repeated, the general condition of the spine will improve and the few spots needing special attention will be apparent. Remember Mr. Stephenson's observation that when any of the spinal curves are disturbed, the others will compensate for it.

➧ **Step 3:** Do the wry neck treatment; see next page.

Examples from Creative Healers

1. After an automobile accident the patient was suffering from back pain and whiplash. He was unable to turn his head either way. At first, unable to touch his neck because of the pain, work was done on the sciatic nerves and wherever sensitivity was found on the back. During this treatment he remarked that he was feeling sensations down his legs all the way to his toes. He was able to perform the sciatic exercises after the treatment. Still unable to work on the painful area of the neck around the cervical region three days later, a light General Treatment was given and a massage to his upper back from the shoulders up to the filter areas. This area was very sensitive and required the gentleness of touch that every Creative Healer discovers. Three days later while administering the general treatment, the triangular area between the "pain between the shoulders" spot up to the filters felt like little bits of gravel or sand. A gentle breaking-up movement over the area while resting the left hand loosely on his head, allowed a slow and gentle circumduction of the head. The fourth treatment took place 3 days later. He reported that his lower back felt much better and that the neck region seemed to be loosening up a little.There was still a gravelly feeling on the back but by placing the thumb along the cervical region with a strong thought of unlocking these painful spots, there was a decrease in the sensitivity and the feeling of gravel in the upper back region. The third step in the general treatment could be done in almost the normal manner. Three days later the area of the upper back that had been so sensitive was normal feeling to the touch.

2. A friend who had studied the introductory course in Creative Healing, asked me to work on her neck. She had had a whiplash two years earlier and was still wearing a neck brace occasionally when her neck was hurting. I insisted that she undress so I could work on the whole back.

When she sat down on the bench, it was immediately apparent that the tenth dorsal vertebra was very visibly projecting outward and to the right. I began gentle quarter-twists in the soft tissue at the base of the lumbar region on both sides of the spine. Reaching the projecting vertebra, I started the quarter twist an inch or more to the right of the projection. As each quarter-twist moved closer to the projection, it slipped back into line with the other vertebrae although it was still projecting out. Two more quarter twist passes from bottom to top and the vertebra moved into line. The general treatment was given to finish up and the problem was solved. This is the reason for working on the entire back for whiplash.

Extreme Cases of Stiff Neck—Wry Neck

Torticollis, wry neck and trouble in the cervical region of the spine happen often after whiplash. The vertebrae appear to be so tightly locked together that no one spot wants to give. These problems can also occur without whiplash.

Treat the spine, vertebra by vertebra, with the thumb of one hand, first one side then the other. Begin this work below the shoulder blades or lower and gently work up the spine and through the cervicals. At the same time, rest the other hand loosely on the patient's head and gently circumduct it opposite the thumb with each spine pressure as in the headache treatment, page 2–39. As the process is repeated a small response will be elicited at first and finally the increased responses will produce a compete unlocking of the spine.

The patient can easily tolerate these gentle movements and once the spine is unlocked and has lost its sensitivity, your work is done.

Lordosis and Disc Trouble

Disc trouble is one of the most painful, perplexing and hard to handle disturbances of the spine because the source of the trouble lies so deep and is apparently inaccessible within the spinal column.

The key concept of this Creative Healing treatment is that the entire substance between two vertebrae is held together by a ligamentous encapsulation and reacts as a unit. No one part of that unit can move or be affected without affecting the whole. For this reason the disc, which is farther to the anterior of the spine, can be worked on from the posterior of the spine, that is, on the outside of the body.

No new treatment methods are involved but you must adapt procedures to free that region of the spine from contractions by feeding, remolding and repositioning the intervertebral substance as needed. There is no rule about how much can be accomplished in any session. Patient comfort is the guide. The aim is to soothe, relax and provide conditions in which the body's healing forces are freed to overcome the injury. This is true even in the most extreme cases when patients are in bed or on the floor with such severe pain that they cannot move. Support with elbows must be firm enough with patient lying face down to prevent the injured spot from being impinged upon. The treatment frees the individual vertebrae to move in relation to each other so that the entire spine can move with some degree of comfort. The treatment may be applied even when an operation on the spine has been performed but has not produced the expected results. Proceed as though no operation had taken place and a completely satisfactory response may be expected, restoring the body to normal function and freeing the patient from pain.

Like the soft vertebra problem, disc trouble occurs most frequently between the fifth lumbar vertebra and the sacrum, with the next most frequent place between the fourth and fifth lumbars; however it could occur anywhere on the spine. In the lumbar region disc problems are often accompanied by a severe contraction of the postural muscles of the spine, causing a severe exaggerated flexing toward the front of the spine, a condition commonly called lordosis. If lordosis persists it leads to more deterioration of the condition within the spine because of increased interference in the nourishment of the tissues concerned. This deterioration adds to the patient's pain which, in turn, causes a still stronger contraction and a vicious circle of pain until surgery is performed.

Not all disc cases are complicated by lordosis, but when they are, the lordosis must first be treated before anything else is done—to forcibly reverse the exaggerated anterior flexing would simply cause more pain. Therefore, the condition must be treated by gentle means without causing further harm and pain.

Position

The patient sits on a bench; the Creative Healer sits behind, hands well-oiled with olive oil.

➧ **Step 1: Releasing tension.** Massage with full palm contact, fingers and thumbs extended but held together, up and around over the buttocks, clockwise on the right and counterclockwise of the left. The patient's pain has caused tension in the buttocks so the lifting of the heavy gluteal muscles often affords great relief.

➧ **Step 2: Check sciatic nerves.** Check the sciatic nerves with the fingertips in the jiggling and smoothing motions described in the sciatica treatment, page 3–23, allowing the patient to relax.

➧ **Step 3: Breaking up movement.** With plenty of oil on the thumbs, use the breaking up movement over the contracted area and test the intervertebral spaces. Work only on the surface. Even though your touch does not visibly penetrate, it will tell you what lies beneath the muscles and will help you determine what will relax in response to a reasonable pressure. When such a spot is reached, the patient will only be aware that a vital place has been contacted but will feel no pain.

➧ **Step 4: Feeding life force to the spine.** With the thumbs, feed life towards the spine as in the side feeding of a soft vertebra. This is done without the thought of molding substance to where it belongs. You will find that, beneath the surface, with no protrusion visible or palpable, substance has bulged out several inches towards the sides. Do not try to remold until the 3rd or 4th treatment unless it can be accepted by the patient with comfort. Think only of feeding in the life force and you may feel a flow or hear a gurgling, which is a good sign, but not the goal of the treatment. In disc problems, the troubled spot is the weakest spot of the spine. In severe lordosis cases, it is most frequently the rivet spot (L5–S1) in the lumbar region.

➧ **Step 5: Patient's help.** As soon as feasible, place your thumb on this weakest spot and have the patient move the pelvis back against it. Your thumb acts without pressure, merely as a support for the patient to lean against, enabling some flex with more comfort. This backward movement of the pelvis causes the intervertebral spaces of that region to open, allowing the flow of life to enter more freely. Then have the patient straighten up and exert a mild pressure with your thumb, right on center, to promote feeding action. Repeat this 2-step process several times, each time slightly increasing the pressure. Intersperse these repetitions with the thumb feeding massage from the sides and the palm massage over the buttocks.

Do this until the patient is able to move a little with comfort while staying strictly within the middle plane of motion: not allowing the spine to rotate at all. Then continue this 2-step procedure to the next space, (placing the thumb between the next two vertebrae, asking the patient to move back against it, and as he/she straightens again, pressing mildly with your thumb) and continue up the whole lumbar and thoracic regions, returning to earlier spaces when necessary.

➤ ➤ ➤CAUTION: Use no force! When there is forced motion, the spot with the disk trouble can be further injured; all stresses connected with force will converge and impinge on the weakest spot .

After the Creative Healing treatment has broken the grip of the lordosis, all the vertebrae can again share in providing motion and this flexibility enables the weakest spot to be fed and get relief from its former pain. By working this way at reasonable intervals, a weak spot will be built into a strong one.

➧ **Step 6: Relax muscles.** Next, the muscles on each side of the spine must be relaxed, one side at a time. To do this, the patient lays on the back with knees flexed. Place a cushion or sandbag against the patient's feet to keep them from sliding and to keep the patient free from strain. Use the hand closest to the knees to steady them by placing the hand lightly on top of both knees. Slide the free hand underneath the patient so that the pads of three fingers are touching the back just above the upper corner of the sacrum. Do not let the patient help you by raising or lifting his/her body. You can press the bed down with the back of your hand as it slides underneath to where the fingers are touching the muscles. Now the cushions of the fingers make small circular breaking up movements on the muscles. If the patient is relaxed, this will feel very good. The lumbar muscles are very thick, and even though the surface muscles appear to be relaxed, the effect of the breaking up circles penetrates to those contracted bundles of muscle fiber, deep in toward the bottom of the muscles worked on. Again, as you work you may hear a gurgling sound. Work up one side through the lumbar and the thoracic regions then move to the other side of the patient and repeat the same movements. Never reach across beneath the spine! Always slide the hand in on the side on which you want to work.

➧ **Step 7: Groin to ankle relaxation.** When the patient is free of tension and pain with the back extended flat on the bed, ask him/her to spread out the legs and work on the groin, thigh and down the legs to the ankle spots. Do not prolong this relaxing work as the patient needs to get up, move about and let the spine carry the weight.

In later treatments, when the patient has improved and is lying with knees flexed, ask him/her to raise the pelvis and stretch the spine, extending it so that, when it is again lowered, it may lie in long contact with the bed, each vertebra lying as loose and far apart from the adjacent ones as possible. This is a good exercise at night before going to sleep, and will enable the weak spot to feed during the night instead of remaining cramped and contracted. This exercise is beneficial in cases of ordinary back fatigue, when there is no lordosis. Another beneficial exercise for lordosis is bending over from the hips so that the trunk, arms and head dangle limply. While doing this treatment the patient should think of each vertebra as part of a stack of dominoes, removed from the stack one by one from the top down as he bends and similarly replaced one by one as he stands erect.

Warn the patient against using heating pads or lamps (sciatica and heat, below).

Sciatica and Heat

As for the kidney patient, warn the sciatica patient against using local heat, either in the form of a heating pad or a heating lamp. Though it may bring momentary relief, it can actually be a source of increased trouble. Such relief is deceptive because when the heat is removed, the pain will return. Moreover, this temporary relief involves a serious risk, causing one tissue to swell in relation to another, because different tissues have different rates and coefficients of expansion. Cartilage and other tissue may not properly fit into position after the application of local heat. This improper alignment may further impair nourishment to the injured spot.

Many people, misled by the deceptive relief provided by the heating pad, conclude that if a little is good, more must be better. They may turn up the heat so that the ease of pain achieved amounts to baking the back to insensitivity. Such a back may have a highly mottled coloration of the skin, with red blotches. This denotes damage to tissue and is a real impediment to circulation.

Work to keep the body at normal temperature. Warm, (not hot) water used in baths, showers, whirlpool baths, and fomentations will always aid circulation and give comfort that is not deceptive and precarious. Water used in any one of these forms will not swell one type of tissue relative to another. Warm water means water at a degree of heat that feels comfortable. This policy can always help the circulation and normalize and equalize the forces within the body in a comforting, soothing and safe way. Such applications of heat impart all the benefits that the heating pad seemingly offers, without jeopardizing the tissues. Furthermore, applying heat throughout the body avoids temperature differentials imposed by local heating. Also, when the strong heat of a heating pad is removed, the tissues, being used to the high temperature, are easily subject to chilling.

Wool Insulating Band for Sciatica

Any chilling should be avoided. For this purpose, it may be advisable to wear an insulating band of wool (not synthetic material) next to the skin, over the sacrum.

Mr. Stephenson's Concepts of the Sciatic Nerves

Mr. Stephenson saw a nerve "harness" fitting over the rump of the human body; this harness conforms roughly to the pattern of an inverted candelabra with a stand or trunk and paired branches on each side. In the human candelabra, there are many collateral branches between the basic ones. The entire nerve network converges again principally into the great sciatic nerves that descend down the back of the legs. If the harness on the rump of a horse is out of position, distorted or asymmetrical, or if the single tree (pulling bar) is crooked, it is obvious to the horseman what should be done to correct the situation. It should be just as obvious to the Creative Healer what should be done to correct the nerve harness on the human body when it is out of position.

Within the great sciatic nerve, Mr. Stephenson designated the upper and lower sciatic nerves. A long-standing interference with these nerves can result in a sagged condition, extending the full length of the leg. This condition causes obstruction and contraction within the muscles controlled by these nerves. The sciatic region is the main distribution center for power and life going to the legs. The constraint imposed by this, upon the comfort of body motion, can be likened to that suffered by a woman wearing a long skirt standing with her heels on the hem of the skirt. Attempts at bending over would be very constrained and uncomfortable. Here again, it is obvious to the Creative Healer that constraints must be released, unlocked and freed up throughout the length of the leg. This is accomplished by working on the muscles and freeing the nerve paths.

The upper sciatic nerve descends through the groin and feeds the front and inner (anterior and medial) aspects of the leg down into the foot. When the nerve sags, it can be compared to a string that cannot control a puppet because of too much slack. Again, it is obvious that the slack or sag must be taken out. This is accomplished by the treatment at the groin as described in the upper leg treatment, page 7–13, and pertains particularly to the area from the knee to the groin.

According to Mr. Stephenson's experience, a person may be 80 years of age, have suffered from sciatica for 10 years and yet can be completely and permanently healed of this trouble, possibly in one treatment.

Sciatica

The painful condition known as sciatica involves the lower part of the back and often the legs. This area is the main distribution center for power and life going to the legs. The pain of sciatica indicates that the flow of nerve life through these nerves is impaired. Therefore, sciatica treatment is directed to these nerves with the aim of removing any obstruction to the flow of life force through them and to restore normal function. In their normal and natural state during walking these nerves glide a little in their grooves in the bone and tissue at the center line of the sacrum. An obstruction to the flow of nerve life may be caused by a displacement of the nerve, a contraction of muscles, or by a nerve plexus that are not centered symmetrically; the treatment must take all these possibilities into account.

Lower Back

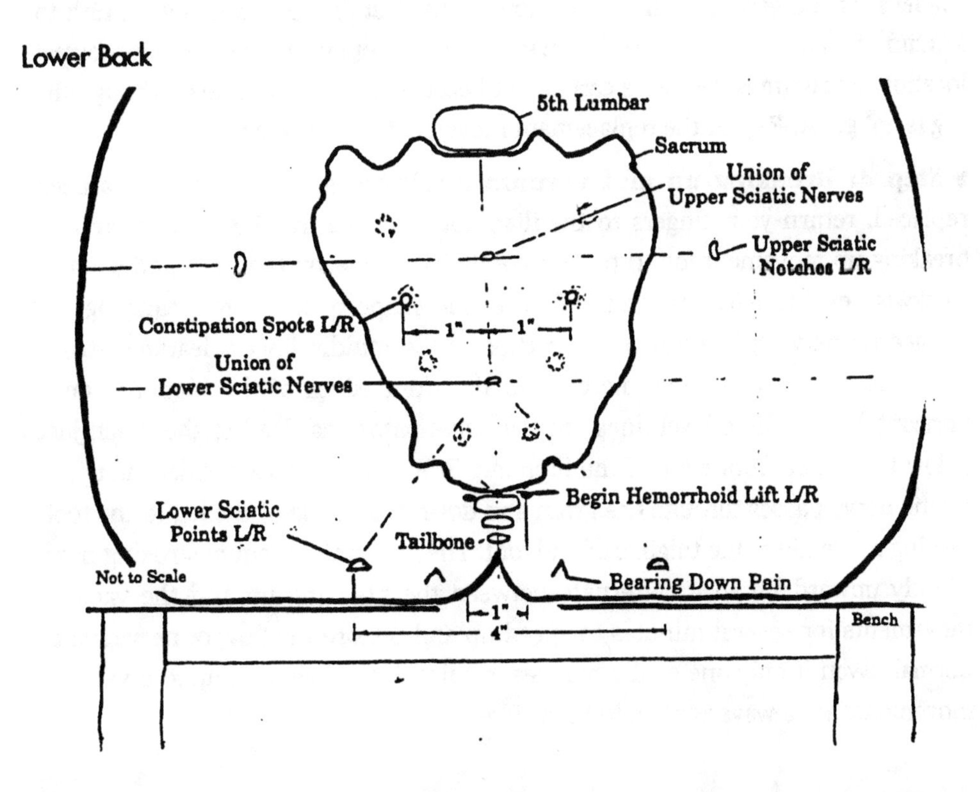

Position

The patient sits on the bench; the Creative Healer sits behind.

Upper Sciatic Nerves

Finding notch and nerve

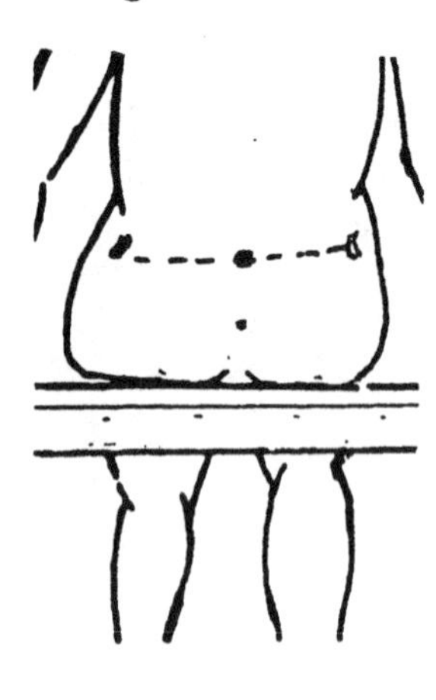

➧ Step 1: Locating the notches. If the patient cannot sit because of pain, treat the ankle filter spots, page 7–28, while patient stands. This will take enough pressure off the nerves so that the patient can sit to receive the treatment. Before beginning the treatment apply oil in an upward only direction to the sacrum. The notches for the upper sciatic nerves, the iliac notches, are found to the side of the joints linking the hipbones to the sacrum and just lower than the crests of the hipbones. The notches are usually farther apart for women than for men. Place the tips of your index fingers firmly in these notches. If the patient moves quickly away from both fingers or only from one, you have located the problem. If neither spot is sensitive or painful the upper sciatics are probably not involved.

➧ Step 2: Finding the nerve. Using a light contact if there is sensitivity on one or both sides, use the thumb to trace a horizontal line to the center line from the notches. At that place there is a small groove across the spine where the upper sciatic nerves form a union that normally rests in the groove. Located on the sacrum below the joint of the fifth lumbar vertebra and the sacrum, the groove is undetectable to the touch.

➧ Step 3: Replacing the nerve. If the upper sciatic nerve is displaced, replace it with the quarter twist movement (see page 3–3) into its groove in the bone and tissue where it should lie. The nerve may be displaced to the right, to the left, or at the center line; the right or left iliac notch will indicate which one. If there is pain at both notches, the nerve must be replaced at the center line. When the nerve moves out of position, it sags downward, so contact the body slightly below the level of the groove with the cushion of the thumb (approximately 1/16th to 1/32nd of an inch below). Use the quarter twist to replace the nerve in its correct location. Sometimes the nerve can be felt because it has swollen even though the sag is not great. Repeat the replacement movement if necessary.

Vacuum stroking

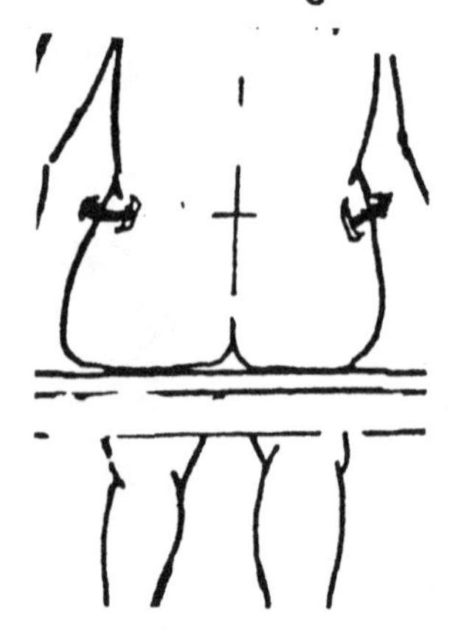

➧ Step 4: Breaking up and vacuum stroking. After the nerve has been replaced, return your fingers to the iliac notches. Use the fingers in a circular breaking up movement for 10 or 15 seconds (clockwise on the right and counter clockwise on the left) that gently follows the shape of the notch, carrying the surface tissue with it. With the fingertips of the middle fingers leading, stroke from the center of the iliac notches to the front edges of the hipbones on a horizontal line. These level lines are the nerve paths that lead to the notch just below the upper front edge of the hipbone. From there, on each side, the upper sciatic nerve passes through the groin and down the inside of the leg to the foot, feeding nerve life to the thigh, calf and foot. The horizontal vacuum stroking has a slightly upward lift to it. Alternate between the breaking up and the vacuum movements for several minutes to speed up and restore the flow of nerve life to normal. Even if only one of the notches is painful, the breaking up and vacuum movements are always applied to both sides.

Locating notch and lower sciatic nerve

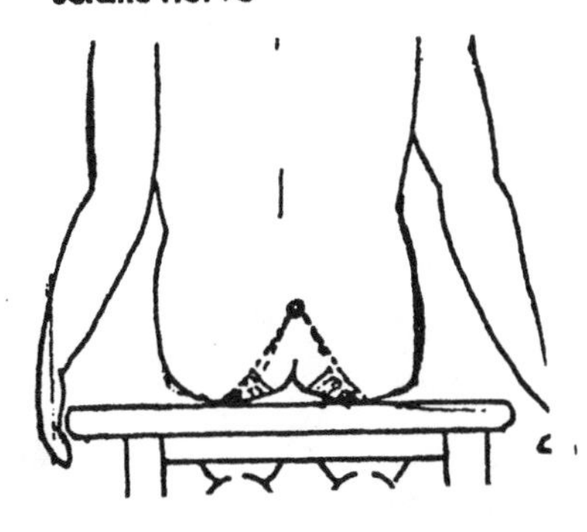

Step 5: Perform the tests described in Step 4 of Lower Sciatic Nerve, below.

Lower Sciatic Nerve

Step 1: Locate lower nerve. The lower sciatic nerves are found at center back about 1 1/2 inches below the groove for the upper sciatics. The lower nerves descend from the spine on an angle of 45° on each side into the muscular tissue of the buttocks forming a 90° angle. Place the fingertips about 4 to 5 inches apart where the buttocks meet the bench and rotate the fingers as they work their way through the muscle into two lower sacral notches. Sensitivity in these notches always reveals which side is involved.

Step 2: Repositioning the nerve. Use the quarter twist to replace the lower sciatic nerve in its groove at the spine in the same manner as described above for the upper sciatic nerve.

Breaking up and vacuum stroking

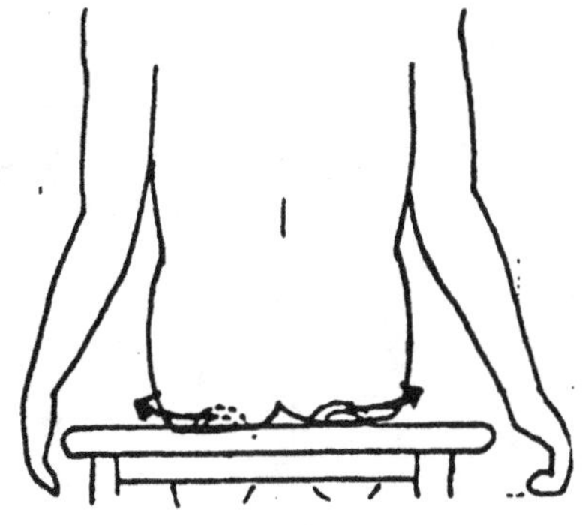

Step 3: Breaking up and vacuum stroking. Perform a circular breaking up movement with the fingers for 10 to 15 seconds at these lower notches under the buttocks, then, with the middle fingers leading, vacuum stroke in an outward direction along the nerve paths (close to the bench) that lead just past the greater trochanters of the femurs (the hip joints). The breaking up movement and vacuum stroking are performed as a unit on both sides simultaneously.

Step 4: Testing the results to embed the nerves in their natural channels. The nature of sciatic trouble demands that the body be used symmetrically, even though pain has forced one to do otherwise. Now, with the pain relieved, the patient should draw the feet back and place them parallel to each other. By leaning slightly forward and pressing upward, the patient may come to a balanced standing position without help, even without thinking it possible. With feet parallel and about 12 inches apart, the patient should bend from the hips so that trunk, arms and head dangle limply as far as the weight of the body will allow without any effort. At first, the patient will think these movements too difficult but by following instructions will be pleasantly surprised. The knees can bend slightly. After returning to the standing position, the patient should also raise each leg so that the knee is horizontal with the thigh letting the lower leg dangle. The ability to perform these movements is "proof" that the nerves are in their channels and the nerve life is flowing freely through them and also helps establish the nerves in their rightful place. This sciatica treatment will take care of the majority of cases; it will give impetus to the flow of life and circulation to enable the body to take over and clear up the condition. Another bend with the patient rocking his weight back and forth over his/her heels will denote a good recovery. In some cases it will be necessary to work down the entire length of the leg to the toes to overcome obstructions and increase the flow of blood to the extremities. The patient may feel the pain is moving down the leg and out the toes. This signifies that the flow of life and fresh blood are coming in.

Testing results of the treatment

Frequency

Treat once a week for several weeks. Sometimes the patient can do the movements described without difficulty, but soon afterward feels the same trouble return, or the patient comes for treatment pointing to spots midway between the 2 sets of nerves as the seat of pain. These are signs that further treatment to the sciatic nerves should not be given at that time but attention should be given instead to the kidneys.

If the kidneys are not fed nerve life properly, they may be forced to operate at above normal body temperature. They then sweat and the secretion that oozes out of them penetrates some membranes and flows down others. It settles in the sciatica region of the sacrum and keeps the sciatic nerves in a high state of irritation. This problem cannot be relieved until the kidneys are restored to normal functioning.

The recognition of the connection between kidneys and sciatica, which Mr. Stephenson saw, enables Creative Healing to help people with sciatica who hadn't obtained relief from any other treatment. For the few cases where these treatments are not sufficient, appropriate treatments may be found under crippled leg treatment, page 7–4.

Pain at the End of the Tailbone

When the tissues surrounding the end of the tailbone are displaced, they usually withdraw upward toward the sacrum. The tailbone then penetrates other tissues and the result can cause severe pain. This condition is brought on by sitting on too soft a surface such as overstuffed furniture, or on hard, irregular surfaces or surfaces subjecting the body to jolts. Without attention, inflammation and swelling of the area and even the formation of an abscess may result. In cases of prolonged agitation, an abscess could develop that might be difficult to detect in the early stages. It can either surround the end of the tailbone or be on the posterior surface; it is painful and swollen and gives off heat. The most indicative sign is that the swollen area, when touched lightly from each side, moves as though filled with something soft; even a light touch is painful. When an abscess is detected, the patient is advised to consult a physician. When there is no abscess apply the following treatment.

Position

The patient sits on a bench so that the tailbone is flush with the edge of the bench. This allows the hand of the Creative Healer clearance as it rotates downward. The Creative Healer sits behind.

➧ **Step 1: Repositioning the tissue**. To reposition the dislodged tissues, place the end of the right thumb, horizontally, at the top of the tailbone on the center line of the body. Gradually rotate your thumb to a vertical position as it moves down and off the end of the tailbone, bringing tissue gently back into place. The pressure is firm and positive but not so heavy as to dislodge the tailbone itself.

After the treatment, the patient should stand up and move around to allow time for the tissues to readjust.

Repositioning the tissue

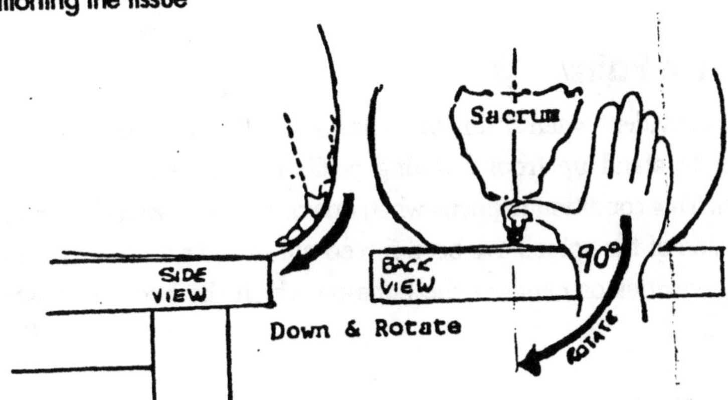

➧ **Step 3: Seating.** Teach the patient to sit down carefully by bringing the body into a light contact with the chair and then sliding backward on the surface. This draws forward the tissues that the body rests on, and downward those that surround the tailbone, thus enabling the repositioned tissues to retain their normal positions. Learning to sit down in a deliberate way will prevent future problems. If the patient is not completely comfortable the treatment can be repeated to be sure the tissues have been fully drawn down into place.

Dislodged Tailbone

A dislodged tailbone is usually caused by having fallen on it or having sat down hard or on an irregular surface with projections. A dislodged tailbone will either point straight forward or forward and to the right or left. The Creative Healing principle involved in healing this condition is that of repositioning substance. By moving the substance surrounding a bone, it is possible to move the bone without actually touching it. In the same way, it is also possible to move tissue, ligaments, nerves, organs, cartilage, etc. Using olive oil on the hands acts like gloves but allows the fingers, thumbs and palms to become more sensitive to what is happening under the skin of the patient.

Quarter twist to replace a dislodged tailbone

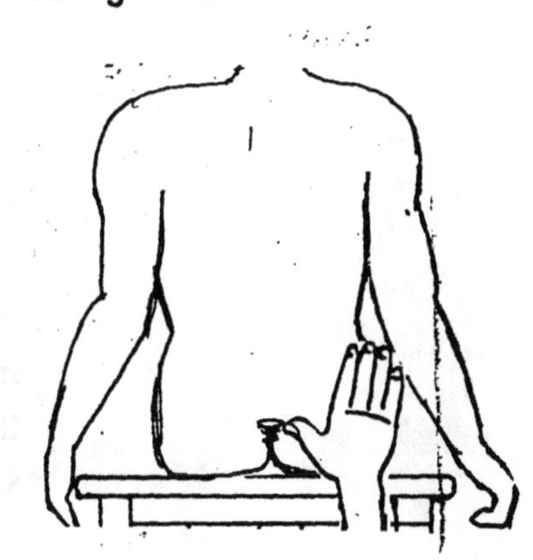

Position

The patient sits on a bench so that the tailbone is flush with the edge of the bench; this allows the Creative Healer's hand to easily move downward. The Creative Healer sits behind.

➧ **Step 1: Use of the quarter twist.** If the tailbone points forward, replace cartilage on both sides of the tailbone (not on the tailbone itself) with the quarter twist. Place your thumb horizontally on the body and gently rotate a quarter turn to the vertical position; see page 3–3. Have in your mind exactly what is to be accomplished with the action taken. If the tailbone points to one side, replace the cartilage on the opposite side. When the cartilage is replaced, the muscles pull the tailbone back into position. There is is no need to enter the rectum to reposition the dislodged tailbone.

Bearing-Down Pain

This pain is not evident when sitting or standing, but the strain is very severe when attempting to stand up from a sitting position or to sit down from a standing position. This condition happens when one or both of two nerve centers located on each side of the spine have been forced out of their normal position, which is in small cavities or dents in the bone on which the body rests when sitting.

Position

The patient sits well back on the bench so that the Creative Healer's index finger can be properly placed without interference from the bench; the Creative Healer sits behind.

➧ **Step 1: Positioning.** We describe the right side. Place your right forearm just above the wrist on your own right leg, above the knee. Your elbow is free and upper arm is straight below the shoulder. The palm of your hand faces upward for the correct placement of the index finger, the tip of which accomplishes the lift. Place your index finger under the buttocks between the hipbone and the tailbone so that it will clear the bench when it moves upward.

➧ **Step 2: Locate notch.** Locate the notch with the index finger under the buttock and vertically beneath the upper side edge of the tailbone. If the finger encounters the tailbone or hipbone, release the pressure and reposition the

➧ **Step 3: Press nerve into notch.** The tip of the index finger will press straight up, parallel with the spine, with the aim of lifting the tissue into the highest point of the notch. The pressing is applied with a slightly arched finger, steadily, firmly, persistently, of long duration and must not be hurried. The shoulder is pressed downward and acts with the forearm and stiff wrist in a lever like action to allow the index finger to move slowly upward and lift the tissues that will replace the nerve into its natural position. The pressure is slow and straight up and parallel to the spine. When the finger ascends very slowly, the muscles will begin to relax with its penetration upward. It is amazing how easily this is accomplished as the index finger, in the correct location with slow and steady pressure, reaches the highest point of the notch between the hipbone and the tailbone. Release the pressure smoothly and slowly, and repeat the treatment on the left side of the body.

To further strengthen the muscles in the floor of the pelvis, the bed wetting spots may also be treated. See page 5–51.

Treating for bearing down pain on both sides

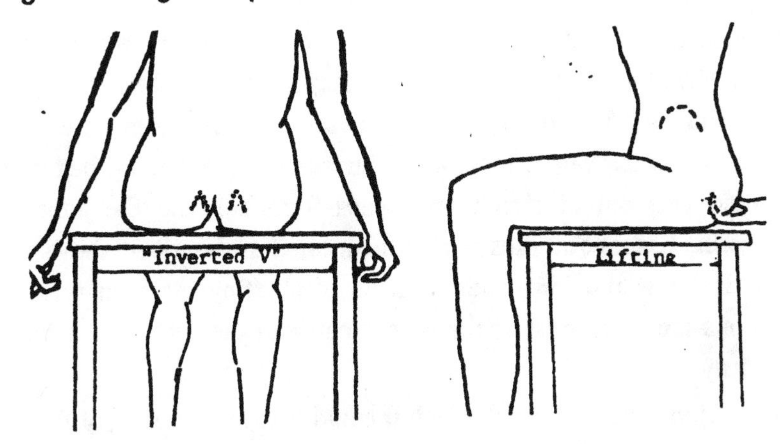

Cordlike Formations Emanating from the Spine

Cordlike formations emanating from the spine can be detected by touching. Such formations are usually present on one side of the body only so comparison of the two sides is always valuable. An effective means of palpating is the scissors movement (see page 3–5), applied from the sacrum to the base of the neck. What is felt as a cordlike formation seems to emanate from between the vertebrae. Though frequently not apparent to the eye or discernible to the superficial touch, it reveals itself to the palpating touch as elevated over the underlying tissues. It is usually detectable for 2 or 3 inches, following a path parallel to the ribs. At its end it is buried in the tissues.

Position

The patient sits on a bench; the Creative Healer sits behind.

➧ **Step 1: Apply the quarter twist.** To correct this formation, start the quarter twist at the innermost end of the cord near the spine. Try to bury the cord in the tissue by repeated quarter twists. Proceed in this manner as far out from the spine as you are able to replace displaced substance.

➧ **Step 2: Stroking movement.** Alternate the quarter twists with stroking movements. Stroke away from the spine and parallel to the ribs in the area beyond that of the quarter twists.

➧ **Step 3: Breaking up movement.** Apply breaking up movements over the cord. By alternating these three movements, the whole formation can soon disappear.

Lumps in the breast can disappear by using this treatment. It has also been used successfully to heal chronic bleeding of the bowel and also used in cases where the arm cannot be raised.

An additional use of this treatment is from a woman who practiced Creative Healing very successfully for 40 years: She found a cord-like connection to the spine in a child with leukemia, which she treated successfully as described above.

Seepage from the Spine

Certain conditions in the lumbar and thoracic regions of the spine can manifest what Mr. Stephenson described as "seepage." It would be recognized chiefly from a burning sensation in the tissues emanating from between the vertebrae and leading diagonally downward. Such burning is due to the fact that lubricating fluid gets out of circuit and seeps from between the joints (the vertebrae) into the tissues and muscle sheaths located as described above. Here, the Creative Healer would have the intention of shutting off such a flow, as molding motions are performed at the spaces between the vertebrae, using the thumbs primarily.

If this condition continued unchecked, it could lead to an apparent flabby or atrophied condition of the muscles lying in the diagonal locations mentioned above, a condition that could persist long after the original burning sensation has disappeared. Mr. Stephenson called the condition "swinneying" (atrophy of shoulder muscles in a horse).

Multiple Sclerosis

Mr. Stephenson would not accept a patient for treatment of multiple sclerosis if the patient, in order to walk, had to sway in the hips because he/she could no longer flex the knees and lift the legs, or if the patient's face wore a hard, constant, unnatural smile. He felt these cases would not benefit from his work. In any case, for successful treatment, a long and persistent commitment must be made and family members should be taught the treatment to give the patient additional help.

In multiple sclerosis the feed to the tracts of the spinal cord has been interfered with and shut off. Accordingly, treatment consists in reestablishing this feed. The principal movement employed is the scissors movement. This movement, done by the thumbs, loosens the obstructions and reestablishes the feed to the spinal tracts.

Position

The patient sits upright on a bench; the Creative Healer sits behind at a comfortable height and distance. Use olive oil on the hands for ease of operation.

➧ **Step 1: Hand placement of thumbs.** Begin the scissors movement by placing the left thumb at the space between the sacrum and the fifth lumbar vertebra, to the right of the spine and the right thumb in the space between the fifth and fourth lumbar vertebrae on the left. The crossing of the thumbs creates "blades" of unequal length with the pivot and the opening of the blades between the two thumbs, over the center of the spine.

➧ **Step 2: Action of thumbs.** To "close the scissors" bring your thumbs towards the two intervertebral spaces on the spine, the left thumb at the lower space, the right thumb at the higher level. Apply pressure by both thumbs straight forward, then as the "scissors" close, the pivoting thumbs enter between the vertebrae. Focus your mind to affect a point 1 inch or more beneath the surface of the skin at the center line. As the thumbs pivot in the quarter twist, they gather and feed new life and they also create a gentle, loosening and rocking movement to the vertebrae. Continue this movement up the entire spine to the base of the neck.

➧ **Step 3: Interchange thumbs.** Interchange the thumbs, the right thumb on the rivet spot on the left side of the spine and the left thumb between the fifth and fourth vertebrae on the right side. Repeat the 2 upward movements from sacrum to neck 5 or 6 times.

➧ **Step 4: Downward stroke.** Draw life into the spinal tracts by stroking down over the spine with the double vacuum: palms following one another so that when the first palm reaches the sacrum the other starts at the top.

➧ **Step 5: Neck treatment.** Apply the treatment described for common headache: beginning with the right thumb in the space between the 7th cervical and the 1st thoracic vertebrae on the right side of the spine, circumduct (see page 2–40) the patient's head forward and away from the thumb to open the space as the thumb applies a slight pressure. Return the head to its upright position. Move the right thumb to the parallel left space and circumduct the head in the opposite direction. Continue this procedure in a zigzag manner up the entire neck. Repeat, beginning with the right thumb on the left side: an adaptation of the scissors movement to the neck.

➧ **Step 6: General treatment.** Give a thorough general treatment (see page 1–8) ending with the thumb and fingers on opposite sides of the spine and drawing down, close to the spine at first, then gradually moving out and back in again towards the spine. Again, stroke down the spine with the palms to bring in the life released by the general treatment.

Duration

This treatment for the back and neck should take from 20 to 30 minutes.

➧ **Step 7: Sciatica treatment.** As the patient improves, begin feeding the life down into the sciatic nerve paths, as described in the treatment for sciatica (see page 3–23). Check all the way down to the feet to resolve any obstructions and massage the legs as needed.

Spinal Meningitis

Spinal meningitis and encephalitis are an aftermath of extreme fevers lodged in the head and neck and possibly in the spine, according to Mr. Stephenson. What he saw was the adherence of the myelin sheaths of the nerve tracts to adjacent tissues and membranes, which blocked the flow of life and nutrition to vital control channels, preventing the body from fully recovering without help.

As the condition of spinal meningitis worsens, the most apparent symptom is the bending backward (dorsal flexing) of the person's spine and neck. This can worsen until the spinal cord finally snaps. In treatment, the Creative Healer must first return the spine and head to a forward position and stabilize the condition.

Position

Patient sits on a bench, if possible. Creative Healer sits behind.

➧ **Step 1: Reduce fever.** If fever is present, first treat to reduce it. To do this, apply the palm-after-palm heat withdrawing treatment, as for pneumonia (see page 4–7). Intersperse this treatment with work on the spine to break the grip of the reverse flexing.

➧ **Step 2: Work on spine.** Begin far enough down on the spine to include the bottom of the strongly contracted area and work progressively upward. Do the quarter twist in the intervertebral spaces with the thumb of one hand while the other hand holds the top of the person's head and exerts a very gentle but insistent pressure forward. This insistence is carried by a clear vision of what one wants to achieve and a firm will to achieve it. In 20 or 30 minutes of such treatment, the heat of the fever is removed and the reverse-flexing grip is broken. With the body at normal temperature, the spine and neck can become erect or even flex somewhat forward of center.

In this manner the vital forces are once again released. When they take over, the threat of imminent death is overcome. The person might, of course, be in need of additional care but the immediate problem has been solved. This treatment for spinal meningitis is an impressive example of the use of simple basic principles to resolve a condition that might be considered irreversible.

Encephalitis

In encephalitis, the patient is never fully conscious and may tend to sleep almost continuously. If not helped, this condition may last indefinitely. Mr. Stephenson saw these incapacities as caused by lagging circulation, especially in the head, the base of the skull, the neck and the spine.

He would apply whatever treatment was capable of speeding up the slow moving action of the closed down body: the multiple sclerosis treatment (see page 3–30), the heart treatment (see page 4–21), the digestive tuneup (see page 5–14). He would tune up the whole body in order to speed up the flow of blood through the head to wake the patient up. The patient would respond by gradually becoming more alert and alive and finally returning to his normal state.

Shingles

Shingles is caused by a particular kind of inner agitation and pressure that leads to either shingles or a nervous breakdown. This type of agitation develops from a progressive building up of stresses, a consequence of voluntarily accepting highly taxing demands in work or in personal life. An example might be of a lawyer preparing for a court case or a student preparing a doctoral thesis. Stress can also manifest as ulcers, digestive upsets, sleeplessness or many other forms.

Mr. Stephenson gave Creative Healers an easy analogy with which to remember the shingles treatment: he compared the way he saw it operate to a queen bee and worker bees. When the queen bee is "killed" the worker bees have no more work to do and the colony dies out.

This treatment for shingles is confined to anywhere it occurs on the trunk of the body. It is most frequent in the mid-region but also found on the upper and lower trunk. When the condition has advanced to the readable stage, 3 features will be distinguishable: the queen spot, the feed line and the debris band.

The queen spot will be found a short distance away from the median line on the back of the body, about 1 inch toward the side of the body that is affected. In the early full-blown stage of a typical case, the location is marked by a bright, more clearly defined red spot than any other; its size can be covered by the pad of the thumb. Sometimes no distinct spot can be seen, but the patient will be able to point to a place on the back that hurts or a Creative Healer may find the spot by palpating.

The feed line is found by moving from the queen spot further away from the spine in an essentially horizontal line; other spots, less bright, are distributed randomly along this line. They may extend around the body to the center in front. The feed line is followed by the workers, as they carry "food" to the queen.

The debris band is of mottled appearance, less distinct in color than the spots. It extends from the queen spot, below and parallel to the feed line, widening as it passes the sides of the body, becoming even less distinct and narrowing into an upward arc as it blends with the feed line.

At different stages, the intensity and location of the markings differ. The description here pertains to a certain time in the development of the disease. If viewed earlier or later the case might look very different and cases vary in the sequence in which the three features appear. In advanced stages of shingles that have lasted without healing, extensive tissue destruction may have happened, where the tissue will have eroded to levels below the surface. The unpracticed eye might be so distracted by this gruesome aspect that it could recognize the "bright" queen spot as only insignificant, while actually this is the key spot to Mr. Stephenson's treatment.

If the right side of the body is affected, the deposits along the debris band may interfere with the functioning of the liver and the gall bladder; if the left side is affected, the heart may be disturbed. If both sides are affected and the two feed lines meet in front, an old saying has this to mean death. Mr. Stephenson conceded that if accumulated poisons and congestion were allowed to persist in obstructing vital functions, death could ensue. But he also said a Creative Healer should never lose a patient to death for these reasons. Creative Healing enables the clearing of affected organs and restoring them to normal function.

➧ **Step 1: Three-minute quarter twist.** With oil on the thumb, cover the queen spot. Treat with the thought of killing the queen and all the action emanating from that spot. This is a different visualization than is usual with the quarter twist movement. Perform the quarter twist (from horizontal to vertical) at an almost imperceptible rate of speed, taking 2 to 3 minutes to complete. Maintain a firm, constant pressure throughout the treatment. The patient will often report an immediate secession of the pain. The treatment is usually performed only once and the spot is left alone. If you feel the quarter twist was inadequate, you may perform it again. *[I ask the patient to watch the clock for me and alert me at the 1-, 2- and 3-minute marks. It makes it easier to do the quarter twist slowly enough.—Ed.]*

➧ **Step 2: Cooling treatment.** If the shingles have developed to such a degree that there are no open areas, soothe the patient's pain and agitation by using the hands, heavily oiled, held in a vertical position. Touch is very light, one hand following the other in horizontal strokes from the queen spot over the band and feed line to the front. This treatment completes the work—the scabs may disappear within the week.

In elderly people, the curves of the spine may be exaggerated and the body appears bent over and distorted. This could even be a consequence of the pain suffered with shingles. In these cases, the spine will need to be treated and strengthened so that healing may be completed and strength regained. When treating the elderly, the scissors treatment could also be given; see page 3–5.

Examples from Creative Healers

1. A Creative Healer reported a case of shingles where the pustules were on the legs. Not sure that he could help, he asked to see the patient's back. He found a discolored spot on the sacrum near the sciatic nerve and the patient said, "That's the place on my back that hurts." He was treated successfully at that spot. The pain stopped immediately. The patient declared a miracle.

2. Soon after I learned Creative Healing, a friend asked me if there was a treatment for shingles as another friend of hers (working on her Ph.D) was suffering with a terrible case. "Yes," I said, "there is a treatment, but I have never done it." She asked if I would try and I agreed to do so. When her friend came to my home, she said the doctor had just given her some stronger pain killers that morning because the pain seemed worse. When she removed her blouse, I saw shingles for the first time. They stretched from her upper back, under her arm and across her left breast: ugly, scabby and red sores. The "queen" spot was easy to detect and I asked that she time me as I gave the quarter twist in extra slow motion. She did, and when she said, "Time's up" she also said, "My God. The pain is gone!" That evening she attended a group in which she shared her "miracle". She later told our mutual friend that within a week all the scabs were gone.

Twisted Hip

A twisted, rotated, or tilted hip may be caused by improper lifting, a fall or an automobile accident or even a muscle contraction. It frequently results in uneven length of the legs.

Position

The patient sits on a bench with a firm surface. The Creative Healer sits behind the patient.

➧ **Step 1: Placement.** The patient sits on a firm treatment bench so that the weight of the body can help in realigning the hips. The pressure of the patient's weight bears more heavily on the flats of the ischial bones and less on the legs (as in the normal sitting position). Sometimes the hip has slipped so far out of its normal position it seems folded under as though being sat on. Draw the patient's leg outward just before sitting so that he/she sits more squarely on both hips.

➧ **Step 2: Check the symmetry.** By placing your fingertips on the crests of the hipbones and your thumbs on the joints connecting the sacrum with the hipbones on the two sides of the body, you can feel the extent of the twist, rotation or asymmetry of the hips. Where the sacrum and hipbones join, the surfaces feel uneven, like little hills and valleys. But these bones are securely fastened together by the strongest ligaments found at any joint in the body. Creative Healing works with the ligaments.

Thumb pad spans the joint between sacrum and hipbone

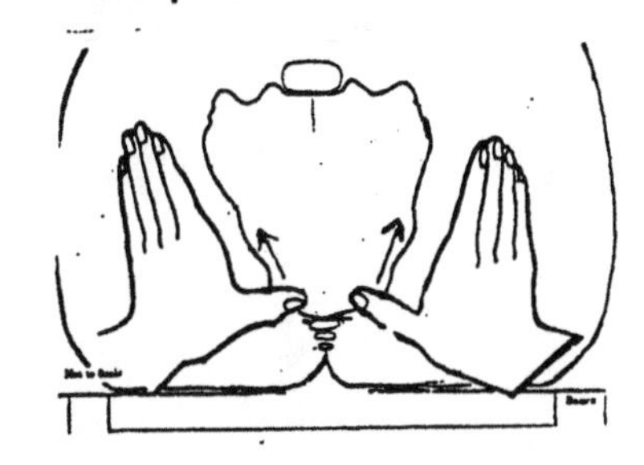

➧ **Step 3: Thumb movement and lifts.** To treat, place well-oiled thumbs, tip facing tip at the level of the top of the tailbone, with the tip of the thumb pad resting on the sacrum and the middle part of the pad spanning the joint between the sacrum and the hipbone. Starting at that elevation, let the thumbs glide slowly and smoothly upward together with a firm, forward pressure, while the elbows are supported by the knees (similar to the hemorrhoid treatment, page 5–35). The part of the thumb that moves on the sacrum exerts a heavier pressure than the part that spans the joint. The thumbs are in a similar position as for hemorrhoid treatment but farther apart.

If you encounter protrusions of cartilage, release the pressure and remold the cartilage by using the quarter twist; see page 3–3. Resume the lift below the level of the protrusion and continue the upward lifting to the top of the sacroiliac joints. Return to the starting position and repeat the process. Occasionally, reseat the person to a more favorable position and continue the lifts as long as changes are taking place. Changes can be limited by swelling, inflammation or disruption of circulation. Sometimes a release of circulation will be felt as pressures are equalized. It is proof that the treatment is effective and the circulation increase will feed and repair as the asymmetric parts are realigned. Alignment automatically occurs through the effect of gravity when the tensions and unequal pressures are released. Also, many other disturbances pertaining to the area are corrected simultaneously when the twisted hip is treated.

Note: Even if only one hip is tilted, the treatment is applied symmetrically to both sides of the spine. Note also, that although bones are repositioned, the intent is always directed by the mind to the softer tissues of the body and when the tension in the ligaments is released, realignment will take place.

This treatment applies when the sacrum seems wedged too far down between the hipbones, appearing too prominent to the posterior. This causes a stress and cross-pull across the sacrum, which is relieved by the lifts.

Frequency

Repeated treatments may be necessary and may be given 3 times a week. In severe cases, a 5-day interval gives the treatment more time when vascular healing is needed yet does not let too much time elapse before it is reinforced. If there is pain when you cross the area of the sciatic nerve, stop and do the sciatic treatment first; see page 3–23. Also check the kidney spots and the back.

Chapter 4 ♦ Chest Cavity

Breathing Correctly

Understanding Breathing

The chest, or thoracic cavity, comprises three chambers: two lateral chambers each containing one lung, and a central chamber containing the breathing tube (as Mr. Stephenson saw it) and the heart. The diaphragm, a sheath of muscular tissue, forms the lower base of the thoracic cavity and separates it from the abdominal cavity below it. In its relaxed condition (exhalation), the diaphragm is dome shaped and arches upward; during contraction (inhalation), the diaphragm flattens into a disc shape, lowering the floor of the thoracic cavity and increasing the chest volume. The movement of the chest wall or ribcage also increases the chest volume. The lungs expand or contract in response to chest and diaphragm movements.

Each lung is encased in its own serous sac, the inner pleura; both lungs are further encased in an outer pleura. A serous fluid lubricates the two pleura, enabling them to glide along each other, maintaining contact without adhesion. In abnormal circumstances an actual cavity forms between the two pleura, i.e. in pleurisy, when air, gas, fluid or pus accumulates between the membranes, breaking their clinging action and separating them. To reestablish normality, foreign matter must be evacuated. While there are actually two pleural cavities, one in connection with each lung, they are spoken of in the singular, treating them as a unit. This corresponds with their evacuation through the one passage we call a breathing tube.

Under normal circumstances, the lung adheres to the walls of its chamber. As this chamber expands from the action of the diaphragm and ribs, the lungs will expand. Atmospheric pressure will automatically fill the lung with air—inhalation. As the chamber contracts, the air previously drawn in will be, in part, expelled—exhalation.

Correct breathing must include the function of the diaphragm in action. Only when the diaphragm contracts will the lower part of the lungs, where their greatest capacity resides, be filled with air. The lungs, in their inflated state, are roughly cone-shaped, with the apex of the cones pointing upward. The volume of the lower half of the lungs is by far the greater. With perfect breathing, the abdomen and chest will simultaneously expand and contract. When one lies down, the chest and abdomen rise and fall together. This is the most effortless type of breathing, so clearly evidenced by babies and animals at rest. In complete repose, the abdominal (diaphragmatic) action predominates.

Educated Breathing

Correct breathing involves the diaphragm and most people are unaware of the correct way of breathing. Creative Healing can enlighten and help a person who has lost the feeling for diaphragmatic breathing and control over the diaphragm; muscles may have to be "reeducated." The high and short breathing treatment may not be enough. Administer the high and short breathing treatment below plus the following instructions for self-treatment.

The person, lying on the back, places one hand on the solar plexus (the nerve center located in the region often referred to as the "pit of the stomach") and the other on the chest. The patient then consciously breathes so that during inhalation the lower hand rises while the upper hand and the chest remain still. During exhalation, the chest relaxes fully and is limp, so that the exhalation is really complete. Practicing this will gradually enable the patient to transfer the pattern to the normal, subconscious performance of diaphragmatic breathing.

A good exercise in conscious diaphragmatic breathing can be carried out during walking. Consciously change the rhythm of the breathing by taking 6 paces to an inhalation, 4 paces while holding the breath, and 4 paces while exhaling. Continue this for a distance and then vary the pattern. Be sure to exhale completely to allow the chest to fully relax as the lungs are emptied of air.

Women, more than men, tend to gradually lose all feeling and ability for diaphragmatic breathing. This might be traced to tight-fitting garments that restrict the body, especially in the waistline and the region of the solar plexus. These people, often show extreme nervousness. As long as clothing discourages deep, diaphragmatic breathing, the condition will not be relieved. Normal clothing marks should disappear from the body within 10 minutes. If they linger longer, it is a sign that the clothing restricts the body too much.

Lung Treatments

High and Short Breathing

High and short breathing frequently occurs with asthma and other respiratory diseases. During high and short breathing the shoulders and chest will heave in the struggle to obtain enough air, and when a patient lies down, there is a big step-off between the chest and the abdomen.

High and short breathing fills only the upper portions of the lungs causing the chest to expand and frustrates the effort to obtain a satisfactory breath, resulting in nervousness and agitation. Also, too much residual air is left in the lungs and the inactivity of the lower part of the lungs invites mucous and other foreign material to settle there.

A frequent cause of high and short breathing is the gasp for air that follows the shock experienced when jumping into cold water or under a cold shower.

Such a gasp can draw air out of the stomach through the breathing tube into the pleural cavity. This breaks the vacuum necessary for the correct functioning of the diaphragm, and the person is not able to use the diaphragm properly for breathing. High and short breathing may also develop as a bad habit, through gradual neglect of diaphragmatic breathing, leaving no alternative but to heave the chest. With the chest over-expanded, the diaphragm becomes taut and overstretched and unable to function properly.

The following treatment (a) makes sure that the vacuum in the pleural cavity is intact, (b) restores the chest to its normal shape, and (c) stimulates the correct action of the diaphragm.

Position

The patient lies down throughout; Creative Healer sits at the patient's right.

➧ **Step 1: Heart treatment.** Administer the full basic heart treatment, page 4–21.

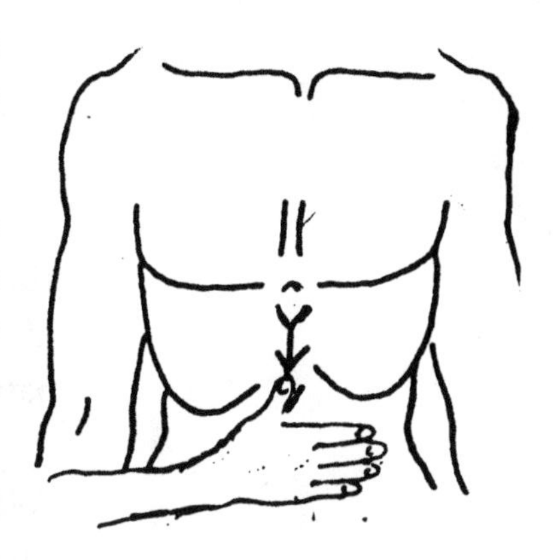

4-minute vacuum over breathing tube

➧ **Step 2: Vacuum over breathing tube passage.** Do the vacuum movement over the breathing tube for 4 minutes; see four-minute breathing treatment, page 4–5. This establishes or reinforces the vacuum in the pleural cavity.

➧ **Step 3: Reduce chest expansion.** Stand at the patient's right side. Place your right hand over the left ribs so that the little finger is on the lowest rib. Place your left hand over the right ribs so that the thumb is on the lowest rib. Your hands must form full contact with the body; thumbs and fingers must be together, extended and touching each other. The hands rest wholly on the ribs, with no part of the hands projecting beyond the ribs. The lower margins of the hands are aligned with the lower margins of the ribs. Keep the hands on the ribs. Do not move the skin over the ribs, as this would destroy the effectiveness of the treatment. Do not allow the heel of the right hand to come in contact with the area over the heart tube.

➧ **Step 4: Inhaling.** Ask the patient to draw a deep breath. During inhalation, be ready, with hands in the position just described, to hold the chest down, should it start to heave. This heaving could draw air out of the stomach, through the breathing tube, into the pleural cavity and would destroy the vacuum that was just established by the 4-minute vacuum over the breathing tube in step 2.

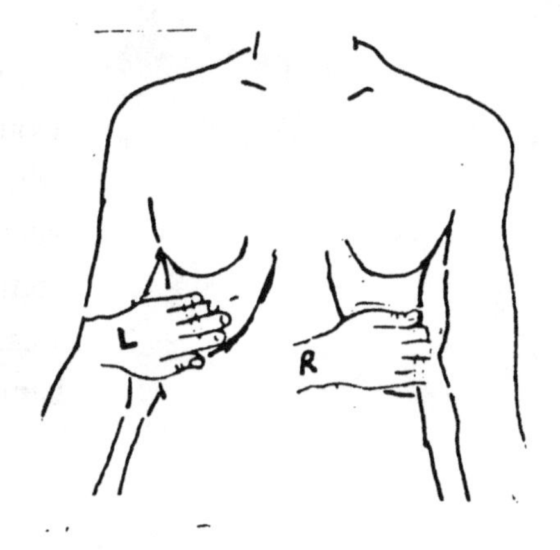

Reduce chest expansion

➧ **Step 5: Exhaling and pressing.** Ask the patient to exhale through the mouth so that you can hear the exhalation end. Assist in emptying the lungs by drawing your hands together and compressing the ribcage during exhalation. The direction of pressure should be toward the center of the body but the pressure is also down toward the spine, and down toward the feet. However, the greatest stress is on the "in" direction. As the ribs are compressed, anticipate the end of the exhalation, always being a little ahead of it. After all the air has been pressed out, retain your pressure firmly for a moment, keeping the lungs in their fully deflated state. Then give a smooth additional pressure (without any thrust) before relaxing the hands. The purpose of this last compression is to change the shape of the ribcage and the set of muscles supporting it. This helps the chest to return to its normal form. Be sure that pressure is exerted only on the ribs that lie below the end of the sternum. Swing them in as a section of the body hinged at the spine, moving them as a unit. By this swinging-in or folding-in pressure, the shape of the chest, as a whole, is changed. The individual ribs will change position moderately, with relation to one another. The shapes of the individual ribs themselves are not changed, however, and no attempt is ever made to bend the ribs. Guard against this by remembering that the stress is on the in-movement, not downward to the feet nor downward toward the spine.

It is important that the pressure exerted on the ribs be evenly distributed over the hands. The beginner may have a tendency to concentrate it at the heel of the hand. To avoid any misconception, it is appropriate to state that the contractile power of the diaphragm works only within that organ. The diaphragm is not empowered to pull an overstretched ribcage in and down.

Frequency

One treatment is usually sufficient for a person under 30 years of age. At a later time of life, more treatments are needed, perhaps 1 a week for 6 to 8 weeks.

Use of a Band Around the Chest

In some cases, it will be necessary for the patient to wear a band to hold the ribs in position. The band holds the chest in and also enforces the use of the diaphragm, which has not been able to function on its own because other muscles have predominated over it.

A comfortable band is easily made out of a 15-inch width of cotton flannel. Fold the edges over 1/3 of the width, stitch them down and add some diagonal stitching across the body of the band for firmness. This now makes a 5-inch wide band, 3 layers thick. Heavily muscled men may be strong enough to inadvertently tear a cotton flannel band. In these cases, it will be necessary to use a non-stretch canvas belt.

Place the band so that its upper edge is level with the lower end of the sternum and spans the area down to the lower edge of the ribcage. Fasten securely with stout safety pins or Velcro, with the overlap and pins on the right front away from the heart. To be effective, the band should be worn snugly. This will give the wearer the comforting feeling that the ribs have something to "lean" against. As the ribcage yields, the band is tightened but never beyond the point of comfort. If the band feels uncomfortable at any time after the first half hour of wearing it, loosen the tension slightly, just enough for comfort. If wearing the band becomes intolerable, it may be removed for 12 to 24 hours. As the ribcage becomes smaller, shorten the band.

The band should be worn at night and whenever possible to prevent the patient from reverting to the old habit of heaving the chest during sleep. Heaving the chest, especially with children, may lead to a panic in the struggle for air that would undo much of the previous gains. For this reason, it is preferred that the band be worn also at night, bringing about the change in the shape of the ribcage more swiftly.

A band can be applied also to the ribcage when muscles or cartilage or tissue have been torn or bruised, even in the case of cracked ribs. The support it furnishes will greatly relieve pain and assure more rapid healing.

Four-Minute Breathing Tube Treatment

Read Understanding Our Breathing Mechanism at the beginning of this chapter. As explained, the outer membrane of the pleura extends continuously over those parts of the ribcage, diaphragm and mediastinum that form the walls of the chambers containing the lungs. This membrane completely covers the inner membranes that contain each lung. While there are actually two pleural spaces, one with each lung, they are spoken of in the singular, treating them as a unit. The pleural space between the inner and outer membranes is normally a purely potential one. The two membranes are separated by a very thin film of serous fluid acting as a lubricant to prevent adhesion, and enabling the membranes to maintain contact and to glide along each other.

Only under abnormal circumstances when foreign matter such as air, gas, fluid or pus has entered and accumulated between the membranes, breaking their clinging action and separating them, is an actual cavity formed. This corresponds with their evacuation through the passage we call the breathing tube. Envision a breathing tube that lies on the center line of the body leading from the pleural cavity into the stomach, whose purpose is to establish and maintain normal breathing, and to evacuate fluid from the pleural cavity, when needed.

The pleural space is like a vacuum in the normal case, and in the abnormal case, this vacuum is partially broken. To reestablish it, foreign matter must be evacuated. This is done by the vacuum movement over the breathing tube. When fluid, pus or gas accumulates in the pleural cavity, instead of having this fluid drained off through an artificial tube inserted into the pleural cavity from the outside, the Creative Healer may draw the fluid through the breathing tube into the stomach. If large amounts of fluid are drawn into the stomach in this fashion, the patient may have to expel this by vomiting.

Vacuum stroking over this tube is a vital treatment and affects a "breathing nerve center" at this location. It calms and relieves tension at this second most important nerve center of the human body, the solar plexus (the first is the brain).

Location of nerve center

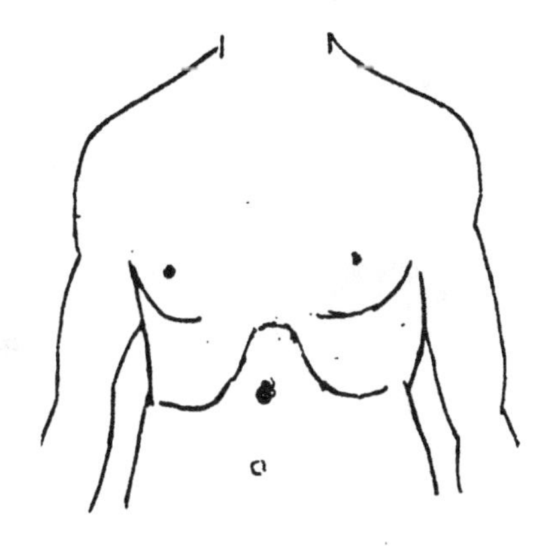

Position

The patient lies on the back; the Creative Healer sits beside the bed.

Thumb and hand position

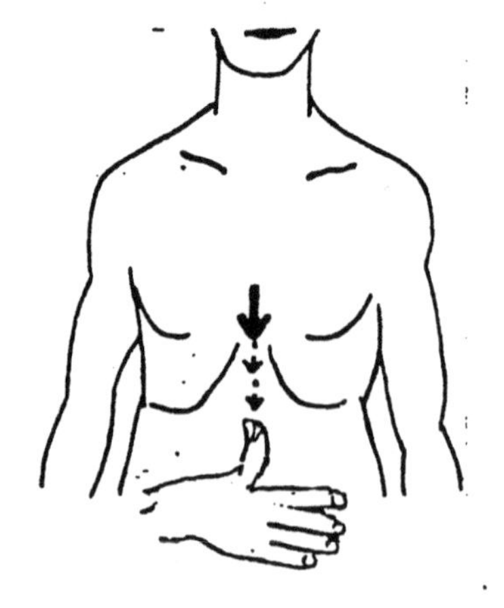

➧ **Step 1: Create a vacuum.** To evacuate the pleural spaces and cavity, create a vacuum by stroking over the center line of the body with the thumb. Begin with the tip of the thumb on the lower end of the sternum. The length of the thumb is in vertical contact on the center line of the body, over the breathing passage. The palm and fingers of the hand are placed at right angles to the thumb and in light contact with the patient's body so that the hand can move easily with the thumb. Draw the thumb downward for 3 inches on the center line over and over to establish the vacuum. Occasionally carry the stroke all the way to the navel. The whole hand moves downward with the thumb. The pressure of the thumb used to create the vacuum in this area must be stronger than most vacuum movements.

At times, when performing this drainage movement over the chest, the Creative Healer can actually feel fluid moving ahead of the thumb and hear it gush down the breathing tube. This action may be audible to the patient as well. Creating the vacuum here not only evacuates the pleural cavity but also cleans out the breathing tube. Volatile vomiting may occur after the 4-minute treatment, but do not be anxious because it marks the end of the patient's problem.

Duration

This is usually a 4-minute treatment. Too long a vacuuming time can occasionally agitate breathing.

➤➤➤ CAUTION When treating a thin person who has a hollow at the end of the sternum where the body should be convex, the vacuum created in the breathing tube must be of only moderate pressure.

Other Uses for the Breathing Tube Treatment

The breathing nerve center is of great importance for the entire respiratory system. We often find ourselves automatically using our thumb in this area to relieve indigestion or gas accumulations.

A collapsed lung can be filled with air by applying the vacuum over the breathing tube for 4 or more minutes quite firmly.

Other treatments illustrate the use of vacuum stroking over the breathing tube. See hiccoughs, page 4–16; baby born with asthma, page 8–19; and high and short breathing, page 4–2.

From of writings of Joseph B. Stephenson

Mr. Stephenson once had a patient lie down for about two hours in his office and every twenty minutes he did the four-minute vacuum over the breathing tube. Then he told the patient to get up and vomit.

Pneumonia

At normal temperature neither the pneumonia germ (nor any other germ that is a threat to the body) can thrive because they need a high temperature. When heat is withdrawn, this warm climate is taken away and germs become inactive. The characteristic feature of pneumonia is a high temperature in the lung region. The heat withdrawal movement for pneumonia is one of the most powerful illustrations of how the palm may be used to restore the body to normal temperature.

Note: It is not possible for the Creative Healer to draw out heat and restore the body to normal temperature in cases like quinsy or pneumonia unless his or her own body is at normal temperature.

In all cases of recurrent pneumonia and other lingering and weakening chest conditions, Vitamin D as found in cod liver oil is recommended in very moderate amounts: 1/4 teaspoon a day. Also, in these cases, milk or milk products should not be consumed.

Mr. Stephenson claimed that he had never lost a pneumonia case and that there was no excuse for losing one.

➧ **Step 1: Positioning.** For treatment on the front of the body, patients always lie on their back. For treatment on the back of the body, patients sit up. If sitting is impossible, treat the back with patient prone. It is advantageous for the patient to move back and forth from flat on the bed to sitting. The following explanation assumes the patient can sit up. The treatment for both front and back extends over the entire lung area, from the top of the shoulders to the bottom of the ribs.

For the Creative Healer, the best position in which to give the treatment at the bedside is to stand with knees straight and feet a comfortable width apart for good balance. Allow the body to bend forward at the hip in a relaxed stance so the arms may be brought over the patient in a free and easy manner for the length of time needed.

➧ **Step 2: Withdrawing heat from back.** Don't worry about uncovering the patient who has a high fever. Just spread oil generously and rapidly over the patient's back and begin to stroke down the spine, fingers pointing to the patient's head, one hand following the other in double strokes from the top of the shoulders to the bottom of the ribs in smooth yet rapid and light repetition. As the hands move toward the right side of the body the double strokes should gradually describe arcs that nearly parallel the ribs.

Withdrawing heat from the back for men and women

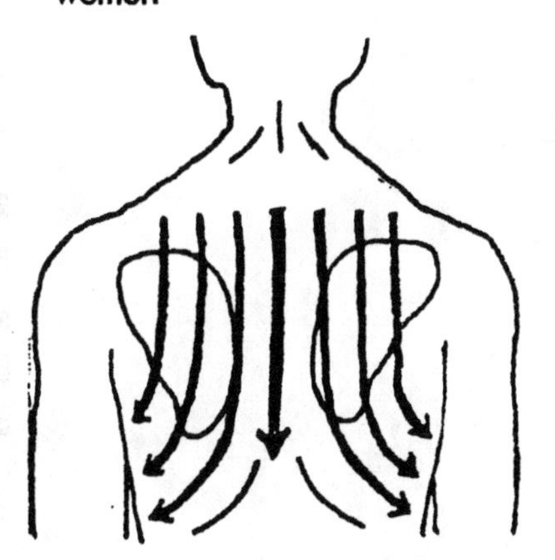

The main power for withdrawing heat lies in the palm, and by holding the extended thumb and fingers together but not rigid, the power is enhanced. Keep the hand supple so that it can readily follow the contour of the body. The stroking movement is easier if you let the elbows hang loosely at your sides, in a natural way. The stroking is always performed in double strokes, one hand following in the path of the other, enhancing the withdrawing power of each individual stroke.

The strokes must be without pressure and swift, at the rate of about 150 strokes per minute (2–3 per second). It is necessary that the heat be withdrawn and carried away rapidly.

After having covered the right side of the back with a succession of 5 or more double strokes, retrace the path back to the spine. Proceed in the same way over the left side of the back. Continue this withdrawing treatment, swinging from side to side across the back until the entire back feels cooler.

It is important that the heat withdrawal strokes be light, swift and smooth. Contact with the body must be made and broken softly, smoothly and without abruptness, slapping or thudding. Do not shorten the individual strokes to make them swift; each stroke must be carried to its full length. Also, as the hand breaks contact with the body at the end of a stroke, do not lift it far off the body but move it to its next starting position by the simplest and fastest route possible.

Drainage movement on back

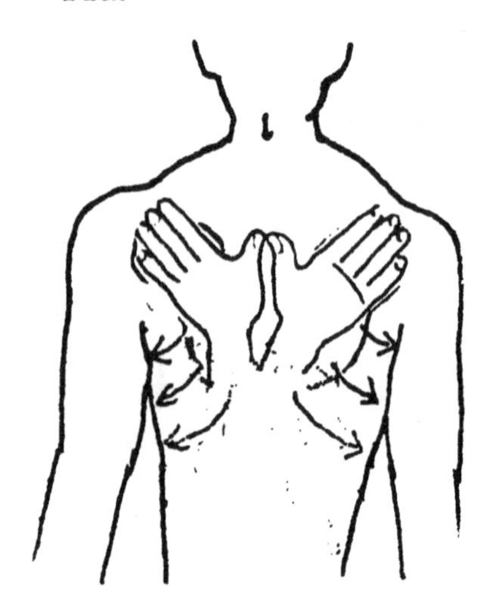

➧ **Step 3: Drainage movement on back.** This part of the treatment decongests and redirects the circulation, which has become disoriented by the fever. Perform this drainage movement with the thought of moving a whole column of blood ahead of the hands, just beneath the surface being worked on. This will draw a fresh supply of blood, from deeper within the body to replace what has been moved ahead of the hands and creates a stronger circulation.

Lay both hands flat on the patient's back near the top of the shoulder blades, fingers together, thumbs extended and touching each other spanning as wide an area across the back as possible. Move the hands down with a firm pressure, letting the thumbs separate as the hands move around the sides of the body, the finger tips pass just below the arms on the first pass. Release the contact.

Return the hands to their original position, just a little lower down on the back and repeat the same drainage stroke, following well around the sides of the body, overlapping the bottom edge of the first stroke area. Cover the entire back in 2 or at most 3 drainage strokes for adequate coverage of the back.

If, after the drainage movement, the back is hotter to the touch, or there are places that have heated up again, withdraw heat and drain again.

This treatment may be used on people who have fever in the lung area, such as in pleurisy, bronchitis, "cold on the chest," etc. and they should sit up for good drainage.

➧ **Step 4: Drainage movement on a man.** In the drainage movement, use both hands simultaneously, one on each side of the body. In front the hands sweep from close under the armpits to the center of the body. In the second drainage sweep, the hands come from the sides of the body under the breasts to center. Then the heat withdrawal may be started once again.

Step 5: Drainage on the front of the chest for a woman. Patient lies on her back; Creative Healer stands. The withdrawal and draining movements for the front of the chest are described for a woman because heat is never drawn through the breasts of a woman. Because of the shape of a woman's chest, the hands are inclined at an angle so that mostly the palms follow in each other's tracks. Begin the path of light double-stroking to withdraw heat over the sternum. Then from the upper part of the sternum, sweep outward on one side with the double strokes below the collarbone to the arm and down the chest, outside the breast, the hands coming around below the breast toward the center line of the body, describing an arc almost parallel to the ribs. Double-stroke again over the sternum then proceed in the same manner on the other side. Repeat several times before repeating treatment on the back.

Removing heat from the front for a woman

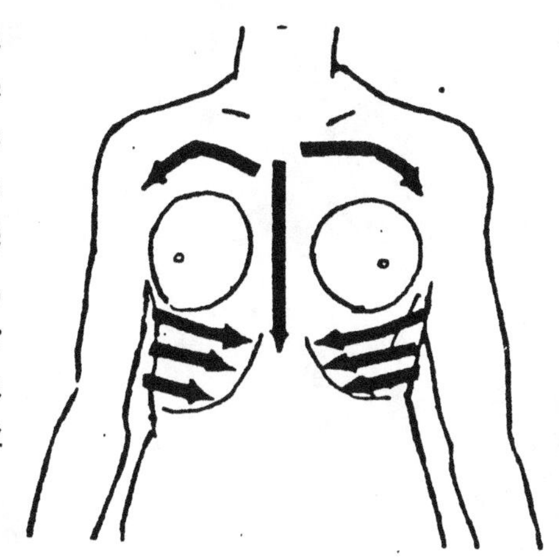

Duration

A pneumonia treatment will require about 20 to 25 minutes. To the beginner, it may seem an arduous task to work that length of time in the bent-over position necessary at the bedside when the patient cannot sit. But be assured, the work will be so absorbing that not even the thought of fatigue will enter the mind. The complete pneumonia treatment consists of applying the steps 4 or 5 times, alternating from the back to the chest or from the chest to the back. Repeated applications are required because, while one side of the body is being worked on, heat will again return (though to a lesser degree) to the other side. The treatment must then be repeated on that side. This alternating treating of the two sides of the body has to be repeated until you are certain that the lung area is remaining at normal temperature throughout.

Removing the fever has such a relaxing effect on the patient that often before the Creative Healer leaves, the patient will have gone to sleep.

Frequency

Treat once a day for at least 4 days. Then depending on the condition of the patient, at less frequent intervals.

From of writings of Joseph B. Stephenson

I was called by one of my patients telling me of their neighbor dying with pneumonia and he had seven children and all young.

"Oh," I said, "You tell the wife I will be there as soon as possible. There are 18 people in my waiting room but I feel this is a case of life or death and in this case it has to be life."

I was there in 15 minutes. I went upstairs and here is what I saw: a man unconscious on the bed and a priest getting ready to give him the last rites. So I spoke to the priest, "What are you going to do?"

"Why, the doctor called me and said to hurry here to give this man the last rites."

"Well, you are not going to do anything of the kind. This man has seven children. He must live."

By this time the priest sat down and I got my coat off and started to treat him. In twenty minutes he opened his eyes and looked up and said, "Hello Father."

The Father never spoke. He was much too interested in what I was doing. In 45 minutes the patient fell asleep.

"You meet me here at 9:30 in the morning."

We met, went into the house but no one saw the Father. The wife had her arms around my neck, the children had their arms around my body. After I got loose we went upstairs and our patient was sitting up in bed with a good-sized breakfast before him. The priest spoke to him in his own language. The man then thanked me for what I had done but he could not remember me being there.

This young priest said to me, "Stephenson, I will never give a last rite to anyone until I send for you. You must be one of the disciples."

"Oh no," I said, "I just know the human body like no one else."

Recurrent Pneumonia and Chronic Chest Congestion

In all cases of chest congestion and especially in the case of pneumonia, the patient must not be given milk or milk products. In the case of all lingering and weakening chest conditions the use of vitamin D as found in cod liver oil is recommended. Mr. Stephenson preferred the plain, unfortified oil and suggested only very moderate amounts: 1/4 teaspoon a day.

Recurrent pneumonia cases, bronchitis, and other long-standing cases of chest congestion, are characterized by weakness, sweating and/or panting with the least exertion, a dry cough and frequently accumulations of fluid under the sternum. Many cases of lingering allergies are due to congestion under the breast bone or sternum. These symptoms often remain after a bad flu or cold and prevent full-strength recovery.

The following steps are applied totally or in part, but always in the following sequence, in the case of any congestive chest trouble.

➧ **Step 1: Bring the lung area to normal temperature.** Restore the body to normal temperature by applying the pneumonia treatment, page 4–7. Then massage, palm following palm, downward over the breast bone or sternum.

➧ **Step 2: Pressure between ribs.** Alternate the massage of step 1 with fingertip pressures centrally along the breast bone. Apply firm fingertip breaking-up pressures on the spaces or depressions between the ribs on either side and close to the sternum. Direct the pressure downward toward the feet and inward toward the spine simultaneously. The pressures are most effective when coordinated with the patient's exhalations. Apply the pressure intermittently at one place during each extended exhalation.

Breaking up pressure between the ribs

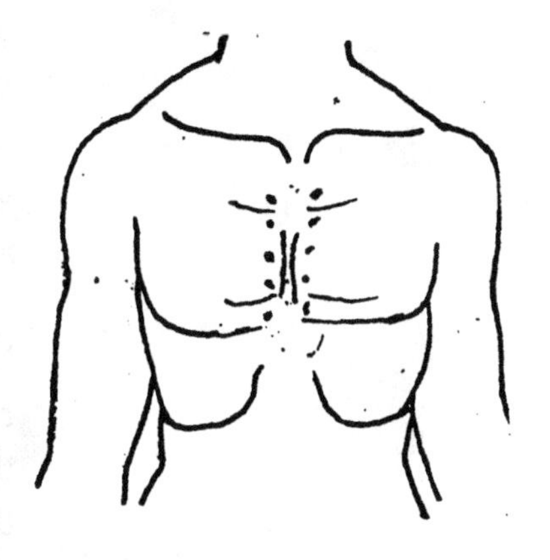

➧ **Step 3: Apply the drainage movement over the lung area.** See steps 2 and 3 for pleurisy, next treatment.

➧ **Step 4: Clean out and drain the pleural cavity through the breathing tube.** Create a vacuum on the breathing tube and draw the congestive material through this tube into the stomach. See four-minute breathing tube treatment, page 4–5. This vacuum movement should be followed up with some firm drainage movements from the back around toward the front. This is the same movement used in the pleurisy treatment, on the next page. In addition, the substance between the vertebrae should be checked for any needed correction.

➧ **Step 5:** Check the diaphragm and reestablish its normal breathing function with the high and short breathing treatment and educated breathing, page 4–2.

Other Uses for the Above Treatments

Emphysema: When the lung region is either above or below normal temperature, treat accordingly, by removing heat (pneumonia treatment, page 4–7) or adding heat (asthma treatment, page 4–13), as needed, to bring about normal temperature. Frequently, correct use of the diaphragm will also have to be reestablished. See high and short breathing treatment, page 4–2.

Fluid on the lungs: In some cases where symptoms seem to linger after a bad chest cold, the patient may complain of a tight chest. Perform a gentle, relaxing massage of the whole lung area (pneumonia treatment without heat to remove). Work with the thought of relaxing the contractions within the chest. Then perform the drainage movement, as in the pneumonia treatment. If the person is unable to take a deep breath, perform the vacuum movement over the breathing tube.

Nervous chills: Perform the heating treatment as for asthma, but only down the spine. Nervous chills occur when nerve life is not sufficiently fed through to the spine, and no amount of external heat will then warm up the body. If the heat treatment cannot be applied, a little whiskey will prove helpful.

Pleurisy

Pleurisy is a condition in which the pleura, the inner and outer membranes covering the lungs, are prevented from gliding freely and smoothly as they normally do during inhalation and exhalation. The characteristic feature of pleurisy is a stabbing pain when inhaling, even in the earliest stages. The pain is usually at the lower part of the lung region, though it can be higher and in either the front or back. This disruption in the smooth flow of lubricating fluids is compounded by a rapid temperature rise in the affected areas. If the condition goes unattended, fluid, pus or gas accumulates in the pleural cavity.

The usual cause of pleurisy is an abrupt loss of body heat through chilling or by suddenly inhaling copious amounts of cold air. People predisposed to pleurisy must be warned against wearing synthetic fibers next to the skin on the trunk of the body. With these non-absorbent garments the slightest draft of air reaching the skin can have a chilling effect. A snug garment of natural fiber is recommended for daytime and even at night. This will keep a warm blanket of air next to the body, directly over the skin.

All the movements described here take place on the back when the pain is in the back.

Position

The patient sits on a bench and will be able to pinpoint the place where the pain is most severe.The Creative Healer sits at a comfortable height behind.

➧ **Step 1: Withdraw heat.** The first movement is to remove whatever heat exists in and around the pain area by applying the pneumonia treatment, page 4–7. Spread oil generously and work quickly to stroke down the spine, one palm following the other from the top of the lung area to the bottom. These double strokes should gradually describe arcs as they approach the side of the body and end nearly parallel to the ribs. The strokes range back and forth across the affected side of the back until the hands feel that side to be at normal temperature.

➧ **Step 2: Drain and redirect circulation.** The draining movement redirects the circulation, which has become disoriented with the fever. The hands lie flat on the patient's back. The fingers of each hand are held together to form a unit and the thumbs are outstretched and touch each other at center back. Move the hands down with a firm pressure until the fingertips can pass just below the arms. Release the contact and return the hands to the original position a little beneath the area just covered and repeat the same drainage stroke, following well around the sides of the body and overlapping the bottom edge of the first stroke. This will draw a fresh supply of blood from deeper within the body to replace what has been moved by the hands. A stronger circulation is created; 2 or 3 strokes will cover the area. This increased pressure gets the lubricating fluids to work to separate the lungs from the lining of the ribcage.

➧ **Step 3: Break up and clean out congestion.** If individual spots remain where the pain still stabs as the hands pass over them or as the patient attempts to draw a deep breath, use the breaking up movement with thumb or fingertips at these points to clean out between or on the ribs from back to front. Though this cleaning out movement is positive it must be gentle with the intention of loosening the adhesion. Continue until the patient can take a deep breath.

Be aware that the heavier pressures in the drainage and cleaning-out movements will add heat so that it will be necessary to again apply the withdrawal and drainage movements to establish normal temperature.

Frequency

If pleurisy is treated in its initial stage, 1 treatment will usually suffice and will relieve the sharp pain.

Asthma

The characteristic feature of asthma is that the lung region is below normal temperature. The asthmatic condition is caused by mucous and possibly foreign particles present in the lungs, as in silicosis (from a chronic inhalation of the dust of silicon dioxide found in stones and sand; this causes fibrosis in the lungs). Mucous forms around the foreign particles, creating congestion within the lung sacs that the body can't overcome. If the condition exists for a long time, the asthmatic may have to sleep sitting up in order to breathe; lying down makes the mucous rise, shutting off breathing. The asthmatic also avoids breathing deeply because this triggers a weakening and unproductive cough. Under normal circumstances, the small, hairlike cilia lining the trachea prevent the mucous in the lungs from accumulating by prompting it to rise, and prevent nasal drip from entering the lungs. However, if the cilia cannot handle the condition, a cough is triggered; a productive cough raises the mucous into the throat from which it can be expelled whereas a dry cough does nothing.

If an attempt is made to swallow the mucous, it may again enter the trachea and then into the lungs. The same thing may occur if the cough is suppressed or stopped by outside intervention (cough syrup, medication). In this way, cases of more serious lung conditions can develop. It is a mistake, or even dangerous, to suppress or stop a productive cough.

In all cases of chest congestion, the patient should have no milk or milk products. In all cases of asthma and other lingering and weakening chest conditions, the use of vitamin D as found in cod liver oil is recommended in very moderate amounts, such as 1/4 teaspoon per day.

Any chilling can prevent the body from re-establishing normal temperature. Synthetic fiber in clothing has little or no absorbency and when compared to natural fibers, little compatibility with the human skin. With a loose, non-absorbent synthetic garment, the slightest amount of air reaching the skin can have a chilling effect. Such chilling is a serious threat to a body with a temperature above normal. Nylon sheets can cause this reaction. Patients must be warned against wearing synthetic fibers next to the skin on the trunk of the body. When the body seems unable to sustain normal temperature, a snug garment of natural fiber should be worn in the daytime and even at night. This will keep a warm blanket of air next to the body, directly over the skin.

Position

The patient sits up for the back part of the treatment, if possible.

➧ **Step 1: Add heat to bring the body to normal temperature.** Apply the same movements as in pneumonia, page 4–7, except that the intent in the mind is reversed. The intent is to add heat instead of withdrawing it. Apply the same full-length, double strokes but with a pressure applied firmly without slapping or thudding, instead of light, cooling strokes. It is easier to apply the additional pressure needed for this treatment if you keep your elbows straight and lean against the patient. The added pressure creates friction between the palms and the body and creates the necessary heat making a "swishing" sound that accompanies the strokes. Also, less oil is used than when removing heat. Use just enough oil to let the hands glide smoothly, without clinging.

The vigorous nature of the asthma massage creates heat, warms the mucous and makes it flow more readily, enabling the patient to cough it up. The patient will continue to cough considerably and with effort, but the cough will, in general, be productive and raise some mucous. As the coughing raises mucous, it frees the lungs by giving them more breathing capacity. An accumulation of foreign matter or mucous that lodges within the lung sacs can be eliminated only by being coughed up and expectorated.

➧ **Step 2: Drainage movement.** Apply the drainage movement as in pneumonia, page 4–7. For asthma, emphasize the lower part of the lung region because the greater congestion lies there. Alternate the treatment from back to front and front to back until the whole lung region is a uniform normal temperature.

➧ **Step 3: Diaphragmatic breathing.** Many people with chest trouble breathe without the proper use of the diaphragm. The breathing nerve center connected with the diaphragm is located about 1 1/2 inches below the end of the breastbone, on the center line of the body. Apply the four-minute breathing tube treatment, page 4–5. The vacuum stroke, as it cleans out the breathing tube and drains the pleural cavity, also works on this nerve center, helping to reestablish deep diaphragmatic breathing.

➧ **Step 4: Breathing nerve center on back.** A second breathing nerve center, is located on the spine at the center line of the body, at the first space below the spot for pain between the shoulders. To complete any treatment of respiratory trouble, replace and center up this nerve center. By working on this nerve center with his thumb, Mr. Stephenson restored respiration to a person who was unconscious from an electric shock and whose breathing had ceased. This occurred several times during his career when he worked in the coal mines.

➧ **Step 5: Reshape chest.** Respiratory disturbances also affect the shape of the chest. The use of a band may be in order to return the chest to normal form; see high and short breathing treatment, page 4–2.

➤➤➤CAUTION When treating a thin person who has a hollow at the end of the sternum where the body should be convex, the vacuum created in the breathing tube must be of only moderate pressure. If it is too strong, it may cause agitation by drawing the breathing nerve center too far downward.

For a baby born with asthma see Chapter 8: Men, Women and Children, page 8–19

Other Problems Affecting the Lungs

Diaphragmatic or Esophageal Hernia, Swallowing Difficulties

The stomach vents air or gas when we swallow food or liquid through a tube Mr. Stephenson called a stomach air tube. It lies immediately to the left of center and continues up to just below the voice box. If this tube does not function properly, difficulties will arise, such as a spastic esophagus and/or a dry hacking cough commonly known as a cigarette cough. The failure of the tube to function is usually because mucus has formed or contractions have developed and the cough is nature's attempt to clear out the mucous.

This treatment may be used in cases of esophageal or diaphragmatic hernia.

Position

The patient lies down. The Creative Healier sits to the right if right-handed.

➧ **Step 1: Four-minute breathing tube vacuum.** Use the thumb to create a vacuum down the center line of the body from the sternum. Although the stomach air tube lies to the patient's left of the center line the thumb stays on the center line, perhaps tilting a little to the left. Care must be taken not to pass over the heart tube. See heart treatment, page 4–21.

➧ **Step 2: Dislodge mucus.** Use your index finger to press down simultaneously toward the spine and toward the feet between the cartilage adjacent to the sternum on the left side. Do this while the patient exhales completely. Begin at the bottom of the breastbone and work all the way up to the collarbone. These firm pressure movements dislodge any mucus and break up contractions that may be present. This treatment can always be applied on both sides whenever there is a non-productive cough that lingers after a chest condition.

Step 3: Repeat the four-minute breathing tube vacuum.

Step 4: Reposition tube. With your index finger, enter into the soft tissue of the V at the upper section of the breast bone on the right side and push toward the left. This puts the tube into position if it has been displaced.

Hiccoughs

Hiccoughs are caused by a little mechanism, about the size of a small fingernail, lying beneath the sternum. It is located about 2 to 2 1/2 inches up from the end of the sternum, slightly to the left of the median. This mechanism can be drawn up out of position if the person swallowed food too dry, hot or spicy. Nature attempts to get the mechanism to relax and return to its normal position but the hiccoughs will persist as long as nature's attempt is not successful. If no help were given, the hiccoughs could persist for days or even weeks, which could lead to exhaustion and ultimately death.

Position

Patient sits. Creative Healer stands.

Step 1: Place your thumb on the spot described in the paragraph above and with a firm pressure directed inward, draw the thumb slightly downward. Do this intermittently while the patient is breathing out and holding, letting the chest fall in. Repeat during several exhalations. This encourages relaxation of the mechanism. As soon as it falls back into place the hiccough spell is broken.

This treatment can be self-administered.

Step 2: Hiccoughs may be stopped by applying the four-minute vacuum treatment over the breathing tube; see page 4–5. However, coordinate the stroking with the patient's breathing so that the vacuum stroke (the down stroke) is accompanied by the patient's complete exhalation.

Step 3: Another factor in breaking the hiccoughing deadlock is suspense. What breaks up the deadlock may take on various forms, but there is always at its base a suspending of the ordinary rhythms, cycles, or patterns. In the common remedy of drinking water from the far side of a glass, the suspense is in the suspension of the ordinary drinking pattern.

From the writings of Joseph B. Stephenson

When it became known that Mr. Stephenson could help with hiccoughs, he frequently had occasion to do so over the telephone. His method was as follows: When someone would call to inquire whether he was the man who could help with hiccoughs, he would say, "Yes, but you must put the person who has the hiccoughs on the phone." As soon as that person began to speak, Mr. Stephenson would at once ask to be excused. He would say that he had to answer the door or give a similar faked reason.

He would remain away from the phone for a minute or two, and then without further inquiry would announce over the phone, "That is all right now." He would then hang up. And it always was all right. The person suffering from the hiccoughs had waited breathlessly for contact with the one who was going to help him. This wait and the interruption subjected the person to a high degree of suspense, and this was sufficient to overcome the condition.

Breathing Nerve Center on the Back

A second breathing nerve center on the center line of the back is helpful in heading off the threat and/or speeding the recovery from flu. When there is flu, this spot will often be sore and sensitive. Mr. Stephenson said he used it to restore breathing to unconscious mine workers.

Position

The patient sits on a bench; the Creative Healer sits behind. This position allows the work on this spot to be done gently with the thumb to break up the strong contraction that has closed down this vital nerve center.

Breathing nerve center

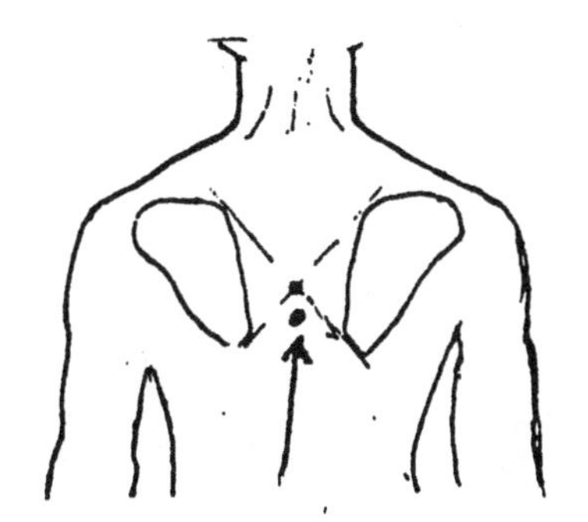

➧ Step 1: Location. The breathing nerve center is at the first space below the spot for pain between the shoulders. At the spine, place the tip of your thumb in the hollow and hold in a horizontal position between the two vertebrae.

➧ Step 2: Thumb action. Hold your thumb straight, the fingers touching the body in a way that supports and adds strength to the thumb. Extend your arm from the shoulder and maintain this position while the thumb is barely moving in a gentle, breaking up circular movement. Visualize the thumb's vibration penetrating and breaking up the strong contraction that has shut down this vital nerve center.

➧ Step 3: You may alternate the breaking up movement with the thumb with stroking down over the spine using the palms of both hands, one following the other. Also replace substance at the spine on each side and on the center line.

The Heart

Understanding Your Heart

The heart is generally thought of as a very delicate organ of precarious balance, subject to many failings. The heart is a highly intricate and delicate mechanism but in performance it is unbelievably rugged, often continuing to function against impossible odds. The heart itself is seldom at fault. Its apparent failings are frequently caused by impositions placed on it by malfunctioning in other parts of the body. The bowel, kidneys, respiratory system, conditions of high blood pressure or poor or blocked circulation are examples. Whenever there is a failure to function properly in the body, this failure ultimately encroaches upon the heart. Thus, when the heart appears to be in trouble, be alert to the condition of the rest of the body. Work to restore it to normal function while at the same time treating the heart.

The heart always gives ample warning of incipient trouble, but its warnings are usually ignored. Be alert to the symptoms of heart trouble. One of the first symptoms is usually experienced in connection with running, such as hurrying to catch a bus. The heart throbs in the throat and doesn't seem to be able to supply the circulation needed for the extra exertion. The person should then understand that the body is imposing too great a load on the heart.

Unfortunately, a person who is convinced that the heart is not functioning correctly, limits activities in an effort to protect the heart. For this reason Mr. Stephenson felt that patients should not be told they had a bad heart; he explained that the body was imposing too great a load on the heart so that it needed help and also treated any other problems.

The following is a brief description of the most essential features concerning the structure and functioning of the heart according to Mr. Stephenson.

The heart is divided by a partition into a right and left half each consisting of an upper chamber (atrium) and a lower chamber (ventricle), which are connected by a valve. The right atrium receives the deoxygenized blood from the systemic (the whole body) circulation. The blood is pumped into the ventricle and from there, into the pulmonary (lung) circulation. The left atrium receives the oxygenized blood from the pulmonary circulation, pumps it into the left ventricle, which in turn, pumps it into the systemic circulation.

The blood vessels leading into the atria and issuing from the ventricles are connected with these chambers by valves. The heart works as two compound pumps, side by side, functioning simultaneously. The pumping action of the heart, which sends the blood from the atria into the ventricles and into the systemic and pulmonary circulations, is done by contraction.

Mr. Stephenson compared the heart to a reciprocating positive displacement pump, with its piston and cylinder. It is a good way to explain the functioning of the heart and the difficulties that arise when it is in trouble. The contraction of the heart corresponds to the movement of a piston, as it displaces the fluid in a cylinder. The return movement of the piston allows fluid to enter the cylinder. This corresponds to the relaxation of the heart muscles, during which time, the chambers fill with blood. Just as the action of the piston is timed with the pump valves, so the contraction and relaxation of the heart is timed with the heart valves. If the pump is fed an incoming supply of fluid and continues its cycle of operation, then, as the piston moves to displace the fluid that fills the cylinder, that fluid must be delivered from the pump.

If an obstruction arises in the delivery lines from the pump, one of two things will happen: either a relief mechanism will begin to operate or the pump will stop. This comparison will be used later in the leaking heart and heart murmur treatments.

This pump comparison describes the working of the heart, except that the heart has no piston and cylinder, but functions instead as muscles do, by contraction and expansion. No muscle can produce work of itself, except by contraction, and the heart is no exception. The flow momentum in the circulation, enhanced by the contraction of the arterial walls, causes the heart to expand and fill with blood each time it relaxes.

Mr. Stephenson saw what he called a "region of relative vacuum" surrounding the heart. It is a region in which lesser pressures prevail than the pressures within the heart during and after contraction. This relative vacuum is a second vital cause for the expansion of the heart after its contraction.

This region of relative vacuum presumably lies within the medial portion of the chest cavity that contains the heart and all chest cavity material except the lungs; it is possibly further confined between other tissues surrounding the heart. The fact that Mr. Stephenson did not indicate the precise location of the region of relative vacuum in no way affects the definiteness and clarity of the treatment that is applied to it. Any congestive matter such as gas, fluid, or pus, present within the confines of this region, will alter the pressure differential, preventing the heart from adequately expanding. Such matter must be removed.

This congestive matter may be drained into the stomach through what he called the heart tube. The delicate heart tube connects the region of relative vacuum, surrounding the heart, to the stomach. It makes possible the removal of foreign material from the region of relative vacuum and obstructions affecting the circulation in the chest. The heart tube is also endowed with a mechanism that regulates the pressure in that region, in relation to the pressure of the atmosphere. This is possible because the tube is connected with the atmosphere through the stomach and the esophagus.

The third purpose of the heart tube is to regulate the speed of the heart. This tube plays an important role in the Creative Healing treatment for the heart.

Emergency Heart Treatment

If you are with someone whose heart appears to be in trouble, make sure the person is lying down and perform this emergency treatment to calm the person and perhaps save a life. The basic requirement is a gentle healing attitude and touch.

Position

Patient lies down; be sure legs are not crossed and arms are at the sides of the body. Creative Healer sits on the right side of the patient.

Emergency heart treatment

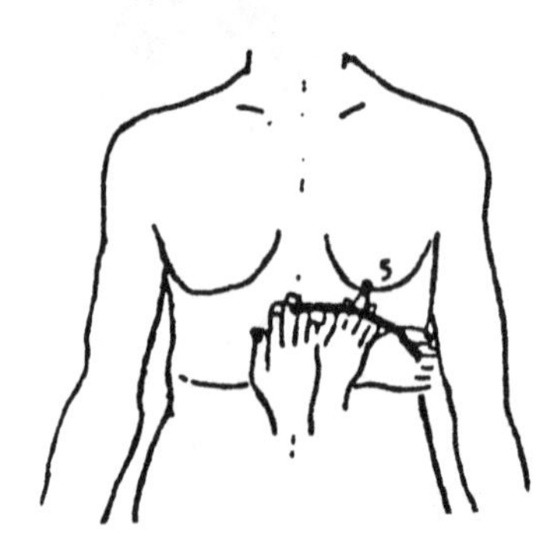

➧ **Step 1:** Your left hand rests somewhere along the right side of the patient's body to give support and comfort. Place your relaxed right palm, thumb and fingers close together, over the ribs on the left side. The hand is in a horizontal position when it contacts the lower ribs of the patient's body, fingers curved and pointing down to the bed or floor. As your hand passes just below the breast outline, turn your wrist so that the fingertips begin to point toward the patient's head. By the time the hand reaches the center line of the body, the fingertips point toward the head and the stroke becomes a gentle arc as it continues toward and across the center line. Exert no pressure, allowing only the weight of the hand to do the work. Keep the hand relaxed. This repeated stroke creates a vacuum from the heart tube and terminates when the palm crosses the center line of the body. Done correctly the hand will be vertical or a little to the left as the stroke ends but in full contact with the body throughout each stroke.

➧ **Step 2:** Lift your hand and return it to the beginning position on the ribs and repeat. This positive, repetitive and calming stroke of the hand creates a drainage action.

Duration

Continue these calming strokes for 4 minutes or until the patient takes an involuntary deep, relaxing breath. This is a sign that the massage has been helpful in relieving a distressed heart and nature will take over the healing process.

If a patient has indicated an awareness of heart trouble, you may listen for the sounds. To do this place your ear slightly above the left breast nipple toward the center of the person's chest, shifting until the lub and dub sounds become nearly equal in intensity. Any sounds occurring before, after, and in between these two are the unnatural sounds. They will disappear as the heart is restored to normal function.

Note: It cannot be overstressed that the heart treatment must be performed very gently. Mr. Stephenson said that a heavy, clumsy hand could not get results in healing the heart; it requires a gentle, healing touch.

Basic Heart Treatment

The basic heart treatment is used for all heart ailments. It is the principal treatment for cases that require regulation of the flow of blood to restore the heart to normal functioning. Many heart conditions, i.e., heart murmur and leaking heart, respond to the five-point heart treatment; others need to be combined with other Creative Healing applications. If the patient has mentioned heart trouble, you may feel free to listen for the sounds. If the patient is unaware of a heart condition, do not cause undue concern by listening to the heart.

Position

The patient lies on the back and is made comfortable, to relax. A pillow may be used at the head; legs or ankles should not be crossed and arms should lie comfortably at the sides, not above the head. The Creative Healer sits on a chair or stool close to the bed at the patient's right side, facing the patient's head and able to reach comfortably across the patient's body with his right hand. The Creative Healer must be comfortable and work without strain, as stress is easily transmitted to the patient.

➧ **Step 1: Vacuum stroking.** Cover your right palm with olive oil; your thumb and fingers, together with the palm are in contact with the body throughout each stroke. The left hand rests somewhere along the right side of the patient's body to give support and comfort. Begin the stroke with the relaxed right hand in horizontal position over the ribs on the left side, fingertips down to where the patient's body touches the bed. As your hand passes below the breast line, turn your wrist so that the fingertips begin to point toward the patient's head. By the time the hand reaches the center line, the fingertips point toward the head and the stroke becomes a gentle arc as it continues across the center line of the body. Exert no pressure, allow only the weight of the hand to work. Keep the hand relaxed. This repeated stroke brings the palm across the heart tube to create a vacuum and the stroke terminates when the palm has crossed the center line of the body. Done correctly the hand will be vertical or a little to the left as the stroke ends. The positive, repetitive and calming stroke of the hand creates the drainage vacuum; continue the stroking for 4 minutes.

Creating a vacuum in heart tube

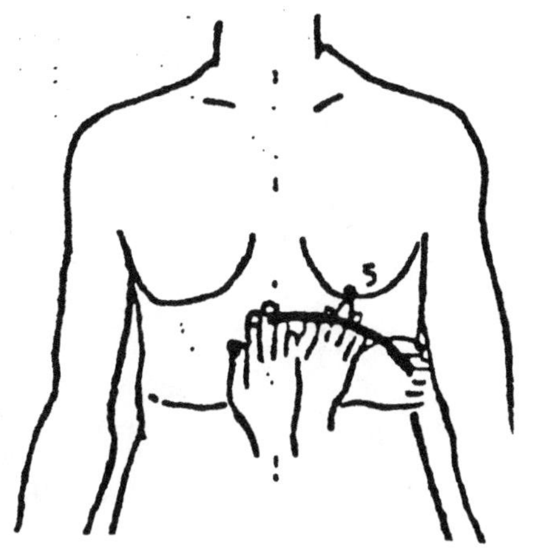

➧ **Step 2: Treating the five heart spots.** In this step, you will treat the 5 special spots related to the heart. These are felt as small cavities between the bones. Their location is more easily described with reference to the female body and can then be transferred to the male body.

Breaking up congestion in the 5 heart spots

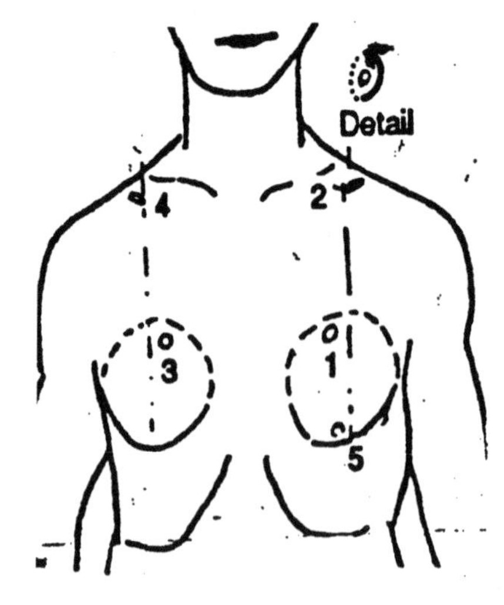

Spot #1 is located inside the upper border of the left breast, on the medial side of a line projected vertically through the nipple.

Spot #2 is located above spot #1, closer to the sternum and immediately below the collarbone. It is felt as an elongated hollow.

Spot #3 is located just inside the upper border of the right breast, symmetrically opposite to spot #1.

Spot #4 is symmetrically opposite to spot #2.

Spot #5 is located just above the lower margin of the left breast, on the medial side of a line projected vertically through the nipple. It is a more pronounced hollow than the four other spots.

These five spots are nerve and circulation centers that regulate the flow of blood. The first four are connected with the blood leaving the heart while spot #5 affects the blood entering the heart. Spot #1 is particularly connected with the relationship between the outgoing and incoming blood. The spots are always treated in their numerical sequence. When a derangement in the flow of blood has interfered with the normal functioning of the heart, the work performed at these five spots is vital in restoring normal functioning.

Use the right index finger for spots #1, #3, and #5. Spots #2 and #4 are more oval in shape. For these, use the index and middle fingers for spot #2; the middle and third fingers for spot #4 fit perfectly into these oval spots.

Perform a circular counterclockwise breaking up movement in these spots while also performing a delicate vacuum by a gradual lightening of the finger contact through the upward arc of the tiny circle. Do this combined breaking up and vacuum movement only a few times at any one spot before moving on to the next.

Hold your hand in a relaxed, flat position, although only the pads of the above-mentioned fingers touch the patient. The 5 spots are never "poked" with the fingertips. While treating the first 4 spots, you must take care not to rest your arm or even your hand on the heart area. Every pressure and strain must be avoided.

The breaking up movement at the 5 heart spots must always be gentle, particularly when the heart is in trouble. One or more spots may be very sensitive or the patient may complain of a feeling of tightness in the chest. As the spots are worked on, the sensitivity and the feeling of tightness will be relieved. Only a few circles of this combined breaking up and vacuum movements at any one spot are done before moving to the next one.

Any material broken up at the first 4 spots is automatically channeled to the fifth spot and from there it is drawn, along with any foreign material present in the region of relative vacuum, into the stomach through the heart tube.

➧ **Step 3: Create a vacuum in the heart tube.** The purpose of step 3 is to create a vacuum in the heart tube and we have already discussed one way of doing this—the safest way—the massage stroke in step 1 with which you began the treatment, with the thought of creating a vacuum and drawing action in the heart tube. When you have touched all the heart spots, return to this massage. While the stroking is performed for about 4 minutes in step 1, it is performed here in step 3 for 1 or 2 minutes.

Then return to any or all of the first 4 heart spots that need further attention by performing the breaking up movement. (Further attention is needed if patient has pain or a disturbed or tender feeling the first time around; encourage patient feedback.) After working again on the first 4 spots, always in sequence, return to work on spot #5 and then, finally, return to the stroking. Repeat steps 2 and 3 several times, but it is vital that each time you work on any of the first 4 spots, you must also work on the fifth spot before returning to the vacuum stroking.

Sometimes a great quantity of flow passes through the heart tube. If the flow is thick and heavy (as would be encountered when removing an abscess beneath the heart) the flow cannot be heard, but can be felt by the hand. If the flow is of lighter viscosity (such as fluids or gases) the flow can be both felt and heard.

The movement of the material drawn through the heart tube is often audible as a "gushing" sound to the Creative Healer and, occasionally, even to others present in the room. The movement of material through the heart tube may start of itself, in the earlier parts of the treatment. However, the treatment should always be carried through to full completion.

➤ ➤ ➤CAUTION: In both cases, be cautious not to draw through too much at one time, since this might change the action of the heart too suddenly. In these instances, a patient might report discomfort at spots #1 and/or #5, which he would describe most often as a "drawing" feeling. In all cases of heavy flow, perform the drainage in gradual steps during successive treatments.

Second way to create a vacuum

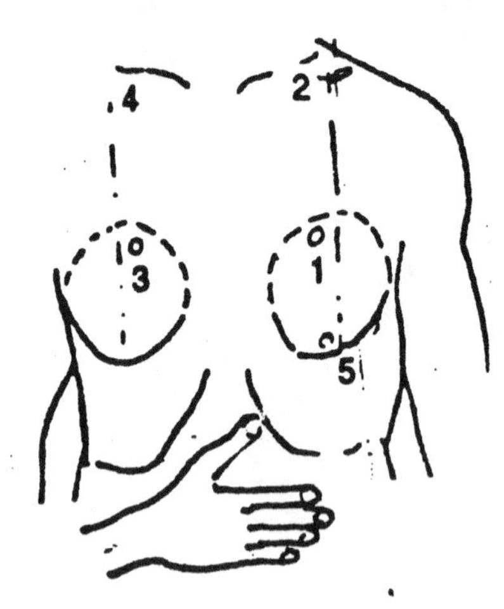

➧ **Step 4: Second way to create vacuum in the heart tube.** The second way of creating a vacuum in the heart tube is by working directly on the tube. Creative Healers are **cautioned** not to use the second method until thoroughly experienced with what actually occurs in the body when the heart treatment is applied. The heart tube is one of the most delicate mechanisms in the human body and should never be probed for or tampered with.

You must be in full control of the treatment. Before starting, be certain that the patient's hands and body are relaxed, the legs are not crossed, and the arms are extended downward and lie loosely alongside the body.

The heart tube is located on a 45° angle with the vertical direction of the body from the cavity of the #5 heart spot. The 45° line passes over the edge of the ribs into the soft, unsupported tissues below the sternum to the stomach.

Place the thumb length-wise on the extension of this line so that its tip rests next to the ribcage, but within the area of the soft tissue. Place the rest of your hand on the patient's body, fingers together, horizontal to the vertical direction of the body and in light contact with the patient's body. Your hand and thumb are now in position for the treatment of the heart tube. The thumb is in little or no contact with the patient's body, certainly without any pressure.

The actual vacuum movement is a gentle and short compound movement. The extended thumb is moved slightly toward the hand, and at the same time, away from spot #5. The entire movement of the tip of the thumb does not cover more than 3/8 inch. The movement of the central part of the thumb, which performs the effective part of the movement, does not cover more than 1/8 inch. After completing the movement, raise the thumb and return it to the original position. Repeat the movement if needed.

If the patient moves or talks, raise the thumb at once. The thumb should be raised at least half the time of the treatment. The palm and fingers, however, remain in contact with the body throughout.

In a great majority of cases in which the heart tube is out of position, it will be too high. Step 4 will automatically draw it into proper position.

Special care must be taken for people who have a hollow at the end of the sternum (where the body should be convex) not to draw the heart tube down, which would result in extreme nervousness. Use the following form of Step 4: place your hand as before but with the thumb adjacent to the hand instead of on the 45° line. The movement is performed with the thumb moving away from the hand while the hand moves away from the #5 heart spot.

Duration

The full basic heart treatment, should be limited to about 15 minutes. Often the patient will, during the treatment, draw a deep, involuntary breath. This is a signal for the Creative Healer to bring the treatment to a close as nature has taken over. To close, always do the breaking up movement at spot #5 and then vacuum over the heart tube. If the patient has not drawn the involuntary, deep breath after 15 minutes, ask him to take a deep breath. If this is done in comfort the treatment is concluded.

If the patient is hesitant in completing a full breath or says there is something like a "catch," proceed with the following: With the hand in position for the heart tube movement, straight across the body but with the thumb lying adjacent to the hand, stroke gently upward with the thumb until its leading edge just meets the 45° line from the #5 heart spot. This relieves the feeling of obstruction and the patient can draw an easy, full, deep breath. Only rarely, will it be necessary to repeat this single stroke.

Frequency

The number and frequency of treatments will depend on the individual patient's particular problem but once a week is usual.

Please note that the heart spot for inward goiter, found on the back, plays a role in many heart conditions, i.e., fast heart, heart murmur, rheumatic and erratic heart.

Leaking Heart

A leaking heart may be completely taken care of by the basic heart treatment. A leaking heart is caused by an obstruction of the flow of blood on the delivery side of the heart. Such obstructions will always be felt at one or more of the first four heart spots. The likelihood is greatest at spot #1 and it will be very sore and tender. The other three spots will probably be less tender.

To explain a leaking heart, remember the comparison of the heart with a reciprocating displacement pump. In this case, there is an obstruction in the lines delivering fluid from the pump. If the pump is to continue to function, some relief mechanism must act. A line or gasket will break in the displacement pump.

The leaking heart corresponds to the breaking of a line or gasket. Because of an obstruction in a small artery on or above the heart, excess pressure develops in the circulation system. The heart then "leaks" to relieve the pressure. The leaking of the heart, as a consequence of obstructions in the flow of blood, is a prime example of the manner in which nature compensates for a malfunction of the body. The arteries leak, in this case, to keep the heart beating in spite of the obstructions.

As soon as the obstructions are removed, the compensating feature of the leaking artery is no longer needed, and nature will quickly heal it.

This blood, leaking into the stomach, creates a circumstance that might lead to further complications because of the inability of the human digestive system to digest its own blood.

Frequency

Basic heart treatments, spaced a week apart, will generally take care of the condition or they may be given more often than once a week, if convenient.

From of writings of Joseph B. Stephenson

A mother came to see me about her daughter who had a leaking heart. They lived out in the country. Would I go to see her?

"We are just poor people but whatever you charge we will pay you sometime. We have no money just now."

She told me where she lived and I told her I would be up at 9 o'clock in the morning. I got there, and lying in bed was a girl 13 years of age and they had ice packs on her heart; at every beat her chest heaved at least five inches. She was in a sitting position.

I took the ice off, then gave her a treatment with great care. In about 10 minutes I saw improvement. In 20 minutes her heart was beating normally. So I told them I would be back the next day.

Just as I was going towards the house the doctor came over. He stopped me and said, "Stephenson, if you can pull that girl through, you can do anything."

"Well," I said, "how did you find her this morning?"

"A hundred percent better."

I went there three times and that girl got well and was out of bed in two weeks. This doctor came to me for a talk on a leaking heart. I gave him a simple illustration of the action of a water pump, pointed out the principal part of the obstruction.

He said, "That is the most wonderful illustration I have ever heard. I will never again say that a leaking heart cannot be healed."

Heart Murmur

Heart murmur is another example of nature's way of compensating for some imbalance in the body. In this case, there is an excessive strain on the heart and the heart valves compensate by purposefully malfunctioning to relieve the heavy strain on the heart.

Such strain may be due to a number of causes. It is often an after-effect of rheumatic fever because the secretion that comes from the thyroid glands in the front of the neck to lubricate the heart has stopped. It is not unreasonable to suspect that a high fever from some childhood illness might have caused this oil to burn out.

Whatever the cause it can usually be corrected by distributing the lubricating secretion to the #1 heart spot.

➧ **Step 1: Administer the basic heart treatment; see page 4–21.**

➧ **Step 2: Create a double vacuum (inward goiter treatment, page 2–18).** Oil your fingers well. As you stand to the right of the patient, let your left hand rest on the nape of the neck. The first and third fingers of the right hand extend with a space of about a finger's width between them and are supported by the middle finger, which lies in lengthwise contact behind them. This spacing of the first and third fingers, provides the double vacuum as you stroke downward with the cushions of these fingers. Hold your hand horizontally as the fingers create a double vacuum from just beneath the larynx along the center line of the body to where the breastbone begins to change shape, a stroke 4 to 5 inches long. The vacuum strokes must be performed with light pressure and rapidly, at the rate of about 200 strokes per minute (3 or 4 per second). The intention during the vacuum movement is to stimulate downward drainage. The fingers may remain in contact with the skin on the upward stroke, but this contact must be very light with no trace of pressure.

To perform the vacuum with greater ease, hold your hand so that your fingers stay in position, but keep your wrist loose and free so that it amplifies the motion of the forearm by providing its own motion. Performing the vacuum in this manner, will be much less strenuous than doing it with a rigid wrist.

During the vacuum, allow your fingers to glide laterally downward into the #1 heart spot 3 or 4 times. Make 3 or 4 gentle, clockwise circles there with the middle finger each time. These circular movements are designed to stimulate and distribute the flow of lubricating oil, secreted by the thyroid gland, to the heart.

Duration

Treat for 4 or 5 minutes without stopping, or more if needed.

Frequency

Two or three treatments, administered at weekly intervals, will generally clear up the condition. A heart murmur of long standing may, however, require a much more comprehensive treatment that takes into consideration other conditions in the body.

It is interesting to note, that while the clockwise movement at the #1 heart spot stimulates and distributes the flow of lubricating oil, the counterclockwise movement (as in the basic heart treatment) is instrumental in breaking up obstructions that interfere with the flow of blood.

Rheumatic Fever

In rheumatic fever, the heart races at a fast pace, due to poisons in the blood stream. The heart pumps furiously to move the poisons through. This occurs primarily in young boys.

In the acute stage apply step 1: vacuum stroke of the basic heart treatment, page 4–23, for 15 or 20 minutes, or until the heart slows. After improvement, apply any of the following, as may be needed:

- Entire basic heart treatment, page 4–21.
- Vacuum step of the inward goiter treatment, page 2–18, for 3 to 5 minutes, to deliver oil to the #1 heart spot.
- Digestive tuneup, page 5–14.
- Feeding the spleen, page 5–13.

Regulating a Fast Heart

Faulty speed of the heart, either too fast or too slow, may be due to many causes. One possible cause is that the heart tube may be out of position. If the tube is too high, the heart beats too fast. If the tube is too low, the heart beats too slow. Restoring the heart tube to its natural position (at the 45° line, mentioned in Step 3 of the Basic Heart Treatment) will restore the speed of the heart to normal. In this sense, the position of the heart tube regulates the speed of the heart.

The caution, stated in step 3 of the basic heart treatment, namely, not to work directly with the heart tube until well experienced with the effects of the heart treatment on the body, applies here. Even the most experienced Creative Healer should only as a last resort attempt to regulate the speed of the heart by moving the heart tube.

A fast heart is frequently caused by the presence of foreign material in the region of relative vacuum. Foreign material in this area may limit the expansion of the heart, causing the heart to make up for a loss in volume by an increase in speed. This is an example of nature's way of compensating for an obstruction. The basic heart treatment is used to remove the obstructive material, so the heart is again able to expand fully. Then it can return to its normal speed.

➧ **Step 1: The basic heart treatment** should always be applied first, page 4–21.

➧ **Step 2: Heart and circulation spot on the back (inward goiter spot).** If step 1 does not reduce the heart speed, apply the treatment for the heart and circulation spot on the back, page 2–17. This is a vital spot for the circulation, particularly that of the left side of the body and is a mechanism acting as a pressure relief valve and by-pass circuit for the heart. Its purpose, under certain conditions, is to smooth out the impulses and absorb the surge of the blood flow so that the flow pressure becomes more uniform. A congestion at this spot, such as a tiny blood clot that prevents the relief mechanism from working, may bring about a condition leading to a fast heart.

Pay special attention to distributing back into the circulatory system the material broken up at this heart spot on the back. Do this by stroking downward from just below the spot and around to the front of the body with the palms of the hands. During this stroking, red blotches may appear on the surface of the skin. The obstructions that they represent must be cleared up.

The patient may feel discomfort below the heart, in the vicinity of the #5 heart spot, as a result of the above treatment. Relieve it by vacuum stroking with the palm as in step 1 of the basic heart treatment, which may now be more fully understood as it continues to bring the broken up material to the front of the body.

➧ **Step 3: Double vacuuming.** It may be desirable to apply the double vacuuming found in step 5 of the inward goiter treatment, page 2–18, particularly if the patient complains of a sensation of extreme nervousness throughout the body, without apparent cause.

➧ **Step 4: Moving the heart tube.** If you have administered these treatments and the heart is still speeding, only then should you move the heart tube. (This is described in the second way of step 4 of the basic heart treatment, page 4–24.) As stated earlier, if a fast heart is caused by the heart tube being out of position, the tube is too high, which means too far in the direction toward the head. Similarly, too low means too far in the direction toward the feet. These terms have nothing to do with the anterior–posterior direction of the body.

To draw the tube down, place your thumb barely 1/2 inch above the 45° line. Using the edge of the thumb, perform a positive, but still gentle movement, downward. Do it with the thought of carrying the tube exactly to the 45° line. This movement reaches into the tissues slightly more than when working directly over the 45° line. Usually, only one movement is necessary to reduce the speed of the heart to normal. At times, there will be a feeling of moving a taut cord so that it "snaps" into position.

Note: The heart tube lies slightly too high in a majority of heart cases, but is drawn into position by creating a vacuum in the heart tube as in the first movement of the basic heart treatment, page 4–21.

Regulating a Slow Heart

A slow heart is most often caused by low blood pressure. (Note that the heart may be a contributing cause in low blood pressure. High blood pressure may overload the heart but the heart is never the cause of the high pressure.)

A patient who's heart is too slow has very low energy; the least activity requires a great effort. Also, the soft body tissue feels too soft. In the case of slow heart with low blood pressure, the Basic Heart Treatment will produce an immediate change. If you place your ear on the patient's heart region, the heart may sound tired. After the treatment, it will have a very different, more vigorous sound. However, the improvement will not last.

Low blood pressure is usually the result of the blood being of insufficient volume and poor quality. This tends to compound the slow heart condition, because the heart muscles are not being adequately nourished. For permanent relief of low blood pressure, other parts of the body such as the digestive system and spleen need to be treated. Feeding the spleen may have a vital influence upon the heart.

If the heartbeat becomes too slow suddenly, and the blood pressure is normal, the heart is not getting enough air. Consequently it gets tired and has to take longer rests between beats to keep it going naturally and to regain enough energy to function again. The heart tube will probably be partially closed and will be too low. When the heart tube is too far down out of position, extreme nervousness may result, so that coordinated movement becomes difficult.

➧ **Step 1: Raise the heart tube into its normal location.** Place the hand as for step 4 of the basic heart treatment (the second way), page 4–24. The hand is horizontal to the vertical body with fingers together, the thumb in little or no contact with the body but adjacent to the hand.

➧ **Step 2: Thumb movement.** With a gentle, short motion, taking in not more than 1/2 inch, move the thumb away from the hand. Move it just to the 45° line. Repeat this movement, to bring the heartbeat to its normal speed. The speed will increase by 2 or 3 beats each time the movement is applied. This treatment along with other heart treatments have been used for enlarged heart and to strengthen weak heart muscles.

Heart and Circulation Spot on the Back

A very important and very delicate spot connected with the heart and vital for circulation is located on the left side of the back, near the upper edge of the left shoulder blade about 1/2 inch toward the spine. In inward goiter cases this spot is always congested and will always be sensitive. It may even show signs of scratches inflicted by the patient who, unconsciously or in sleep, attempts to quiet it. If the spot is heavily congested it will feel hot to the oiled palm.

Heart spot on the back

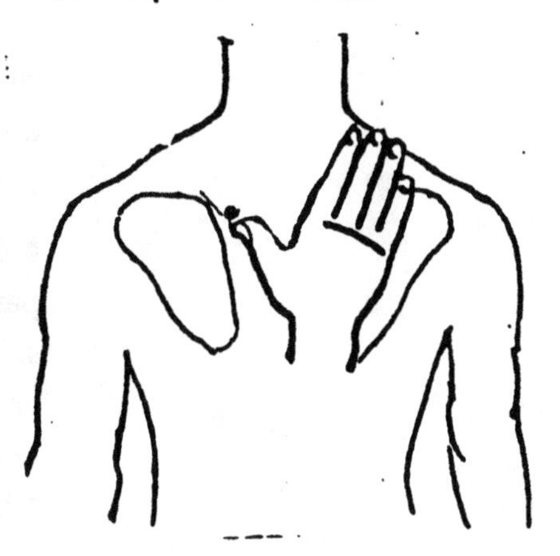

The location of the heart spot on the back may be found described in a different way in inward goiter treatment step 2, page 2–17. Both explanations are correct. To accurately locate this tiny spot (about as big as the eraser on a pencil), place your thumb horizontally on the spot for pain between the shoulders, page 3–10, your palm and fingers flat on the patient's back, parallel to the spine. Using the middle finger as a pivot, swing your thumb upward until it approaches the margin of the left shoulder blade. This movement will carry your thumb very close to the spot and the patient's reaction will indicate the exact location if it is congested.

Relieve congestion by a very gentle clockwise breaking up movement with the cushion of your thumb. The thumb should not be too heavily oiled, allowing it to cling to the skin, carrying the surface tissue with it. As the thumb circles up and around it creates a delicate vacuum and should not receive any pressure. Continue this for 2 to 4 minutes. Do not return to this spot during this treatment session.

Disperse broken up substance

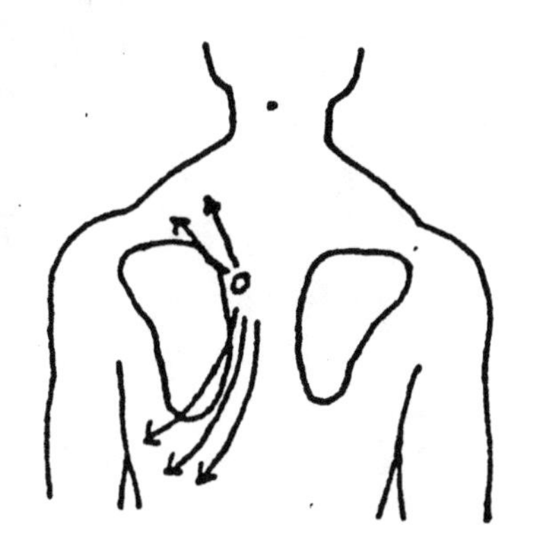

Being careful not to touch the spot again, use the hands to stroke up over the patient's left shoulder to distribute what has been broken up into the circulation, including some circular motions to the filter area at the left side of the neck. Then, stroke downward and forward just below the spot. Carry the movement toward the front of the body, with the fingers of the right hand leading and the left following, alternating the movement of the hands. If red blotches appear along the downward stroke, break them up individually by the circular movement and stroke over them with the thumb toward the heart to carry them off.

Never massage over this spot when it is congested. This spot is described in step 2 of the inward goiter treatment.

Swollen Column

If a patient requires treatment in the thoracic region of the back, check first for a swelling, a swollen column that runs parallel to the spine on the left side only. It is located about 1 inch to the left of the spine and will be a raised, enlarged band of tissue about 1/2 to 1 inch wide and 3 to 5 inches long. Occasionally, it will be a reddish color. See swollen column in Chapter 3, page 3–13.

Erratic Heart Beat

This entire sequence of treatments for erratic heart beat (missing and skipped beats), applies also when the patient suffers from a pronounced thumping or thudding of the heart, especially when lying down. The hardening in the region between the shoulders is also related to problems known as congestive heart.

➧ **Step 1:** The basic heart treatment, page 4–21, is administered first to regulate an erratic heart beat.

➧ **Step 2:** If this is not effective in relieving the condition, then treat the heart and circulation spot on the back; see page 4–30. This spot plays a vital role in many heart conditions. Pay special attention to the circulation below this heart spot. Work well around to the front and clear all obstructions through the #5 heart spot.

➧ **Step 3:** Before doing any other work on the back, check for a swelling that runs parallel to the spine. It is most often located about 1 inch or more to the left of the spine. It will be a raised, enlarged band of tissue about 1/2 to 1 inch wide, and 3 or 4 inches long. Occasionally, it will be a reddish color. It may feel above normal temperature and may be highly sensitive. It is vital that it be cleared before any other work is done on the back; see the swollen column treatment, page 3–13.

➧ **Step 4:** Clear any contractions between the spinous processes below, above and around the spot for the pain between the shoulders treatment, page 3–10.

➧ **Step 5:** Clear all obstructions through the #5 heart tube into the stomach; see the basic heart treatment, page 4–21.

From of writings of Joseph Stephenson

This was a young girl seventeen years of age who had a bad leaking heart. Her seven doctors, including heart specialists, had all given her up to die. The last doctor told her parents to send for Dr. Stephenson. They had not heard of me, but the mother came over to see me.

I said, "I will be over to see her tomorrow."

"Yes, but that may be too late, Mr. Stephenson."

I said, "I don't think so. I cannot see the end so near."

The next day I got to her and gave her a treatment. The following day the doctor came, examined her and was very much pleased with her condition. He asked the mother when I was coming back.

She said, "Tomorrow. He told me he would come two more times, and she would live for many ears."

I saw her the three times. She was sitting up half of the day and I told her mother not to feed her any milk for at least six weeks and nothing ice cold.

Six weeks after that on a Sunday morning, the doctor walked along our street. When he got to our place, I was sitting on the porch. He stopped and said, "Good morning, Stephenson."

I said, "Good morning, Doctor."

Then he said, "Would you mind if I came up to talk awhile?"

I said, "Why no; come up." So he did.

I knew what was on his mind, so I kept quiet. Then he said, "Stephenson, you were to see Mrs.X's daughter?"

I said, "Yes; she told me you told her of me."

"Yes," he said. "Stephenson, you did wonderful work on that girl."

"Oh, I don't know. Those things are easy."

"Yes, to you, maybe but we medical doctors say that a leaking heart cannot be helped."

"I know," I said. "The reason you people say so is because you don't know the cause. A Creative Healer must know the cause of everything; he works on cause and effect. If he does not know the cause, then he keeps hands off but the cause of a leaking heart is simple and easy to know; once the cause is removed the effect comes of itself and nature is always ready to step in and do its duty."

"Will you tell me the cause then, Stephenson?"

I said, "Yes; you see I was a miner, and had lots to do with pumps to clear the mine of surplus water. I found out that if there ever was an obstruction at the delivery end of the pump and the pump kept up its capacity of water, the pressure became greater against the obstruction. This forced back the water to the cylinder and wherever there was a weak spot that part gave way."

The doctor began to see my point. So I went on and told him the heart was the pump in the human body, and the only thing that could cause a leak was an obstruction on the delivery end. So I looked it over, found the obstruction and also found out how easy it was to remove it, and results came quickly in every case. I told him I had had hundreds of such cases and I never failed in any of them but the girl was one of the worst I had had.

I know he wanted to stay longer, but he felt uneasy, so he got up and as he was leaving he said, "This is one doctor who will never say a leaking heart cannot be stopped. Good morning, Stephenson, and I thank you for what you have taught me this morning. We doctors don't know it all, do we?"

I just smiled and said, "Come back again some time."

But he only came back when I sent for him on two or three occasions when I needed a doctor to keep myself safe from the law.

He told me later he felt honored to be called in by me.

(This is told just as it happened in 1926 in Johnstown Pennsylvania.)

Chapter 5 ♦ The Abdominal Cavity: Digestion and Elimination

Understanding our Digestive System

The digestive system acts as the guardian of the blood stream, selecting and governing what should enter the blood. The digestive system is located in the abdominal cavity, which contains the liver, gallbladder, pancreas, spleen, stomach, kidneys and the large and small intestines; each organ plays an important role in digestion.

The liver, the largest gland of the body, is located on the right side, beneath the ribs. Its convex top surface fits under the diaphragm, which separates the abdominal and thoracic cavities. The liver's concave base fits over and partially displaces the right kidney. The gallbladder, a pear-shaped muscular organ, nestles in a cavity underneath the liver. The stomach, the main digestive organ, receives food through the esophagus at its top end. At the other end, it connects to the U-shaped duodenum, the beginning of the small intestine. The pancreas, on the left side of the abdomen behind the stomach and in front of the first and second lumbar vertebrae, is divided into head, body and tail. Its head lies just beyond the center line of the body in the curve of the duodenum and its tail extends behind the stomach to the spleen. The spleen, a bean-shaped organ under the diaphragm, behind and to the left of the stomach, is shrouded by the curvature of the lower ribs.

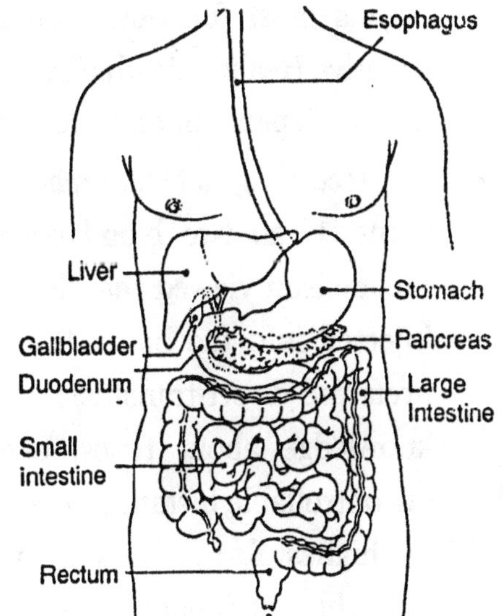

The health of the entire body is dependent on the proper functioning of all these organs. The solar plexus, a network of nerves, connects each part of the digestive system and governs its efficiency. Mr. Stephenson explained the digestive process this way, "If all the digestive organs are in perfect working order and if the solar plexus is unimpaired in its functioning and under no stress or agitation, then, when a certain amount of a certain food is put into the stomach, the solar plexus would call forth from each of the digestive organs the exact amount of its secretion needed to digest that food so that its nutrients could be absorbed into the blood stream and its wastes discarded. The duodenum acts as a mixing chamber for the digestive secretions and also funnels the food from the stomach into the rest of the intestines."

This selective power by which the solar plexus governs digestion is the key to understanding the digestive mechanism. It is also the reason Mr. Stephenson questioned the wisdom of injecting substances directly into the bloodstream (via shots) in a way that bypasses this guardian of digestion. It might benefit one person and go directly against another, so that its results are not predictable. Mr. Stephenson said the secretion of the gallbladder is the strongest of the digestive juices and is reserved for foods that are difficult for the body to digest. When such food is introduced, the gall receives a signal from the solar plexus causing it to contract and eject its strong secretion to begin digestion. If the gall is removed, this mechanism can no longer function and the liver and pancreas must compensate.

According to Mr. Stephenson, incomplete combustion is the essential cause for the accumulation of poisons within the body, which overloads the eliminative organs so that wastes turn into poisons.

To stay healthy, Mr. Stephenson gave three eating guidelines:

1. Eat only foods you like. If eating a food causes a lump in the throat or a feeling of revulsion, that food could not possibly do any good at that time; at a later time such a food may prove wholly acceptable. However, be aware of taste perversion or the influence of society on appetite; false appetites invite overeating and poor nourishment. Be aware of what you are eating.
2. Eat only foods that agree with your system. When eating new foods, determine by experience what is good and nourishing for yourself. Reliance on this guide has been neglected.
3. Don't eat if you don't desire to do so. Overeating causes incomplete combustion and overloads the eliminative organs.

Mr. Stephenson said, "If individuals followed these guidelines from early on, they would be skilled adults on what is good for them." Restoring the body to true balance means the vital organs must function normally. The restoration of normal function is the sole endeavor of Creative Healing. With all the organs functioning normally people have their own true health and are not dependent on anything administered from the outside.

According to Mr. Stephenson, no two people have identical blood streams, not even identical twins. If no two blood streams are identical, then neither are two digestive systems. Mr. Stephenson viewed the digestive system as the body's guardian, and he was skeptical of shots injected into the body. However, he was not averse to blood transfusions to save lives, but preferred direct transfusions from person to person. He said that in spite of the most complete knowledge about types, categories, etc. of the different kinds of blood, there are still uncontrollable instances where the transfusion is given and the recipient dies. As people aspire to the highest form of healing, they will recognize and respect the role of the digestive system and work through it but not around it.

The Digestive System

Abdominal Preparatory Massage

To treat any of the organs of the digestive tract, a gentle massage to the abdominal area is given first, except in the case of appendicitis.

➤ ➤ ➤CAUTION: The only exception is when there is heat in the abdomen. Never massage an abdomen when the abdominal region feels at a temperature higher than normal. Massaging at such a time could cause peritonitis (acute inflammation in the spaces between the abdominal organs and the peritoneal folds). Heat must always be removed before giving a massage and any other treatments must be given another day. (See cooling treatment, page 8–27.)

Our lifestyles today lack the activity that keeps the abdominal wall muscles strong and circulation vigorous. We do too much sitting and too little walking, causing the abdominal organs to sag onto the pelvic floor; their function is impaired by being cramped together. The abdominal massage must restore circulatory vigor in, around and under the abdominal organs and help to get them back into their natural positions.

The patient should be reminded not to eat before a digestive treatment and should be asked to empty the bladder before beginning the treatment.

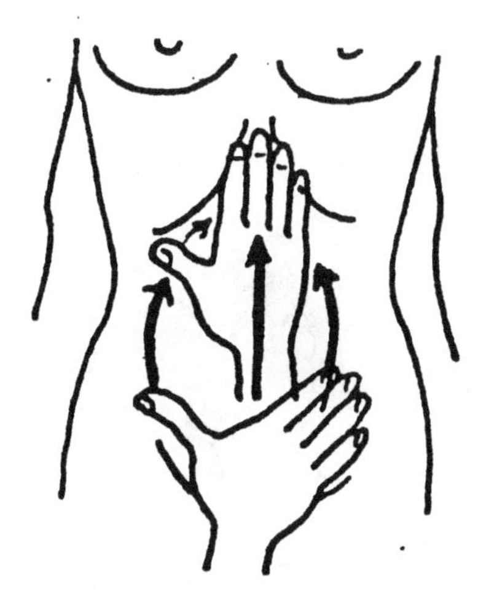

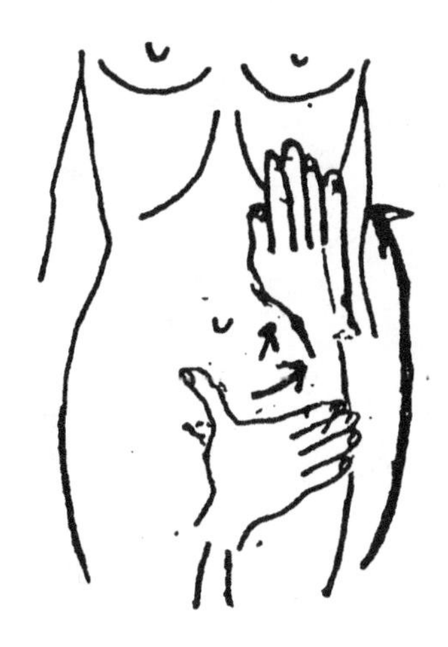

Abdominal preparatory massage: stroking abdomen front (top) and abdomen sides (bottom)

Position

The patient lies on the back. The Creative Healer sits at the patient's right. Use olive oil on the right hand and begin the stroke at the pubic bone. The left hand is placed on the patient's arm or right side to give comforting support.

➧ **Step 1: Abdomen.** This massage extends from the groin and the pubic bone up to and beyond the lower margin of the ribs. During the main part of the principal strokes, keep your fingers together with the thumb apart from them at a wide angle. The strokes start with the leading edge of the hand, formed by the edges of the thumb and the index finger. When the pubic bone is cleared the entire hand is in contact with the abdomen and is essentially flat. As the stroke tapers off at the ribs, bring the thumb and fingers together.

➧ **Step 2: Sides of abdomen.** Perform strokes over the sides of the body changing the hand position. Bring the thumbs and fingers together with the hand essentially flat but with the fingers pointed toward the sides of the body or toward the surface on which the patient is lying. Massage upward from the groin area, cover the side of the body and follow the direction of the ribs up to the sternum (breast bone). The massage is always upward. Cover the entire abdomen with a combination of the two hand positions, which should be smooth and gentle so the patient can relax this vital area.

In performing the massage preparatory to giving any other treatment you might occasionally find soreness and sensitivity in the region just above the pubic bones. Such a condition is relieved by moving the fingertips in a rolling motion, gliding over the edges of the pubic bone in a horizontal direction toward the groin. When full comfort is obtained, proceed with the sought-after treatment.

Duration

Perform the strokes for at least 10 minutes.

The Appendix

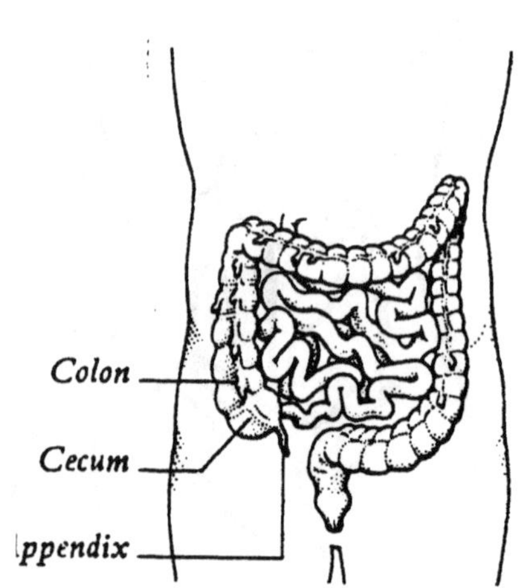

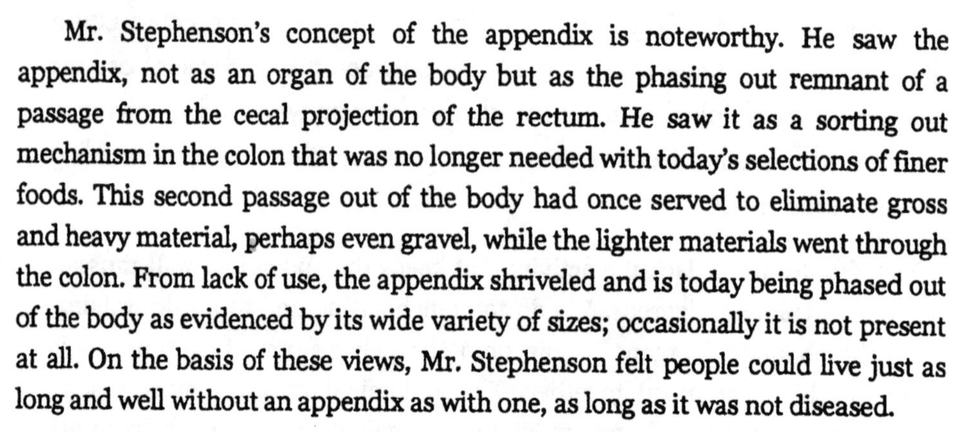

Mr. Stephenson's concept of the appendix is noteworthy. He saw the appendix, not as an organ of the body but as the phasing out remnant of a passage from the cecal projection of the rectum. He saw it as a sorting out mechanism in the colon that was no longer needed with today's selections of finer foods. This second passage out of the body had once served to eliminate gross and heavy material, perhaps even gravel, while the lighter materials went through the colon. From lack of use, the appendix shriveled and is today being phased out of the body as evidenced by its wide variety of sizes; occasionally it is not present at all. On the basis of these views, Mr. Stephenson felt people could live just as long and well without an appendix as with one, as long as it was not diseased.

More serious appendix cases are evidenced by heat and a very painful condition localized at a spot about 1/3 of the way down on the line leading from the navel to the superior spine of the hipbone. The spot might be red and in some cases raised and swollen, and might feel as though half the shell of an English walnut were embedded beneath the surface. Any such condition viewed by a doctor would be an immediate surgical case.

➤ ➤ ➤ CAUTION: Mr. Stephenson warned not to probe deeply as this could cause rupture and lead to peritonitis. In a case of peritonitis there would be no localized heat or pain but the whole of the abdomen would quickly become inflamed, with a feverish painful condition over a wide area. In such conditions massage must NEVER be applied.

Position

The patient lies on the back. The Creative Healer sits on the patient's right.

➧ **Step 1: Use of hands.** To take care of a localized swelling and heat, Mr. Stephenson used the middle finger of his left hand lying in lengthwise contact with the body and beginning to the left of the inflamed spot (from the operator's point of view) and directed toward the cecum, and performed gentle vacuum strokes from 1 to 2 inches long. Meanwhile, his right hand rested very lightly on the medial side of the swollen area as a contact and a gentle support of the movement. These movements released an inner flow that he could feel and hear in 3 or 4 minutes of the vacuum stroking and then he knew that a little while later the area would no longer be swollen or have localized heat. This was all he did on the first day.

➧ **Step 2: Another vacuum stroke.** The next day he used the left middle finger and adjacent ones in light contact, to stroke completely across the affected area, starting approximately 1 inch on the medial side of the critical spot. The complete stroke now was 3 or 4 inches, beginning with a delicate vacuum stroke and slowly increasing it to a slightly heavier contact as though to drain, always governed by the patient's comfort.

➧ **Step 3: Moving released material.** Then to draw the material from the appendix into the ascending colon he performed the cecum and ascending colon treatments, page 5–25, returning to the vacuum strokes until all was cleaned out and the patient was comfortable.

The Liver

The liver is the body's largest gland and is located beneath the ribs on the right side of the body. Its convex top fits closely under the diaphragm, while its concave bottom fits over and partially displaces the right kidney. The liver performs three vital functions: 1. it purifies the blood stream; 2. it manufactures bile; and 3. it remanufactures foodstuffs that are already in the blood stream but not yet usable by the body.

One sign of liver trouble needing treatment is the inability of the person to digest, without distress, chocolate, milk or cream. Liver trouble indicates a restriction in the duct leading from the liver into the duodenal passage, causing the liver's natural flow and response to slow down. This condition is possibly caused by a coating on the walls of this duct, which causes bile to back up. The accumulation of bile slows down liver cell production and secretion. At the same time, bile might accumulate in the liver to such a degree that it is released mechanically, without any relation to digestive demands. The liver, operating under these conditions, delivers too little or too much bile, but never the amount necessary for proper digestion, causing indigestion and distress from gas. At times, the sudden release of bile may cause the patient to vomit.

The aim of the liver treatment is threefold: it must clean out the bile duct; it must relieve the liver, if necessary, of accumulated bile; and it must bring about a balanced secretion and release of bile, thus restoring normal function.

Position

The patient lies on the back; the Creative Healer sits to the patient's right.

➧ **Step 1: Locate the liver notch.** With your right thumb, trace along the lower margin of the ribs (not the floating rib) on the patient's right side, from where the body touches the bed toward the median. Follow the smooth curve whose curvature increases as it swings upward. On this upward swing, the thumb contacts a notch that is more pronounced than any other irregularity, the liver notch. When the liver is in trouble, the liver notch may be sensitive.

Locate the liver notch

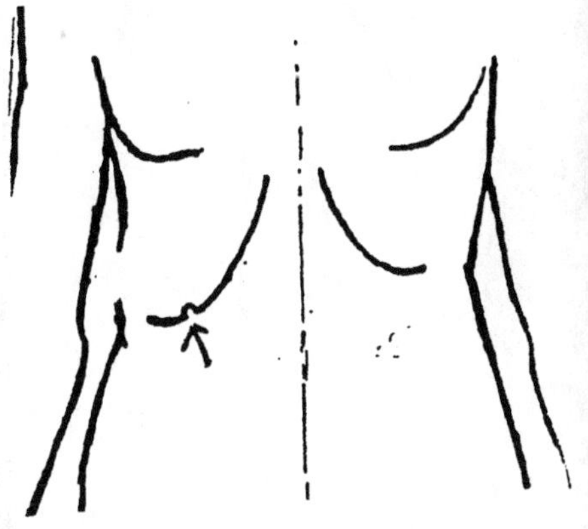

Create a vacuum

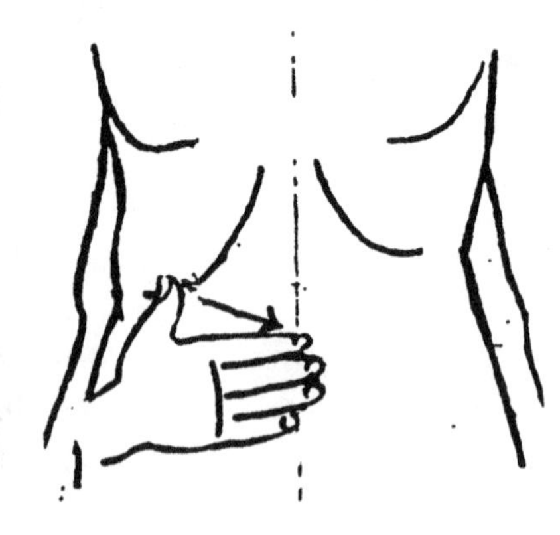

➧ **Step 2: Create a vacuum.** Hold the fingers of your right hand together and place the hand flat on the body at right angles to the median line. Extend the thumb away from the fingers, resting it on the ribs just above the liver notch. The pad of the thumb begins each stroke on the ribs, descends through the notch, and moves toward the median. The thumb is always in full contact with the body. Its motion describes a straight line that forms an angle of 60° with the center line of the body. Move the palm and fingers slightly on the body to compensate for the straight, diagonal stroke of the thumb. Don't abbreviate the stroke, but always carry out its full length to the median or center line of the body. The movement performed by the thumb, as it repeats the strokes, creates a vacuum or displacement movement. This draws through bile that may have accumulated, and cleans out any corrosion that may be present in the duct. At the same time, this movement creates a suction immediately behind the thumb that draws upon the accumulation within the liver. Successive strokes will draw through whatever has been accumulated and will create a vacuum within the liver cells. This changes the condition of stasis in the liver to one of action, by stimulating the liver cells to increase their production.

A beginning Creative Healer need not be concerned about tracing the path for the vacuum over the liver duct incorrectly. Because the thumb is in full, long contact with the body, the path will be covered, even if not by the pad of the thumb. The more experienced Creative Healer, learning to sense the true path, can then accordingly adjust the movement. You need not use more pressure in treating a heavier person. Even though the organ is deeper within the body, the effect of the vacuum strokes will be transmitted through the tissues without any need for increased pressure.

According to the lesser or greater amount of bile that is drawn through, the patient may develop a bitter taste in the mouth, may have loose bowels for one or two movements or may vomit. Because vomiting is caused by the mechanical release of a great amount of bile not required by digestive demands, it will probably have been experienced by the patient previously. These unpleasant effects are unavoidable; the static condition of the liver, caused by the accumulation of bile, must be overcome in order to restore normal function. It is impossible to predict the amount of accumulated bile in the bile duct and the liver before treatment; thus the liver treatment is one of the few in which the patient may feel worse immediately afterward than before.

With successive treatments, the liver will become more and more enlivened and secretion production will improve. The number of treatments needed to fully restore normal function will depend on the severity of the condition and how long it has been going on. The displaced material may be felt flowing through, under the thumb. If you feel the flow while giving the liver treatment, continue the vacuum until the flow ceases and then another minute more. This extra minute produces a suction within the liver cells, enlivening the cells and stimulating their production. The flow is not always felt, even by an experienced Creative Healer. When the flow is not apparent to the touch, continue to treat until you sense that the patient's need has been met.

Kneading action

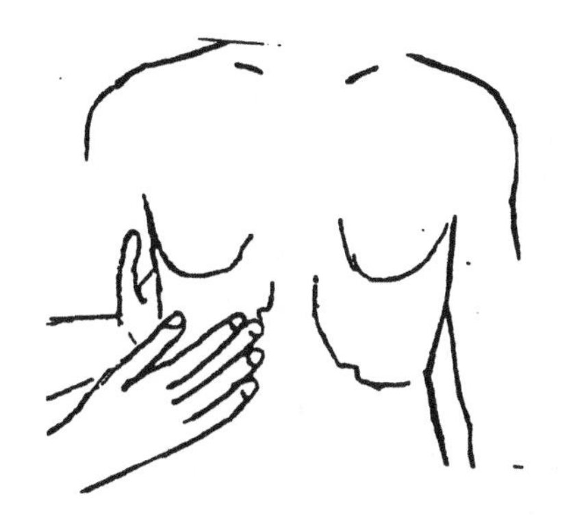

Step 3: Kneading action. Sometimes, further stimulation of the liver is needed. In that case, use a "milking" or "kneading" action between the hands. Place your left hand flat, fingers together, on the patient's back under the body. Place your right hand flat, fingers together, on top of the ribs as though you were holding the liver between your two hands. Milk or knead with both hands at the same time. Alternate this kneading with the vacuum and use the thumb to work on any sore spots between or on the ribs, always working in the direction toward the median.

Sometimes the patient complains of a strong and maybe even nauseating pain, pointing to the spot under the junction of the liver and gall tubes. In this case, with the thumb between the two notches, just below the ribs, let it descend with a positive, single stroke directly toward the spot indicated. As the thumb descends, it enters more and more deeply into the tissues of the abdomen. As it approaches the junction, a little formation like a bulb of fluid may be felt moving ahead of the contact. The pain ceases immediately.

Cirrhosis of the Liver

Cirrhosis (hardening) or enlargement of the liver is usually caused by excessive consumption of alcohol or foods. Under such abuse, the sensibility of the liver is deadened so that a more severe and deeply seated stasis develops within the organ. This type of stasis leads to hardening, or enlargement, or both. To relieve liver sclerosis and enlargement, first give the liver treatment, then massage over the ribs that cover the liver.

Position

The patient lies on the back. The Creative Healer sits to the right of the patient.

Step 1: Massage. With a firm stroke start the massage on the ribs as close to the back as possible, thumb and fingers together, the palm exerting the main pressure, and massage to an imagined line parallel to the median and slightly beyond the liver notch (see step 1 of previous treatment). Let one hand follow the other as for double vacuum. As you perform this massage during successive weeks, let the thumb work on any sore spots between or upon the ribs, always massaging in the direction toward the median.

Step 2: Sore spots. It may be necessary to have the patient sit up in order to detect and treat sore spots, possibly as far back as the spine, where substance may need to be replaced. These sore spots are located at the spine at a level considerably higher than the level of the liver.

Step 3: Kneading action. Follow the procedure for step 3 in the liver treatment, above.

This massage treatment is not only for an enlarged or hardened liver. It may be helpful in many liver cases, i.e., hepatitis and jaundice.

Duration

Alternate the movements. Each may last 2 or 3 minutes. The entire treatment may last about 20 minutes.

Another Liver Outlet

In Mr. Stephenson's view of the body, there is a tube that leads from the liver to the bladder. Through this tube, the liver disposes of wastes. This tube is cleaned out with the pad of the right thumb. Trace along the lower edge of the ribs in the flesh of the abdomen on the right side of the patient's body from where it touches the bed to mid-way between the liver and gall notches. With the tip of the thumb pointing toward the patient's right side move the thumb lengthwise in a feeding pressure, which is a more positive movement than a vacuum contact, but it is never heavy. This is the same stroke for feeding the pancreas.

Beer

Mr. Stephenson said that if beer was drunk merely for sociability it would tend to cause a liver disease. Beer drunk simply for enjoyment would not have this effect.

The Gall Bladder

Location of gall notch

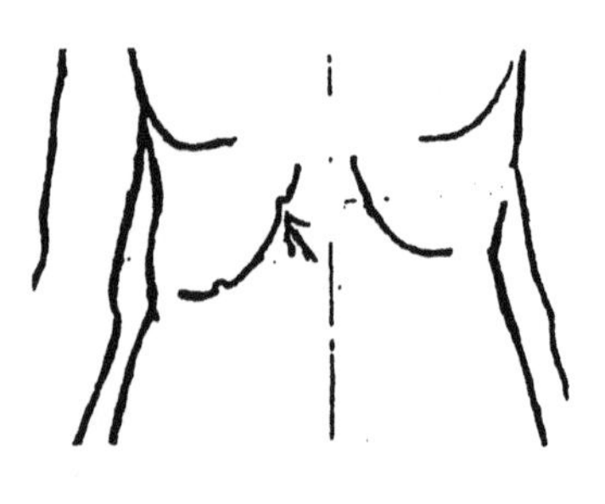

The gall bladder is a muscular organ housed in a cavity under the liver. When full, it looks like a pear-shaped sac, sometimes palpable. It is the organ in which bile from the liver is stored. This bile is used when fats in the small intestine need digesting. According to Mr. Stephenson, the gall bladder also produces a secretion of its own that aids in digestion. The gall duct descends and joins the liver duct at a point near the end of the liver duct. Here the two ducts combine to become a short, common duct that empties into the duodenum (the first section of the small intestine after the stomach).

Position

The patient lies down; the Creative Healer sits to the patient's right.

Direction of vacuum

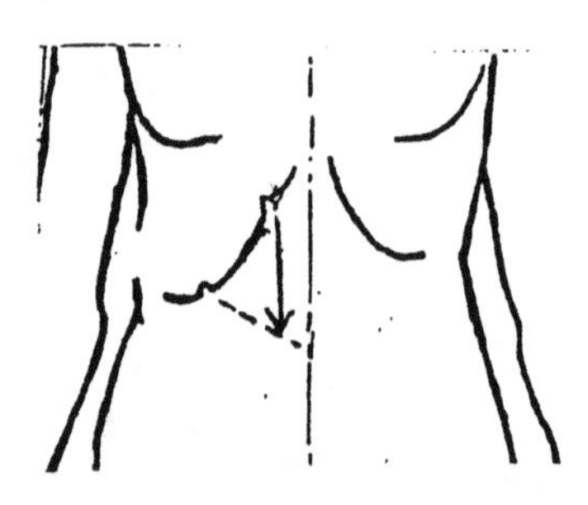

➧ **Step 1: Locate the gall notch.** From the liver notch, trace along the lower margin of the ribs upward. On this path the thumb will encounter a notch that is more pronounced than any other irregularity in that area. This is the gall notch, situated about 2 1/2 to 3 inches from the liver notch. Beneath it lies the nerve center controlling the gall bladder. The gall notch is usually more sensitive than the liver notch. When the gall bladder is in trouble, it may be so sensitive that the patient shrinks away from the slightest touch.

➧ **Step 2: Create a vacuum.** From this notch, create a vacuum with your thumb in a straight stroke downward almost parallel to the center line of the body. The stroke is 4 to 5 inches long and ends at the path of the liver bile duct on the center line. Use the long line of the thumb on the body not just the tip. Continue the vacuum until you sense that the patient's need has been met. This treatment is sufficient when there is no pain and is done as part of the digestive tuneup.

➤ ➤ ➤ CAUTION: Do not vacuum over the gall tube when stones are suspected. Instead do the treatment for gallstones (below).

Pain at the junction of the gall and liver ducts while the treatment is being given is eliminated quickly by directing a vacuum stroke through the intersection of the two ducts to move a bulb of fluid on through to the center line. The pain will cease.

Stroke through intersection of gall and liver ducts

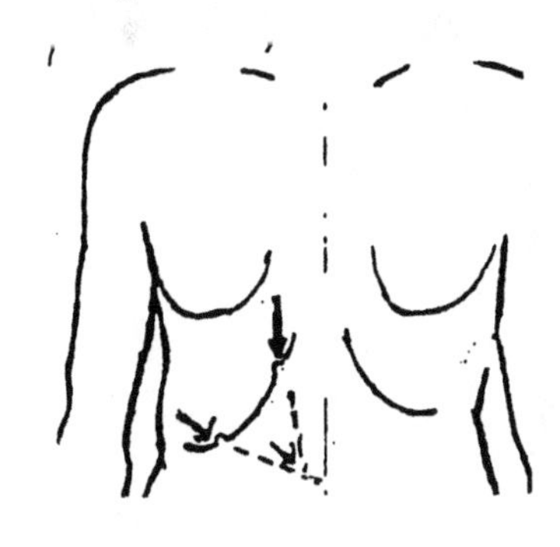

Gallstones

If you know that the patient has gallstones or if the gall notch is extremely sensitive, proceed with this treatment with the light pressure that is always used in Creative Healing.

Position

The patient lies on the back; the Creative Healer sits on the patient's right.

➧ **Step 1: Locate gall notch.** The gall notch is the second notch found at the lower edge of the ribs on the right side toward the center of the body and about 3 inches from the first large notch where we treat the liver.

➧ **Step 2: Light rib pressure.** Place the thumb on the ribs above the gall bladder notch, and use a medium pressure as you bring the thumb downward to the notch. Have your mind direct the pressure downward toward the spine and the feet simultaneously. This is a very small stroke.

➧ **Step 3: Remove congestion.** Change the thumb position so that it rests against the notch from below. Here draw the tip of the thumb downward in very short, small oscillating strokes while the thumb pad blocks any downward flow. Have a strong intention that this movement will tease and stimulate the nerve center beneath the notch such that the flow of gall bladder secretion increases. This secretion acts as a solvent and dissolves the gallstones into sand-like material. This may decrease or eliminate the sensitivity.

➧ **Step 4: Vacuum tube.** After completing steps 1 to 3 every week, a week apart and the pain is greatly diminished, the flow from the gall bladder resumes and a vacuum is created by applying 4- or 5-inch thumb strokes downward toward the liver tube. This will fully drain and cleanse the gall bladder and the duct. Use the oscillating strokes in step 3 above and the vacuuming alternately as needed. Sometimes press lightly downward with the thumb on the ribs as in step 2, follow with the vacuum strokes and omit the oscillating movement. This creates a kind of milking action.

➧ **Step 5: Check spine.** The flow of nerve life to the gall bladder is increased when sensitive spots along the spine are restored to normal with the quarter twist. The sensitivity is found between vertebrae to the right of center back at a higher level than that of the gall bladder.

Frequency

One or more treatments a week may be needed.

The Pancreas

The pancreas is on the left side of the body behind the stomach and in front of the first and second lumbar vertebrae. It is divided into head, body and tail; its head lies just beyond the vertical center line of the body in the curve of the duodenum and its tail extends behind the stomach to the spleen.

One of the functions of the pancreas is to secrete a fluid that mixes with the food in the duodenum. An overactive pancreas could bring on prolonged periods of acid stomach and heartburn. In the underactive pancreas, digestion suffers in another way if the pancreas begins to dry out because this condition can lead to diabetes. One indication of the pancreas drying up is a dull ache beneath the ribs in front on the left side in an area that can be covered by the hand. The patient will often place a hand over the area to indicate the pain, which is a relentless, dull ache not alleviated by moving or changing position. Another indication is an unquenchable thirst, the body's attempt to obtain enough liquid to dilute the unnaturally rich substance in the blood stream caused by the failing pancreas. A third indication of a drying up pancreas is an inordinate drowsiness. In pancreas cases, the stomach will often feel below normal temperature.

Position

The patient lies on the back. The Creative Healer sits to the patient's right.

Decongestion vacuum for pancreas

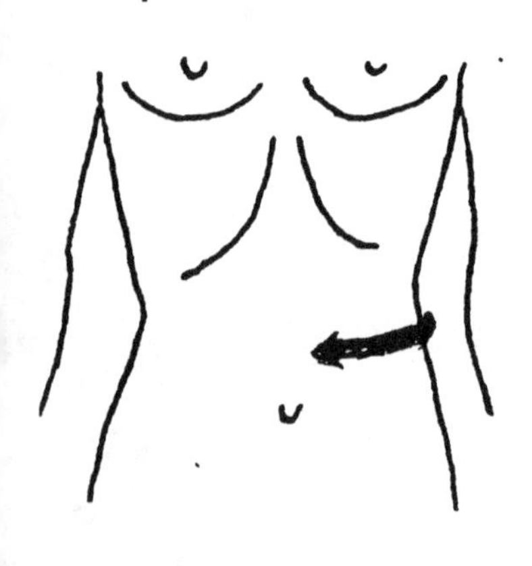

➧ **Step 1: Decongestion vacuum.** With the thumb on the ribs, place the three middle fingers, extended and held close together, just below the ribs on the left side of the patient's body. Using the thumb as a pivot and keeping the fingers extended, move the hand so that the fingers create a vacuum as they retract toward the palm and stretch outward again to repeat the movement. (Creating this vacuum would be very tiring if the whole arm and forearm had to move to produce the required motion of the fingers but the vacuum could be created that way.) This vacuum movement must be light and delicate with the stroke extending as far to the front of the body equalling the start of the stroke at the back. The fingertips should touch the bed so the length of the stroke is determined by the depth of the body. The speed varies from slow at the beginning to a fast and free movement that harmonizes with the movement of the patient's body created by the stroking; however, the stroke is never a compressing action. Occasionally slide the palm to the pit of the stomach to see if it is warming then go immediately back to the decongestion strokes.

Thumb movement for feeding the pancreas

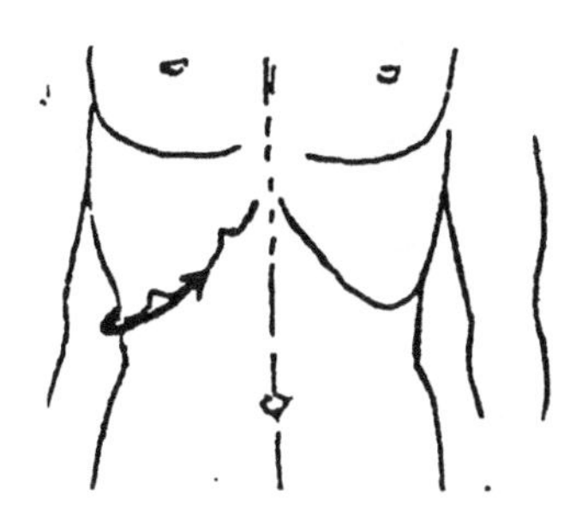

➧ **Step 2: Feeding movement.** With the pad of the right thumb trace along the lower edge of the ribs in the flesh of the abdomen on the right side of the patient's body from where it touches the bed to midway between the liver and gall notches. With the tip of the thumb pointing toward the patient's right side move the thumb lengthwise in a feeding pressure, which is a more positive movement than a vacuum contact, but it is never heavy. This stroke is repeated in proportion to the length of time of the vacuum stroke, i.e., for 20 minutes of vacuuming, 8 minutes of feeding (20:8, 10:4, 5:2). The decongestion movement cleans out, enlivens and starts action in the pancreas while the feeding movement strengthens it by nourishing it. The feeding of the pancreas automatically cleans out the tube that Mr. Stephenson said leads from the liver into the bladder, for the disposal of liver wastes.

Duration

Both decongestion and feeding are done in each treatment. The length of the treatment may vary from 7 to 28 minutes. The longer treatment is applied in cases of severe ache, thirst or diabetes. In general, the vacuum movement is complete when the pit of the stomach feels warm to the palm.

Frequency

Treat at least once a week until the desired result is obtained. If the treatment is part of the digestive tuneup, 1 treatment will suffice.

Diabetes

A drying-up pancreas can lead to diabetes; see above for characteristics of a dry pancreas. Diabetes results in the presence of a tacky substance in the blood stream, which puts a great strain on the purifying action of the kidneys. This tacky substance also causes poor blood clotting, which makes the healing of wounds difficult. The sediments of the blood stream tend to settle in the lower extremities of the body, explaining improper healing in a diabetic, first becoming apparent in the legs and feet.

In order to treat a diabetic person, the Creative Healer must be assured that the diabetic will fully cooperate. This cooperation means essentially that the diabetic be willing to govern daily life according to certain standards of regularity. From day to day, meal times and amounts and kinds of food should be the same, duration and time of activities should be the same, and the time and length of rest periods should also be the same. It is indispensable for the diabetic to follow an appropriate diet and avoid burdening the system with those foods recognized as offensive for diabetics. This regularity will stabilize the daily routine, keeping demands on the body uniform. Widely varying demands on a diabetic's body will upset the precarious blood sugar balance, whether or not the diabetic is taking any medication. Persons who have been testing their urine will have already been alerted to the vital importance of sustaining regularity. The Creative Healer must be certain that this regularity will be observed, otherwise, the effectiveness of the treatment is jeopardized.

Children may be the most gratifying cases of diabetes to treat because they usually respond quickly, and it is gratifying to think that a successful treatment will spare them a life of burdensome routine. The Creative Healer should not feel discouraged about treating cases of diabetes at a more advanced age, even cases of long standing. However, in all cases the indispensable basis for success is a completely regular daily routine and a diet that omits foods offensive to diabetics.

The treatment for diabetes is comprehensive. However, the sequence in which the various parts of the whole treatment are administered is immaterial.

1. Treat the pancreas. Apply the vacuum stroking for at least 20 minutes. Apply the feeding for 8 minutes; see page 5–11.

2. Give the kidneys a complete treatment. This will help them with the overload that diabetes always imposes upon them; see page 5–42.

3. Check and treat the liver, as necessary; see page 5–5.

4. Treat the gall bladder, as necessary; see page 5–8.

5. Finally, check the left side of the spine for sensitive spots, particularly at a level slightly above that of the pancreas; see step 5 of the gallstone treatment, page 5–10.

Frequency

Treat at least once a week until the desired result is obtained. As you continue treatments, the patient's need for medication will lessen; however, medication changes should only be done under the guidance of the patient's doctor. These treatments may need to continue for as long as 6 months.

Congested Spleen

Hand movement to decongest the spleen

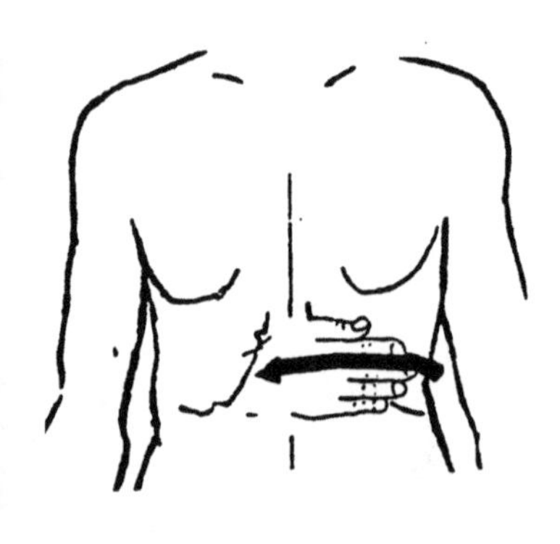

The spleen is a bean-shaped organ located on the left side of the body behind and to the left of the stomach and directly beneath the diaphragm. Its concave side is toward the tail of the pancreas and is shrouded by the lower ribs. If the spleen is congested the area over it will be sensitive and at times painful even to the lightest touch. The patient may complain of sore ribs and the region will feel hot to the touch.

This spleen treatment is also used for infectious mononucleosis, leukemia, sluggish lymph system (which can result in repeated illnesses) or trauma to the spleen. This treatment has been used in AIDS cases, also.

Position

The patient lies on the back; the Creative Healer sits at the patient's right side.

➧ **Step 1: Decongest the spleen.** Begin the vacuum stroke with the right palm centered over the region of the spleen where the heat is and with the fingertips touching the bed on the patient's left side. Your hand follows a straight path across the rib cage, past the center line on the front of the body. The hand placement is lower (toward the feet) on the ribs than the first stroke of the heart treatments. Look for a release of congestion in a flow of action beneath the area stroked. It may cause the patient to shake or ask for a drink of water but usually all the effects will disappear within 5 minutes, the length of time it takes the blood stream to absorb the material released.

Duration

The vacuum stroke should continue for 20 minutes.

Frequency

One treatment is often sufficient, or, if needed, once a week until the congestion is relieved. If the spleen needs feeding do not do it at the same session as decongestion, but wait a week.

Feeding the Spleen

The spleen feeding treatment increases flow of life to the spleen through what Mr. Stephenson described as an artery. The spleen is never fed when it is congested and never more than once a week. It is fed ONLY in the following conditions:

1. When giving the digestive tuneup there is a specific need to feed the spleen when the person has low blood pressure, anemia, or loss of appetite. Mr. Stephenson called the notch for feeding the spleen the appetite spot and he considered it the governor of the digestive system, putting it to work to make more and better blood.

2. After the heart treatment has restored the heart to normal functioning, there is sometimes a lingering, burning pain that starts at the level of the feeding notch for the spleen. It travels toward the spleen and extends over the left chest region up into the left side of the throat. Such a pain will usually be removed by a single spleen feeding treatment.

3. To ameliorate the after effects of rheumatic fever; see rheumatic fever, page 4–28.

Position

The patient lies on the back; the Creative Healer sit on the patient's right.

Thumb movement for feeding the spleen

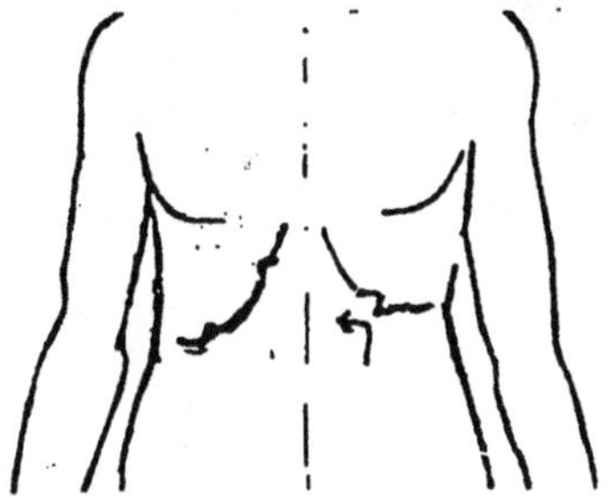

➧ **Step 1: Locate the notch.** With your right hand, trace with the thumb or first finger along the lower margin of the left ribs from the side, toward the front of the body. Where the edge of the ribs change direction, the finger will feel a vertical ascent and a narrow but pronounced horizontal ledge. This is the notch for feeding the spleen. It cannot be confused with the location of the heart tube because it is an inch or more lower.

➧ **Step 2: Feeding motion.** Place the tip of the thumb in the soft tissue 1/2 to 3/4 of an inch below the horizontal part and just far enough away from the vertical to not be in contact with the rib. Move the the thumb gently upward until its motion reaches the horizontal limb of the notch and, without releasing, draw it about 1/2 inch toward the median. This hooklike angle movement involves no gliding, stroking or rubbing and there is no need to use oil. The index finger is more useful for self-treatment.

Mr. Stephenson mentioned two indications that the feeding has been accomplished: the sensation of a flow passing beneath the thumb toward the spleen, or feeling something like a taut string slipping into place beneath the thumb as it moves upward and toward the median, as though something had gone back into position. If neither of these indications occur, the treatment may be repeated 6 or 8 times. As your experience with Creative Healing grows, you develop a sense of when to stop.

Feeding More Power to the Spleen

There is an additional way of feeding the spleen that differs from the above treatment and is used less frequently. It provides an increased flow of life to the spleen through a nerve. The need for it may be recognized (a) when the failing appetite is not restored by the treatment described above, (b) when a person lingers after a severe illness with a lack of power or strength, (c) when the body refuses to accept and use food to develop the needed power.

Position

The patient sits on a bench; the Creative Healer sits behind.

➧ **Step 1: Locate the nerve.** The spot is found on the left side of the spine 3 or 4 inches above the level of the spleen. This is the nerve embedding point at the lower end of the column described under swollen column on page 3–13.

➧ **Step 2: Embed the nerve.** Embedding a nerve between vertebrae is the same movement described in treating the swollen column. At this location a gentle quarter twist is used repeatedly to bury the nerve. Sometimes it is necessary to begin 2 or 3 inches left of the spine and stroke gently to carry the nerve toward the spine. Then gently embed it between the vertebrae.

➧ **Step 3: Soft stroke toward spleen.** In addition, using the hands on both sides of the body, lightly stroke from this feeding spot to the region of the spleen on the left side and symmetrically on the right. This will bring the feeling that a previously collapsed passage has been opened.

Digestive Tuneup

If the digestive organs do not all function properly or if the solar plexus is disturbed, the various organs will not give the correct combination and amount of juices, and digesting food will ferment and form gas, due to the heat of the body. A small amount of gas is always present in the intestines and is needed to stimulate their peristaltic action. But if this normal amount is exceeded indigestion sets in and the person is aware of discomfort.

To tune up a sluggish digestive system, follow the steps below.

➧ **Step 1.** Begin by giving the abdominal massage, page 5–3.

➧ **Step 2.** Give the liver, gall bladder and pancreas treatments, pages 5–5, 5–8 and 5–11.

➧ **Step 3**. Give the heart treatment, page 4–21.

➧ **Step 4**. If the solar plexus is tense, encourage deep, diaphragmatic breathing with onc palm placed over the solar plexus to calm any agitation or give the high and short breathing treatment, page 4–2.

➧ **Step 5**. If low blood pressure, anemia, or loss of appetite are present add the feeding of the spleen treatment, page 5–13.

Frequency

This could be such an important use of Creative Healing methods that a treatment once a year might be as important as a physical exam: an action similar to the tuneup we give our automobiles on a regular basis.

Barium

This substance must be removed from the body. A barium drink or enema, if not cleared, leaves a cement-like material in the body. Apply the digestive tuneup (above) and the colon treatment, page 5–25.

Acute Indigestion

The digestive process comes to a complete halt in two cases: acute indigestion and ptomaine poisoning. "The digestive system goes on a sit-down strike," Mr. Stephenson said. Acute indigestion is caused by conditions inside the body. Ptomaine poisoning is caused by the introduction of a poisonous or indigestible substance into the body from the outside. The effects of both problems are identical, but this treatment discusses only acute indigestion.

Inadequate functioning of the digestive process forms gas. If the digestive organs do not all function properly or if the solar plexus is disturbed, the correct combinations and amounts of digestive juices will not occur. Instead of being properly digested, food will ferment and form gas due to the heat of the body. This incomplete digestion is the main cause for accumulation of poisons within the body and results in overloading the eliminative organs; wastes that should be eliminated remain within the body and turn into poisons.

If the process of digestion stops completely, gas formation increases in intensity and volume, which may cause extreme discomfort and cramping in the abdomen, stomach, mid-chest region, and over the heart. It can push high up under the ribs, rib cage and back, and the pressure over the heart is agonizing. As Mr. Stephenson saw the body, the pressure builds up and, without relief, may push gas up the heart tube and break the vacuum surrounding the heart. If this happens, it is fatal. The breaking of the vacuum around the heart in this manner is frequently the cause of death attributed to a heart attack.

Position

A person with acute indigestion often cannot lie down because of the strong gas pressure, especially on the back. The patient should sit on a bench; the Creative Healer sits behind.

Drainage movement for acute indigestion

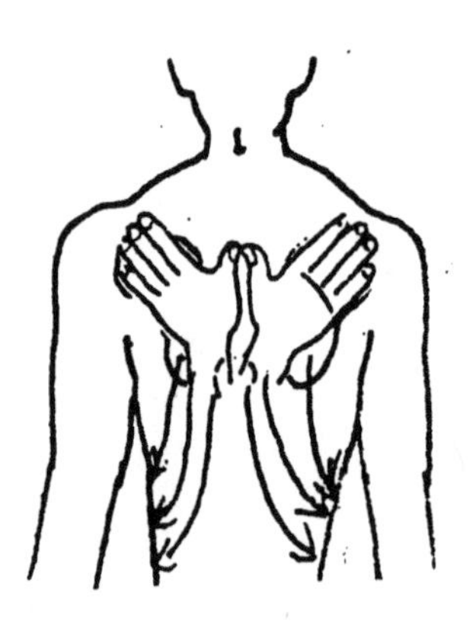

Step 1: Drainage movement. Apply the drainage movement to bring the gas under control; see pneumonia: redirection of circulation, page 4–8, step 3. With thumbs touching at the spine, place the hands, fingers together, high up on the shoulder blades. Bring them down firmly with strong pressure all the way around to the front of the body, pushing the gas ahead of the hands towards and into the stomach so that it can be expelled. Repeat over and over until there is relief from pain or until the patient stops burping.

Step 2: Restore normal temperature. When most of the gas pressure is relieved and the patient is able to lie down, bring the body to normal temperature. The sides of the body will feel hot while the pit of the stomach will feel cold because the circulation has been slowed down there. Massage to equalize the temperature (the movements as for asthma, page 4–13) by letting one palm follow another with the intention of putting in heat. With fast movements and just a bit of oil on the hands, create friction by drawing the hands from the sides of the body over the lower chest, from below the ribcage and from below the stomach so that the strokes all converge towards the cold region. This warming massage brings circulation back into the region of the solar plexus allowing the digestive function to resume. If the body cannot accept the warming up treatment as a complete stage in itself, then administer as much of the digestive tuneup (step 3, below) as possible and alternate between the warming massage and the tuneup until the body is back to normal temperature and the digestion functions normally.

Step 3: Digestive tuneup. When the distress from gas is relieved and the body is at normal temperature, administer a digestive tuneup, page 5–14. Occasionally, about 1 hour after the treatment for acute indigestion, the patient develops a fever all over the body. The trunk and extremities seem to be "on fire" and sensitive to the lightest touch. The head is also affected. This condition is caused by toxins that have been absorbed but not disposed of by the blood stream. To relieve this condition, give a withdrawing heat treatment as in pneumonia (page 4–7) over the back and chest and a thorough treatment to the back of the neck. The fever and sensitivity in the extremities will automatically disappear when the heat is removed from the trunk and the head.

In all instances, to restore the body to true balance, the vital organs must be restored to normal function which is the sole purpose of Creative Healing.

Foul Breath, Chronic Indigestion and Sick Stomach Caused by Post Nasal Drip

Older people often develop a post nasal mucous drip. According to Mr. Stephenson, this does not come from the head sinuses, but from the brain, and is caused by the weakening or deterioration of the gelatinous substance that keeps the brain firm. If a person lives long enough, this weakening or deterioration, together with the ensuing drip, will inevitably develop. While mucous from the head sinuses can be coped with by the digestive system, this discharge from the brain cannot. It coats the walls of the stomach and small intestine and interferes with proper digestion. Food becomes embedded in it and for want of being digested, putrefies. The symptoms are chronic indigestion, a sick stomach and foul breath. Mr. Stephenson felt that such accumulations from the brain could lead to a certain kind of cancer of the stomach and even to death.

People are cautioned never to swallow this mucous when it drips during waking hours. It must be drawn down from the nasal passage, coughed forward and spit out. The detrimental effect of the drip during sleep still remains and there is no way of preventing its accumulation. However, *Eno* fruit salts will gradually loosen the coating in the stomach and intestines. In a glass, add 1/4 teaspoon of *Eno* to 1/2 cup of lukewarm water; drink it either while it still fizzes or when the fizzing has stopped. Drink the mixture in the morning 1/2 hour before eating anything and continue each morning for 2 or 3 weeks; stop for 2 weeks and repeat, if necessary. The effect is nullified if greater amounts are taken in an attempt to accelerate the action. In this weak solution, the coatings crumble away. An accentuated foul odor of the stools, noticeable in a few days, indicates that the coating is crumbling away. In a case of heavy coating, after the patient has taken the *Eno* for a while and it has its crumbling effect on the walls of the stomach, induced vomiting would bring up the loosened material. See below for induced vomiting.

Vomiting

Induced Vomiting

To induce vomiting, locate a spot about 1 inch below the first notch found on the base of the ribs on the left side of the body (feeding spot for spleen). For a heavy person it may be 2 inches below . Reach into the soft tissue at this location with the first 2 fingers and gently push up.

Uncontrolled Vomiting

To stop uncontrollable vomiting that has reached the stage of dry heaves when nothing comes up, Mr. Stephenson recommended eating white rice, thoroughly cooked and steamed to a tacky consistency; a little butter can be added to make it more palatable. Even though the person continues to retch, the tacky substance will adhere to the stomach and not come up and as more is eaten the vomiting tendency will stop and the tacky substance will pass into the intestine. Since the rice is fully cooked, the stomach does not have to hold it for digestion. It is able to inflate the intestine and create a readiness of the body to accept more food. The rice also acts as a blotter in the stomach, sweetening it by absorbing the unpleasant secretions that cause the bitter taste.

Violent Vomiting

Repeated violent regurgitation can cause the stomach to be inverted and sucked into the mouth of the esophagus, a condition caused by reverse peristaltic action, which is present in such violent vomiting. This can choke a person to death because the displacement of the tissues will not allow him to breathe. The type of vomiting referred to might occur in severe, prolonged sea sickness. If the condition is recognized, the stomach may be drawn back to its normal position by creating a vacuum downward over the breathing tube with the palm and thumb. When the person is again able to breathe, he/she should immediately swallow something to keep the stomach down. Steamed rice is best, but use milk or water or anything to hold the stomach down until rice is available.

Fallen Stomach

According to Mr. Stephenson, there are three ribcage lengths in people: short comes to or below the breast; the second type is 5 inches further down; in the third type, the ribs extend so far that they knit together at the bottom of the parting zone and cannot expand. Only long-ribbed people can have a fallen stomach because they cannot get flesh in this area as others do. The doctors say that only through a major operation can the stomach be lifted, but Mr. Stephenson proved that it could be done, having lifted more than a hundred in his years of work with Creative Healing.

A fallen stomach will only occur in thin or medium weight people. If a person is filled out and well supported from the pubic region up, the stomach cannot fall because all the organs below it are too firmly held in place to shift out of position. Where there is a fallen stomach, the abdomen will often reveal a sunken aspect in the region of the solar plexus and a protrusion in the lower abdomen. Fallen stomach may be brought on by an auto accident or a high fall, but it most often is caused by improper lifting.

Fallen stomach affects people in different ways: loss of appetite, feeling hungry but feeling full after only a few bites of food, or more severe digestive disturbances, such as frequent vomiting. In extreme cases not even soup or broth or water will stay down. A person with a fallen stomach can't take in enough nourishment and is always weak and has no way of regaining strength.

There is always a pulse beat in the region of the solar plexus whenever there is a fallen stomach but a pulse beat in that region does not necessarily indicate a fallen stomach. In the latter it could be caused by tension or contraction of the muscles that affect the blood vessels. A pulse beat in the case of a fallen stomach is caused by the bending of arteries that have been displaced by the sinking of the stomach and other organs. This pulse beat may be felt anywhere between the lower end of the breastbone and the navel. The farther down it is, the farther down the stomach has fallen. To detect a pulse beat lay your hand lightly on the patient's body with no pressure applied and the fingers over this region.

Whenever a pulse beat is detected in the region of the solar plexus, give an upward directed massage over the entire abdomen. Never massage downward!

➤➤➤CAUTION: Mr. Stephenson warned, "A pulse beat near the base of the sternum would say to us, 'Don't massage downward', a pulse beat midway between the base of the sternum and the navel would say, 'Do NOT massage downward', while a pulse beat at, or immediately above, the navel would say 'DON'T YOU DARE MASSAGE DOWNWARD!' " This warning applies to giving liver or gall bladder treatments with their vacuuming in the downward direction. The lower the pulse beat the more dangerous the situation. The upward directed massage is the same for all cases of pulse beat in the stomach and the cause of the pulse beat cannot be identified until the massage is given and sometimes not until the second step is completed.

Position

The patient lies on the back. The Creative Healer sits at the patient's right side.

Abdominal preparatory massage

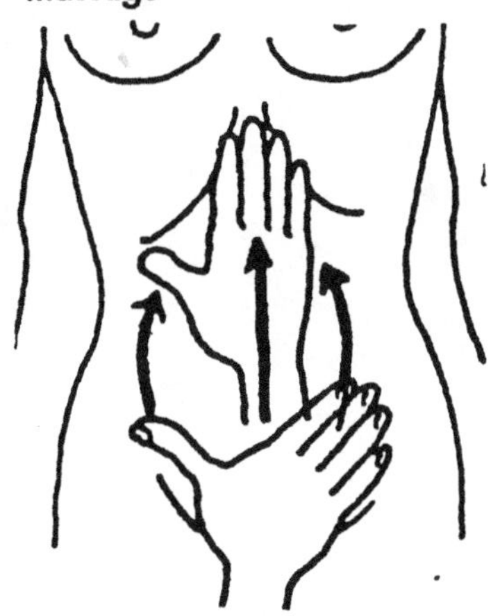

➧ **Step 1: Abdominal preparatory massage.** With oil on your hand, stroke upward from the groin and the pubic bone up to and beyond the margin of the ribs. Hold your fingers together with the thumb apart from them as the stroke begins; as the stroke tapers off gradually bring the thumb and fingers together. See abdominal massage, page 5–3. The purpose of this preparatory massage is to equalize pressures and to make the abdomen soft and pliable for the lift, if it is needed. This treatment must be smooth and very gentle so that the patient can be relaxed and at ease. The massage is not intended to be deep or painful, just soothing and should take about 10 minutes. If, after these 10 minutes, the pulse beat has disappeared, it was not due to a fallen stomach but to tensions and contractions that interfered with the circulation.

Stomach lift

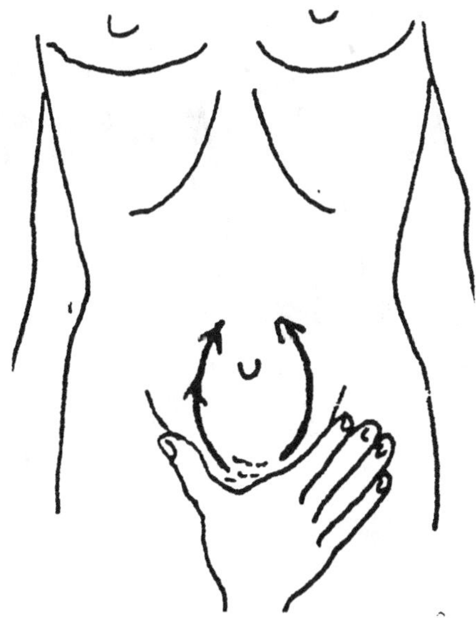

➧ **Step 2: Stomach lift.** If the pulse beat has not disappeared, proceed to the stomach lift. Before starting, place your hand lightly over the bladder area, imparting a gentle pressure, to see if the patient is prompted to void. The bladder must be empty before the lift is done. Ask the patient not to speak during the lift. To perform the stomach lift, the fingers and thumb are separated, as in step 1. Adjust the distance so that your arm is extended and your elbow straight, to give the necessary lifting force. When the hand clears the pubic bone it must lie absolutely flat and in full contact with the body. The lift must be straight up and very slow, advancing mainly as the patient exhales.

Hold the fingers and thumb apart until the lift does not want to proceed any farther. With the hand remaining flat on the abdomen, bring the thumb and fingers toward and away from each other in a gentle scissor-like movement directed upward. The purpose of this scissor-like motion is to coax whatever obstruction there may be into giving way. During the lift, the Creative Healer should proceed with the feeling that he/she will never use force but will coax the stomach, with its contents, through the small opening in the folds of the peritoneum. (The stomach broke through this area as it fell.) As it moves up, it can once again expand into its natural shape and position above the opening. Observe that in the actual lifting operation and scissors movement, substance yields more readily and the hand advances more easily during the patient's exhalation periods; time your movements to occur during exhalation, thus treating in the most gentle manner possible.

If the obstruction does not yield, change back to the general preparatory abdominal massage for a few minutes. Then attempt the lift again. It may be necessary to alternate between the preparatory massage and the lifting movement several times. If dealing with a fallen stomach, the obstruction will ultimately yield. The obstruction actually is the fallen stomach. The treatment will have succeeded in putting the stomach back where it belongs, when it is "sucked up" into place. This will occur near the end of the last part of the lift, during the scissors movement. The stomach has then made its way up through the folds of the peritoneum and expanded into its natural position.

When the lift is completed, the pulse beat will most often have disappeared. If it has not, it will feel as though there is still a portion, about the size of a goose egg or a golf ball, left behind. As a rule, it will underlie the region of the navel. This, too, belongs with the stomach. Apply the lift to this part also. This obstruction will slip into position, yielding to the scissors movement. Because the remaining obstruction is small, perform the scissors movement essentially with the thumb and the index finger only. The thumb and fingers will come completely together, with nothing left for them to grasp. In this obstruction, there is a convoluted mass of blood vessels that belongs up with the stomach. Once they are back in their natural position, they will smooth out. The pulse beat will then have disappeared.

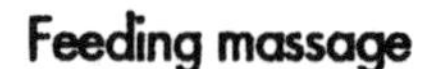
Feeding massage

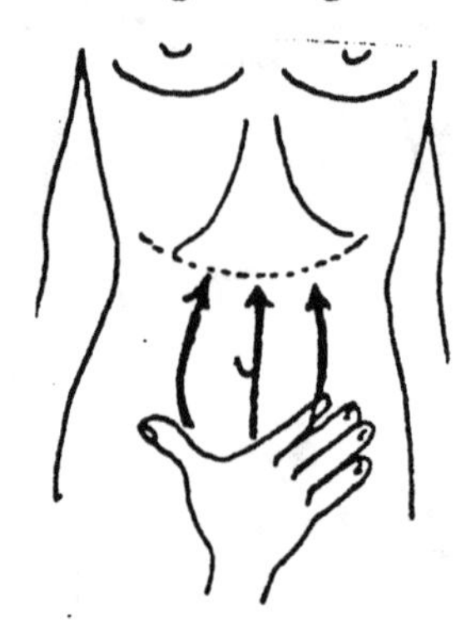

➧ **Step 3: Feeding massage.** After the stomach lift, this massage is directed upward toward a shallow arc that swings gently upward from the navel toward the sides of the body. This feeding massage is like the preparatory massage except that the preparatory massage extends beyond the margin of the ribs, but the feeding massage goes up only to the arc described, and the thumb and fingers come together earlier than in the preparatory massage. The purpose is to feed and strengthen the tissues that hold up the stomach and the abdominal organs. It also equalizes the pressures within the abdomen, to accommodate the new positions that these organs have assumed through the return of the stomach to its natural position. Do this for 15 minutes.

Duration

The entire treatment may take 30 minutes, including the preparatory massage, the actual lifting and the feeding massage.

Frequency

Treat once a week for 7 weeks, even if after the first few treatments the pulse is completely gone. If the patient is very weak and thin, the pulse beat may have reappeared by the second treatment, but it will not be as far down and the situation may be similar for the following treatments. But if the pulse beat moves down again it shows that the patient has been lifting something and is not yet prepared for it. The patient should be warned at the start to refrain from any appreciable lifting until full recovery.

If the pulse beat does not return during the week intervening between two successive treatments, add a digestive tuneup to the treatments, either after or combined with the feeding massage.

An Obstruction that is not Fallen Stomach

If, as the lift is completed with the scissors movement, the obstruction refuses to yield and responds but little to the preparátory massage, there may be an obstruction that is much more massive than a fallen stomach. In this case, the pulse beat extends over a much broader area. This condition can represent a very serious situation in that it may comprise a grave derangement of the blood stream in the vital region of the solar plexus. Such a massive obstruction must be treated with gentle, breaking up movements from below. Also, use fine lines of contact applied straight upward, with the fingers working more or less along a single line. The patient can be instructed to self-administer this treatment, if he/she proceeds very gently and always in the upward direction. It may take weeks to break up such an obstruction and may be helped by attempting the lift from time to time.

According to Mr. Stephenson, "Striving for hollow goals, driven by false ambitions, entertaining unwholesome emotions or struggling for a long period of time to fulfill obligations that seem overwhelming are often connected with such a massive obstruction. Emotional conflicts have their effect upon the solar plexus. If this seat of energy is disturbed, it cannot empower the body as it should."

Example from Creative Healers

A number of years ago, a good friend introduced me to Creative Healing and I benefited immediately because I had a fallen stomach. In the days following the treatment I experienced no more gas attacks and better digestion. For most of my life I had been very thin. even anemic, but after the treatment I gained weight and felt better. I recalled that in my youth my wise mother remarked that she "suspected my stomach had fallen" after a season of broad-jumping in high school sports but she did not know what to do about it.

Stomach Ulcer

The stomach is a continually undulating muscular organ. To illustrate the power of the stomach acids, Mr. Stephenson said that if you could tie a string onto a human finger, lower it into a human stomach and withdraw it again after 2 or 3 hours, there would be no flesh left on it, but only the bone. If you lowered the finger into a dog's stomach there would not even be any bone left. When the stomach is empty, and thus collapsed, a person will feel discomfort and hunger pangs, caused by the walls of the stomach rubbing against each other. This characteristic of the stomach contributes toward the development and perpetuation of ulcers.

A stomach ulcer develops when the linings of the stomach, in a certain region, have been weakened and broken down by the introduction of destructive substances or poisonous food into the stomach or when worry, anxiety, apprehension, or shock are registered in the solar plexus. A person always under pressure and in a permanent state of high nervous tension is most likely to develop a stomach ulcer. The ulcer is most likely to occur on the front side of the stomach. Friction develops when the muscular wall comes in contact with acidic contents through a weak place in the lining of the stomach. When this happens, the muscular wall of the stomach beyond these linings is no longer protected and contracts sharply. This creates a zone of high heat and friction. The friction of the raw muscles rubbing against each other is perpetuated by the never-ceasing undulation of the stomach.

The more forcibly the muscles at the ulcer point are forced to contract, the less nutrition they can receive. This causes more tissue deterioration and possibly bleeding, and the ulcerated spot may become enlarged. The increased exposure of muscular tissue to stomach acids brings on more violent contractions. A vicious cycle develops and the body cannot right itself without help.

An ulcer patient always feels the need to have some food in the stomach because the food expands the stomach and tends to pull the muscles apart in the highly contracted region, but the never-ending friction prevents the healing circulation from entering. An ulcer treatment must, therefore, break the friction within the sharply contracted muscles at the point of the ulcer and separate the raw surfaces rubbing against each other. This separation enables the forces of nerve energy and circulation to enter and healing can begin.

Position

The patient lies on the back; the Creative Healer sits at the patient's right side. The patient will usually be able to designate the spot where the pain is most acute with considerable accuracy, because the pain is so severe and so localized. This hot spot will usually lie somewhere within the lower part of the anterior (front) side of the stomach.

➧ **Step 1: Stroking up.** After the patient has pointed out the location of the hot spot, apply a stroking massage that will reveal its precise location. Administer the strokes with the oiled palm of your right hand. The contact should not be heavy. Perform the strokes along a line that passes through the hot spot and the pit of the stomach, starting at a place on the opposite side of the hot spot from the pit of the stomach and at least as far from the hot spot as the pit of the stomach. The strokes must not draw the surface tissue far out of position: firm, yet gentle. Use the mind strongly, to cause the hand to create a drawing action that brings the heat of the ulcerated spot through to the surface. This stroking actually aggravates the condition slightly but not distressingly, because it pushes the tissues that are already heavily contracted, closer together. The stroking teases the ulcer into revealing its exact location. If the stroking is done correctly, a well-defined red spot will appear after 4 or 5 minutes. Its size corresponds to the size of the ulcer: if the red spot is, for example, the size of a dime, the ulcer will be that size. If too heavy a pressure is used in the stroking, the heat will still be drawn through to the surface, but instead of a well-defined red spot, a pink one with a blurred contour will appear.

Step 2: Placing hands. Once the red spot appears, use the left hand to keep the tissues that it contacts in place, with the fingers together, the thumb separated; place this finger unit at right angles to the path of the stroking just performed. Place it at the upper edge of the red spot or on the side of that spot nearest the center line of the body. This hand remains in this position throughout the treatment. Now, present the finger unit of the right hand to the body in a vertical position with the length of the little finger on the opposite side of the spot from the left hand.

Hand placement and stroking for stomach ulcer

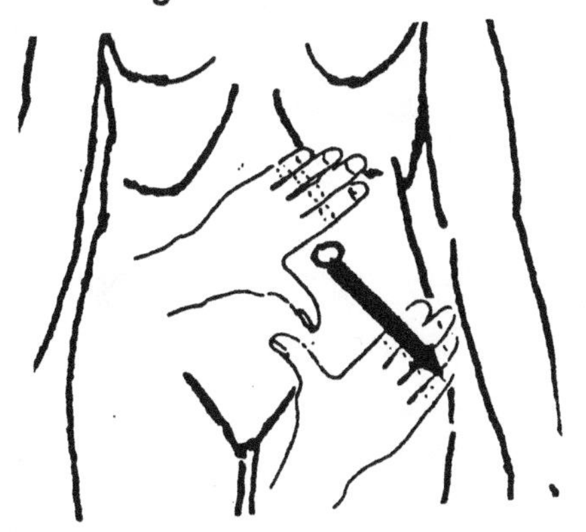

Step 3: Stroking in opposite direction. Perform a vacuum action beginning with the length of the little finger in the opposite direction from the previous stroking but along the same line. As the little finger clears the edge of the spot, bring down the third finger and similarly the middle and the index fingers, so that finally all four fingers are in contact with the body. Each finger, as it comes down, establishes a firm contact with the body and retains it throughout the stroke. The fingers are applied in their full length, not just their tips. The strokes are long; they extend from the hot spot to a place two or three times as far away from the spot, as the spot is from the pit of the stomach. They must be performed slowly; do not curtail either their length or their duration. Apply these long, enduring strokes with a strong, firm pressure. The stroking is guided by the thought of creating a vacuum so that the lower part of the stomach and the adjacent contents of the abdomen will be drawn downward in a straight or diagonal direction, depending on the position of the ulcer. The continuation of the stroking, drawing the lower part of the stomach downward, separates the muscles at the ulcerated spot. In this manner, the friction described earlier is broken.

➤➤➤CAUTION: Be careful that the last of the vacuum strokes are the last stroke of the treatment.

Duration

The vacuum strokes are performed for 10 minutes or until the red spot disappears, whichever comes first.

Frequency

The ulcer is treated once a week, for 7 weeks. In connection with an ulcer treatment, it is vital to have the patient understand the importance of keeping the solar plexus undisturbed.

The Duodenal Ulcer

The second type of ulcer in the stomach region is the duodenal ulcer. The duodenum is the U-shaped first section of the bowel connected to the stomach. The red spot denoting this ulcer will appear somewhere along the line overlying this part of the intestine. The treatment is exactly the same as for a stomach ulcer, except that the Creative Healer will have to shift position in order to be able to place the hands in the right directions in relation to the pit of the stomach.

Use of Egg White

After the basic ulcer treatment has been performed, nature steps in at once and the healing of the ulcer begins. To assure that this healing is not interfered with, the patient is directed to take the white of an egg for 7 mornings, 1/2 hour before swallowing anything else. The egg white should be pure, raw, not salted or mixed with a juice or otherwise adulterated. It is drawn to the ulcerated spot by the heat of that spot which will "cook it," just as surely as the heat of a stove would. It will cover and protect the spot so that food cannot get into the space between the raw muscles to cause irritation and friction. Ulcer patients will often mention that they have been confined to bland foods. It may be well to have them continue on these foods until the healing is complete. In all cases, the patient should not make drastic tests with foods that have given him trouble before.

Bleeding Ulcer

This ulcer treatment applies also to bleeding ulcers, even if bright red blood is vomited or the stools are black from the bleeding of the ulcer. When blood is present in the stools, the color of the blood is a clue as to the location where the bleeding is occurring:

- Bright red: bleeding is within 10 or 12 inches of the anus.
- Light brown: bleeding is higher up in the intestine.
- Dark brown: bleeding is at medium intestinal height.
- Black: bleeding is high up in the duodenum or stomach.

The progressively darkening and finally black color is due to the action of the digestive juices on the blood. In other words, the higher up in the bowel that the bleeding area is located, the darker the blood appears in the stool.

Conditions that are not Ulcers

Many supposed cases of stomach ulcers, especially when their location is higher than the regions designated in the foregoing paragraphs, do not yield to the first step of the ulcer treatment and no red spot appears. The distress they cause may, however, well approximate that caused by true ulcers.

In cases where the ulcer treatment does not apply, stop the treatment and check over the entire area of the body that is subject to distress or discomfort. Check the area to detect where normal function may be deficient and then apply the treatments appropriate to restore it. Most frequently, the solar plexus is involved in some way. It may be that this vital nerve center is disturbed because the patient is a faulty breather and fails to breathe through; thus, the diaphragm does not function properly. This keeps the solar plexus in a perpetual state of agitation, and is further aggravated by nervous pressure and anxieties.

Failing to breathe correctly may mean the patient is a high and short breather or has lost proper breathing habits. It is important that the Creative Healer review high and short breathing, page 4–2, to appreciate the connection between the solar plexus and breathing. When the ulcer treatment does not apply, the four-minute breathing tube vacuum treatment, page 4–5, is indispensable in restoring that all-important region of the solar plexus to normal function.

The vacuum over the breathing tube may be very helpful in other instances of pseudo-ulcers. In particular, it may be helpful when a deficient functioning of the digestive system causes a disturbance to the solar plexus. The vacuum movement may be used here as a supplement to the basic treatment for restoring normal function to the digestive system. A disturbance of the digestive process may, at times, be caused by eating agitating food and drink. The patient is, in these cases, advised to stop until the nerve centers have been settled.

The Large Intestine (Colon)

The lowest points of the large intestine (colon) on the two sides of the body are the cecum on the right and the sigmoid flexure on the left. These two places in the approximately 5 feet of large intestine are most affected by the sagging of internal organs and this affects digestion. Therefore, after the abdominal massage is given as part of the digestive tuneup or for enhancing the constipation treatment, these two areas should not be overlooked.

Cecum and Ascending Colon

The intestinal system

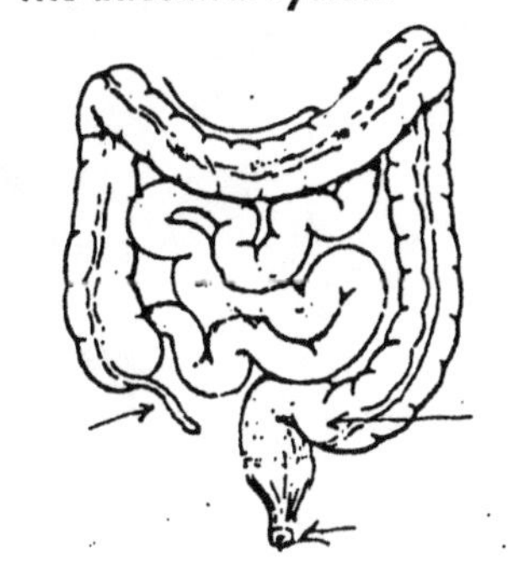

The cecum is the dead-end pouch that forms the beginning of the ascending colon. The small intestine (ilium) empties into the ascending colon through the ileo-cecal valve, which is situated on the medial side of the cecum, several inches above its bottom point. Because this pouch-like end of the colon is below the main flow of action through the bowel, it can accumulate and trap static material, which deteriorates. This condition is fostered by wearing garments or belts that are too tight at the waist as well as eating quantities of foods that are gas-forming.

When the accumulation in the cecum reaches an advanced stage, it may lead to appendicitis. The appendix is another dead-end but deflated pouch attached to the cecum. Gas in the intestine may inflate the appendix and force decomposing trapped material into it, which further putrefies, causes acute pain and in extreme cases, ruptures the walls of the appendix. Mr. Stephenson believed that the appendix was a remnant of earlier times and not needed in the body today; see the appendix, earlier in this chapter, page 5–4.

It is important to gently break up any accumulation that has formed in the cecum and move it up the ascending colon. Fortunately, since the cecum and the sigmoid flexure are so close to the abdominal wall, they may be felt and reached from the outside as part of the abdominal massage. The treatment must be unhurried and the patient fully relaxed.

Position

The patient lies on the back; the Creative Healer sits at the patient's right.

➧ **Step 1: Clear the cecum.** Start at the groin with the fingertips leading and the fingers coming into flat contact with the abdomen as the hand moves upward in a lifting movement. When within 1 or 2 inches of the hepatic flexure (where the large intestine turns to cross the body), begin to release the contact so that the fingers glide up and off before they reach the ribs. The movement must be very gentle and slow and at the same time positive, with the fingertips penetrating as this gentle lifting is repeated until all the material is felt to have been moved out of the cecum ahead of the fingertips.

The patient may have sensitivity in the region of the cecum but with the gentle lifting the pain will disappear, a sign the cecum has been cleaned out. The operator will be able to feel the movement of the fecal matter up the ascending colon, which is another guide to the success of the treatment. In cases of severe obstruction, it is helpful to have the patient flex his/her legs in order to allow the fingertips to enter into the abdominal wall more easily.

➧ **Step 2: Encourage movement.** After the lifting treatment, stroke along and below the margin of the ribs on the right side, with the thumb (as for feeding of the pancreas, page 5–11). The patient may be instructed to self-administer this treatment.

Sigmoid Flexure

The lowest part of the descending colon on the left side of the body is the sigmoid flexure. It is in the form of a twisted letter 's' and is the bend the colon makes before it joins the rectum. Here the folds of the colon, by sagging, obstruct the passage of fecal material descending from above. Mr. Stephenson compared this condition to that of a gunny sack into which one is trying to pour potatoes. If the sack is held up straight it is easy to pour into but if it sags down with lots of folds, the flow is obstructed. The idea behind this treatment then, is to straighten out the folds of the colon.

Position

The patient lies on the back. The Creative Healer sits at the patient's right.

➧ **Step 1: Lifting the folds.** This lifting movement covers only a small area and takes the surface tissue with it. With the fingertips, reach into the abdominal wall just above the groin and next to the hipbone. Gently lift almost straight up, perhaps a little toward the median line until reaching the top of the hip about 2 inches. Gradually release the contact as the fingertips move off the body toward the left side of the body in a smooth clockwise arc. Repeat the movement until it feels that the fecal matter is moving through. Again, it is helpful to have the patient flex his/her legs in order to allow the fingertips to enter into the abdominal wall more easily.

➧ **Step 2: Vacuum.** When the sigmoid flexure feels cleared, perform a succession of short, vacuum movements downward over the mid-section of the descending colon. The drawing action of these vacuum strokes will enliven the bowel and material from the transverse colon will begin to move through. This vacuum movement has a settling effect and can be used in cases of vomiting and sick stomach. The person may be taught to treat this important spot. For helping to release barium or constipation, you can apply gentle, breaking up movements and vacuum on any area of the colon. You would stroke up on the ascending colon, across from the right side to the left side on the transverse colon and down on the descending colon. Show special attention to the bends (flexures) where the ascending turns into the transverse on the right side by the liver and on the left side by the spleen where the transverse turns into the descending colon.

Barium

This substance must be removed. Such a drink or enema, if not cleared leaves a cement-like material in the body. Apply the digestive tuneup, page 5–14.

Uses for *Eno's Fruit Salts*

Mr. Stephenson never recommended the use of anything that could be classed as a medicine. However, although *Eno's Fruit Salts* is obtainable in drugstores, its only active ingredients are bicarbonate of soda and cream of tartar, staples common in any kitchen. For decades previous to and during his boyhood in England, the preparation *Eno's Fruit Salts* had been in use. For full effectiveness use *Eno* according to Mr. Stephenson's directions, not the directions on the label. It should be understood that these uses of *Eno* are intended as emergency measures and are not meant to be relied upon in lieu of restoring proper function to the body.

Note: While *Eno's Fruit Salts* are available in Canadian and British drug stores, they may not be available in the U.S. Mr. Stephenson saw three important uses for *Eno*: as an antacid, as a physic, and in certain cases of chronic indigestion, sick stomach and foul breath of a special kind. See post nasal mucous drip, page 5–16.

As an antacid: In a glass, add 1/2 to 1 teaspoon of *Eno* to 1/2 cup of lukewarm water and drink the mixture while it fizzes. It will cause belching and bring relief from gas on the stomach and pain or distress from having eaten the wrong food. It will help cases of flatulence and biliousness and may be used to calm the solar plexus.

As a physic: Begin with 1 level teaspoon of *Eno* in 1/2 cup of lukewarm water; the amount needed for the desired result must be adjusted individually up or down to avoid griping. *Eno* can be used without fear of dependency. It can often be taken in conjunction with the digestive tuneup or the treatment for constipation to wean the patient from the use of other laxatives and get the bowel to move by itself again, without prompting.

Discharge from the Navel

In this condition, the navel secretes a sticky, whitish matter that has a tendency to dry in the air and crust over the navel. The crust seals off the navel, so that healing from within cannot take place. The oozing of the matter is repeated each time the crust is removed. Advise the patient suffering from this trouble to put 1 drop of olive oil into the navel after every bath. This will prevent the sealing-off crust from forming. In addition, you, the Creative Healer will treat the area once a week with a feeding massage that moves in toward the navel from all directions. Hold your fingers together as a unit and separated from the thumb. Move your hand, laid flat on the abdomen, so that the space between the thumb and the fingers is directed toward the navel and decreased as you approach the navel.

Mr. Stephenson saw that discharge from the navel was coming from the small intestine.

Low Blood Sugar

A low blood sugar condition is indicated if a lump of sugar taken in a cup of hot tea produces a noticeable lift within 5 minutes. This is, of course, only a test, and the lift will be but temporary. A condition of low blood sugar develops when the body consumes more of the natural, essential sugars in the blood stream than are being replaced. The body needs these blood sugars to power its muscular processes. They are even necessary to process the food the body must receive to keep its energy up. In extreme cases of low blood sugar, an acute loss of energy, severe agitation or a ravenous desire for food can result. In a diabetic, a condition of low blood sugar may be brought on by an overdose of insulin. In other instances the condition may be caused by too little rest, by over-exertion or by not eating regularly. All of these conditions result in a depletion of the blood sugars.

Chronic cases can be greatly aggravated by the excessive use of refined sugars or foods containing such sugars, and of other highly refined carbohydrates. They contain no building blocks for the body. They supply heat and also stimulate the blood stream but this is false nutrition. If the body is fed true nutrients it will manufacture essential blood sugars for itself.

For the relief of a low blood sugar condition, the patient must stop eating refined foods. When this dietary change has been made, administer the digestive tuneup as needed, page 5–14. Give special emphasis to the liver and the pancreas and, at times, the spleen. With restored function, the body will once again be able to remanufacture the food it receives. It can then produce the blood sugars that are so essential to the body.

Low Blood Pressure

Mr. Stephenson's concept of low blood pressure is one in which the quality of the blood is not up to par, and the volume of blood may be less than normal, factors that impair the functioning of the body in a critical way. In this low blood pressure condition the heart slows down because its muscles are not properly nourished, which further reduces the blood pressure and a vicious circle arises. A person with low blood pressure describes the sheer will power needed to achieve anything, because of being in a continuous state of fatigue.

An extended general treatment in every low blood pressure case, will open up the back of the neck and keep the circulation in that vital part of the body free and stimulated. A heart treatment is also indicated. The application of the heart treatment will immediately make the heart work better, evidenced by a more vigorous heartbeat. The whole condition of the person will improve but this lift will only be temporary. To put the digestive system to work making more and better blood, combine the heart treatment with the digestive tuneup and the feeding of the spleen. In addition, because low blood pressure involves the inadequate functioning of the digestive system, always examine the person for a condition of fallen stomach.

In summary, the treatment for low blood pressure includes:

- **Step 1:** Administer the heart treatment, page 4–28.
- **Step 2:** Administer the digestive tuneup, page 5–14.
- **Step 3:** Administer the feeding the spleen treatment, page 5–13.
- **Step 4:** Administer the general treatment, page 1–8.

A person with low blood pressure usually lacks all zest for food. It is a sure sign that the treatment is taking effect when the appetite resumes. The person will gradually develop a hearty appetite and pink cheeks. Then it is time to advise on the importance of choosing truly nourishing foods.

Protruding Abdomen

There are different proportions in the structure of the male and female pelvis. In a woman, the pelvic girdle presents a larger diameter than in a man. The spanning of this opening puts a greater demand on the abdominal muscles of a woman. Because of the larger opening provided by nature for the birth canal, the muscles on the floor of the pelvis are subjected to greater stress than in a man. For these reasons, women are not built as well as men for heavy lifting. They are more vulnerable to a dropping of the abdominal organs by straining the abdominal and pelvic muscles.

The muscles of the abdomen can also be sprained by being subjected to forceful stretching such that the tissues are torn apart and not able to return to their natural position. The pain in these cases can be great, even excruciating and last for an extended length of time, until nature has compensated for displaced tissues, but it will be by way of repair (connective tissue) rather than a return to the natural, former state. When this condition of sprained abdomen is recognized, particularly before compensating repair has been completed, and when there is not a case of pregnancy, the remedy is simple. It consists of binding the abdomen so that the tissues can come into their proper position and heal correctly. The binding will, almost immediately, relieve all aspects of pain. In lieu of a better provision, a piece of sheeting, or a towel securely fastened around the abdomen to draw it in and cradle it comfortably, will be adequate.

If abdominal tissues are very weak, the abdomen may fall out of place when the person stands. These may be very heavy people, women after childbirth, injuries caused by a fall, or other reasons causing a severe distension of the abdomen. In such cases the muscle fibers may have become stretched, even torn so that they cannot reach against the distended abdomen to pull themselves together and knit again.

Support for protruding abdomen

A temporary support is necessary to bring the organs and muscles of the abdomen into position and hold them there until they are sufficiently strengthened. At that time, the support can be dispensed with. The use of such a support, for a certain period, will not make the person dependent upon it.

The support should provide a lift like that provided by the hands when held, fingertips touching, far down against the abdomen, drawing it upward and a little inward. The support should exert pressure only over the area described by the hands. Pressure exerted at the waist, for example, would be contrary to the purpose of the garment. The purpose is to lift and to have the circulation above the supported area unrestricted. Pressure at the waist tends to push the organs of the abdomen down into the pelvis, like into a funnel.

The support should be a panty-type garment not an open girdle type; should be made of a firm, two-way stretch material without bindings; and should fit snugly around the hips and over the groin. If, in a very thin person, the hips stand out too far, so that the garment cannot have the desired snug fit, a body-size powder puff should be placed under the garment in the depression over the groin. The back of the support may come up to the waist but the front should be folded down to the groin and tacked so that it lies smooth. It will form a double-walled supporting sling for the abdomen to lie in.

Because of the snug fit over the hips and legs and the quality of the material, a massage-like action is transmitted to the weak tissues as the person walks and bends. If the person is fleshy, there may be a considerable bulge over the sling. Do not be concerned about it. The abdomen will soon reshape itself and the bulge will disappear. The garment need not be worn at night.

The support described is effective in any case in which an organ is out of place. These include cases of fallen womb or bladder, fallen stomach or floating kidney. In all these cases, the abdominal wall is weak. The garment may also be used when no organ is out of place, but when the abdominal wall is so weak that the skin hangs down over the upper legs like an apron. Whatever the case may be, the pertinent Creative Healing treatment for organs that are out of place, i.e., bladder, stomach, and uterus, is given once a week until the tissues are so strong that the support may be dispensed with.

The foregoing refers to organs that are out of position in both men and women but for a man a more appropriate form of garment may be found among the athletic-type abdominal supports available in sporting goods stores.

A binding can be applied also to the muscle, cartilage or tissue that has been torn or bruised, even in the case of cracked ribs. The adequate support it furnishes will greatly relieve pain and assure more rapid healing.

Hernia

The type of hernia most frequently encountered is the rupture of the abdominal wall caused by too heavy or improper lifting. However, if the muscle fiber is already weakened, even grunting or coughing may cause it to break down. With treatment, a hernia can be completely healed if the person is less than 16 years of age, no matter how long the condition has prevailed. The possibility of complete healing resides in a peculiar aspect of the growth factor. In an older person, complete healing can be expected only if treatment is begun within the first five days after the hernia occurs. Unless it is alarming, however, the average hernia case is not even detected much less treated in that time. After the five days have passed, nature will do its best to heal the rent in the tissue.

At the site of the hernia the tissues bulge and protrude. This prevents the edges of the opening from lying close together. Muscle fibers immediately begin the healing process, but because they cannot knit together, a faulty healing takes place. The muscle fibers heal but the area is still left with a rent, or hole, in it. Therefore, surgery is necessary, which makes the edges raw again and brings them together so that they can heal properly.

Hernia Treatment

The treatment for hernia consists of massaging, with the intent of feeding, toward the center of the opening. Massage from the perimeter toward the hernia to the greatest degree from the bottom, to a somewhat lesser degree from the sides, and least from the top. Use the flat sides of the fingers, thumbs and in some cases both hands to massage with the thought of closing the opening and, at the same time, feeding the tissues so that the muscles are strengthened. This massage is valuable because it strengthens the muscles, even if surgery is required.

If the massage is expected to be effective, the area of the hernia must, at all times, be properly supported. The tissues must be kept together at all times whether the massage is intended for strengthening, prior to surgery or whether it is intended for full healing. One of the best ways to achieve this is with a belt-shaped band, which gathers the tissues from all around the body with special attention to the hernia area and supports it like a hand. Support at the critical place may be built up by adding a flat pad, especially necessary if the hip bone is prominent, where the depression caused by its prominence must be adequately filled. Under no circumstances may the support be of a knob-like nature. Such a support would only tend to keep the tissues separated and cancel out the work. The person must, for some time, avoid lifting or any other activity that strains the hernia area, which could cause the tissues to separate again.

Edema, Ascites, Dropsy

The word dropsy was once widely used to describe a certain problem but has now largely fallen into disuse. The current medical term in use is edema, defined as an abnormal accumulation of watery fluid in body tissues or cavities. The use of medicines so strongly diuretic that they wring fluid out of the body, can mask the conditions causing dropsy. If the causes are not recognized, they cannot be worked on to allow the body to restore normal function.

Mr. Stephenson recognized two kinds of dropsy. He designated as low dropsy, the condition in which the tissues of the legs fill up with excess fluid. He designated as high dropsy, the condition in which the abdomen fills up with excess fluid. Ascites is the term now used for this fluid in the abdominal cavity. High dropsy is the more dangerous of the two because the abdomen may fill to the extent that breathing is stopped and death ensues. In some life-threatening cases of high dropsy, in which the patient is not using powerful diuretics, the fluid has often been allowed to accumulate to such an extent that it could cause breathing to stop if the person were to go to sleep. In such cases, Mr. Stephenson would not allow the person to go to sleep until the condition was brought into balance.

Three causes can bring on high dropsy: a leaking heart, malfunctioning kidneys and a porous stomach; this treatment addresses all three.

➧ **Step 1: Give the basic heart treatment, page 4–21.**

➧ **Step 2: Give the complete kidney treatment, page 5–42.**

➧ **Step 3: Closing seeping pores.** If steps 1 and 2 do not completely relieve the condition, treat for a porous stomach. In connection with porous stomach, Mr. Stephenson warned his patients not to eat unripe green apples. In certain cases, the acids of such apples would perforate the stomach and cause the porosity. He saw the stomach seeping fluids into the abdominal regions where they accumulated. To close the seeping pores, Mr. Stephenson used a solution of 1 pound of white sugar dissolved in 1 gallon of spring or well water. He did not heat the solution. He had the patient drink this in place of any other liquid. The patient would drink no water, tea, coffee, juice, etc. The sticky sugar substance would seal the pores of the stomach until the porosity of the stomach was gradually overcome. During this time, Mr. Stephenson administered a massage over the bladder spots to remove the fluid from the abdominal region and draw it directly into the bladder.

➧ **Step 4: Locate bladder spots.** To locate the bladder spots on an average-size adult, place the heel of the hand just above the pubic bone, and the thumb and middle finger on the lower abdomen at a distance of 4 1/2 to 5 inches apart. The thumb and finger will lay on the centers of the bladder spots. These spots are to be thought of as small areas. See illustration on page 5–50.

➧ **Step 5: Create vacuum.** The vacuum-type movement starts on the lateral-most position on the spots, proceeds to the uppermost central position, then draws nearly straight downward, and releases. With your finger and thumb, carry the surface tissue through the small movement except, of course, at the release. Even then, do not break contact with the surface. The movement is small because the spots comprise areas of only 3/4 to 5/8 of a square inch. The movement might be thought of as describing a circle but it more nearly approximates a semicircle. Perform this movement with the intent of gathering and feeding the natural secretions to the walls of the bladder, to cool it.

The stomach should also be well cared for by eating reasonable foods. There are cases of high dropsy in which the amount of fluid produced in the abdomen proves to be greater than the amount of liquid knowingly taken in. Mr. Stephenson in such cases, based the treatment on the fact that all other possibilities having been eliminated, the fluid must have been taken into the body out of the air. Therefore, after the fluid had been extracted, the body was shielded from the air by wrapping the trunk in surgical rubber sheeting. He then alternately treated in the manner described above and protected the body from air until balance was restored.

Low Dropsy

For low dropsy, presuming adequate kidney function, adequate circulatory volume, and adequate heart capacity, work with the intent of regulating the flow of life and blood through the legs. See leg treatments in Chapter 7, and the bladder treatment, page 5–49.

Typhoid Fever

Typhoid fever causes the walls of the stomach to swell, coating them heavily with a gelatine-like substance. The stomach is thus unfit to receive solid food. A fast is indicated. As the body struggles against the disease, it is helped in the process of eliminating the poisonous wastes arising from the shedding of the stomach coating. This is done by the sustained, gentle, cleansing effect of frequently drinking a weak solution of *Eno* (1/2 to 1 tsp *Eno* in 8 to 12 oz of water). It prevents a stagnation of the eliminating process, which could cause further poisoning of the body and a lingering of the disease.

Twice in his life, Mr. Stephenson suffered an attack of typhoid fever. Both times, he recovered quickly and both times attributed his rapid overcoming of the disease to his use of *Eno*. He took no medicine and no food. He took only tall glasses of water to which very small quantities of *Eno* had been added and sipped this quite frequently. He took no other drink.

The Elimination System

Constipation

The bowel is susceptible to induced habits. It can therefore be trained to respond to good patterns consciously established. Every person should set aside one or two times a day for consciously and leisurely prompting the bowel to void, allowing sufficient time for the natural action to take place.

The main cause of constipation is the failure of two glands to function as they should. Their function is to keep the contents of the bowel moving smoothly after the natural action of the large bowel has withdrawn much of the fluid. The glands emit a mucous secretion that prevents the bowel contents from becoming too dry and hard; if this secretion is inadequate, constipation results. A treatment for constipation must, therefore, feed nerve life to the glands, stimulating them to secrete the quantity and quality of mucous necessary for the bowel to function smoothly. The spots that activate these glands are called the constipation spots.

Position

The patient sits on the bench; the Creative Healer sits behind.

Placement and movement of thumbs and knees

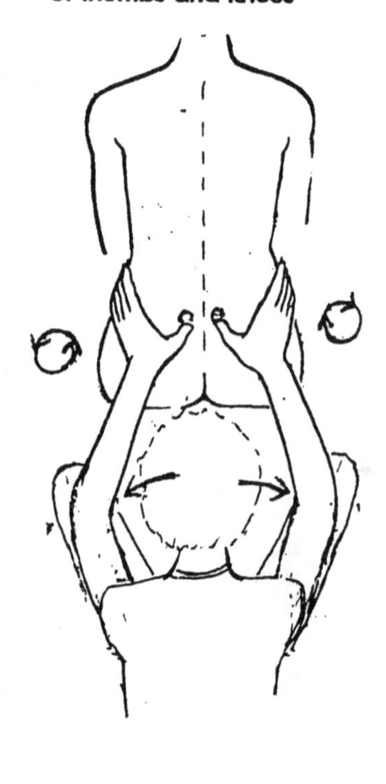

➧ **Step 1: Locate the spots.** The constipation spots, which often look like dimples, lie on a pair of sacral foramen (depressions), the second pair from the top of the sacrum about 1 inch from the center line of the body. They are recognized by their sponginess. If, because of the person's build no dimples are visible, the spots are located by imagining a line between the upper and lower sciatic nerves. The correct spots will be found 1/3 of the way down from the upper to the lower.

➧ **Step 2: Hand and arm placement.** Rest your forearms on your own separated thighs and the fingers of both hands around the buttocks. The thumbs are placed just below the constipation spots.

➧ **Step 3: Feeding movement.** Move your thumbs in a circular movement that feeds directly into the spots—clockwise on the right and counterclockwise on the left. The movement is brought about not by moving your arms but by moving your legs toward and away from each other—this motion moves the arms. Give pressure on the upward strokes of the thumbs and release as thumbs reach the highest points of their paths. With a little practice, the circular feeding motion can be performed quite rapidly. You will find, as you grow familiar with the treatment, that for each individual patient, a natural speed and rhythm establishes itself. It will be in harmony with the slight jiggling motion by which the patient's body responds to the cycles of applied and released pressure of the circular feeding movement.

Duration

Perform the feeding for 6 or 7 minutes. As in the case of hemorrhoids, the treatment may be interspersed with a massage upward, over the sacrum.

This treatment for constipation is all that is needed in most cases. In the exceptional case, a digestive tuneup and the large intestine treatment, especially the sigmoid flexure lifts are done as well. See pages 5–14 and 5–26.

Eno For Constipation

One teaspoon of *Eno* in 1/2 cup of lukewarm water. Drink while it fizzes. The amount of *Eno* actually needed to produce the desired result and avoid unpleasantness or spasmodic pain in the bowel must be adjusted individually up or down, from the 1-teaspoon amount. *Eno* can be used in this manner without fear of inducing dependency. It can be used to wean the person from other laxatives and get the bowel to move by itself, without prompting.

Hemorrhoids

Hemorrhoids develop when the natural feed to the rectal muscles is cut off or interrupted for too long a time. This may be caused by sitting on a cold surface, sitting or standing too long without a change of position or by using unreasonable pressure trying to perform a bowel movement rapidly. Such forcing may injure rectal tissue, which then obstructs the continual feed to the muscles and causes them to deteriorate. When the blood and nerve life to the rectal muscles is restricted, the muscles will sag and cause blood vessels to herniate out and penetrate into the tube of the rectum. Hemorrhoids are swollen blood vessels of the rectum. They may protrude beyond the anus and are easily ruptured. The result is known as bleeding hemorrhoids, which always produce bright red blood.

Distension of the mucous membrane at the anus is caused by the inability of the muscles that support the rectum to hold the tissues in place. This causes the protrusion and exposure of this membrane on the outside of the anus. When these tissues are protruding, patients should be cautioned not to use toilet paper, since wood fibers in the paper adhere to and become embedded in the swollen mucous membrane and cause continual irritation. A soft wet cloth or sponge can be used instead, until the hemorrhoids are completely healed. (If you look at paper under a magnifying glass, you see a mass of splinters.) Repeated embedding of these fibers is the sole cause of itching hemorrhoids. It can cause a swelling, shaped like a ring formed in the protruding membrane at the anus. During this condition, the strength of the rectal muscles will be insufficient to draw all rectal tissues back up into position. Mr. Stephenson stated that if this condition continued over a period of 2 or more years, it could cause cancer of the rectum. Thus, it is very important to avoid using toilet paper until all tissues are in position and the mucous membrane is no longer exposed at the anus.

This Creative Healing treatment will feed the rectal muscles, restore the rectum to its proper position and stop the herniation of the blood vessels within the walls of the rectum. This treatment illustrates what the term "Creative" signifies. The thumbs lift the tissue on the outside of the sacrum , but the mind concentrates on seeing what is lifted on the other side of the sacrum. The inner tissues respond to this combination of manipulative work and creative thought. The "lifts" will stop the herniation of the blood vessels within the walls of the rectum.

Position

The patient sits on a bench in the usual upright position and is asked not to move the hands in conversation during the treatment. The Creative Healer sits behind, hands oiled with olive oil.

➧ **Step 1: Hand and arm placement.** To treat, place the thumbs horizontally, tips about 1 inch apart, on either side of the center line of the body where the sacrum joins the tailbone. The fingers are on the patient's buttocks. This position allows you to rest your forearms on your own separated legs.

Slow knee movement moves thumbs upward

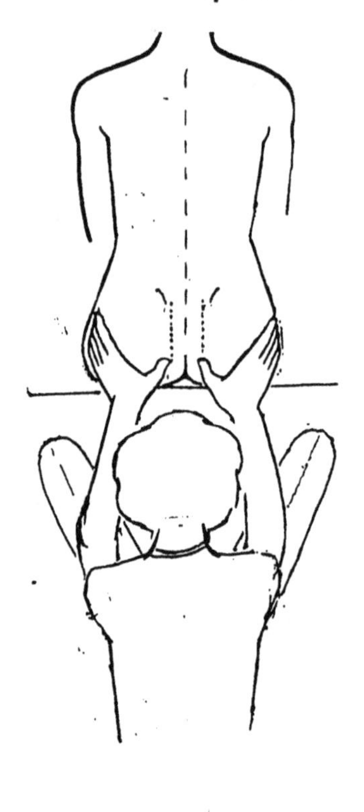

➧ **Step 2: Movement of thumbs and knees.** By slowly moving your legs together and keeping the fingers in the same relative position, your thumbs will be pushed up over the natural channels of the sacrum. At the top of the sacrum, the thumbs arc outward, away from the center of the body and will be about 2 inches apart at the end of the movement. The entire movement is performed **very** slowly with the mental intent that everything that passes under the thumbs is lifted. The pressure is firm and constant without any change of intensity. Using the legs allows the thumbs to proceed without fluctuation until they reach the top of the sacrum and as they diverge the pressure is gradually released. A treatment consists of 6 lifts.

➧ **Step 3: Massage.** Because the thumbs will tire from the lifting, an **upward only** massage may be interspersed between the lifts. Your hands are held in the same position as for the lifts, but the thumbs are in full lengthwise contact with the sacrum. This massage also rests the tissue and builds circulation that strengthens that entire part of the body.

Several days after a hemorrhoid treatment the patient may notice a small amount of red blood in his stools. This is caused by the breaking of a herniated blood vessel. In the process of the strengthening of the muscles and the return of the rectum to its natural position, some tiny blood vessels are squeezed into the passageway and a firm bowel movement may break them. This is of no consequence as they will quickly dry up and heal.

Frequency

Three or four treatments, spaced 1 week apart, should be sufficient for the average case. Sometimes it is necessary to correct other conditions also, such as constipation and bearing down pain.

For the self treatment of hemorrhoids, use the first finger of each hand supported by the second and steadied by the placement of the thumbs on the buttocks.

It may be necessary to strengthen the pelvic area by performing the treatments for bearing down pain, below, and bed-wetting spots, page 5–51.

Note: Failure of the hemorrhoid treatment, after ruling out constipation, swollen tissue from wood fiber and bearing down pain, may be caused by a "gusset" or pocket-like formation of scar tissue in the rectum. A condition of this kind requires surgery for its correction.

Collapsed Sphincter Muscle

It sometimes happens that after a successful hemorrhoid treatment, the bowel movements are still not full-formed but remain thin and stringy. This continues to impart a feeling of unsatisfactory emptying of the bowel, as compared to the sensation that accompanies a full-formed movement.

This condition is most often due to the upper portion of the rectum and the upper anal sphincter muscle not being in proper position relative to each other. The upper sphincter may be collapsed and telescoped down into the rectum. This precludes the adequate filling of the rectum, without which, the expulsion of a full-formed movement cannot take place.

To correct this condition, proceed as for the regular hemorrhoid treatment above, except place your hands a little higher on the patient's buttocks. In this position the thumbs will tend to swing closer together, instead of further apart, as they are pushed upward by the movement of the legs. As the thumbs move closer together, their contact surfaces are gradually concentrated into contact points near their ends.

In this treatment, move your thumbs still more slowly than in the regular hemorrhoid treatment, and the movement becomes slower the closer it comes to its end. The pressure is well sustained, already, at the level of the upper sciatic nerve. Sustain this positive lift for 1 minute or more to nearly the top of the sacrum. Then gradually and smoothly taper off into nothing, as in the regular hemorrhoid treatment.

To correct the condition of a collapsed upper anal sphincter, first give the regular hemorrhoid treatment, applying as many lifts as you feel are necessary, and then perform 1 or 2 of the lifts just described.

Bearing Down Pain

The bearing down pain often accompanies hemorrhoids. If this is so the hemorrhoid treatment should be given first. The causes of both are the same: sitting or standing too long without change of position and occasionally from rectal examinations. The term used, bearing down, is very descriptive. It is a severe pain around the rectum and in the muscles of the body adjacent to the rectum and similar to an urgent bowel movement that has to be delayed. In some cases it may cause the loss of control of the anal sphincter. In each case, whatever the cause, the coccygeal nerves, near the tailbone have been displaced. This causes the muscles adjacent to the rectum to pull down the tissues that they normally support. The nerve or nerves to be replaced lie between the hipbone and the tailbone, lower than and nearer to the tailbone than the sacral notches connected to the lower sciatic nerve. Here lies a notch, shaped like a tent or an inverted "V" below and a little to the right and left of the upper edge of the tailbone. The treatment is given individually for each side of the body.

Locate the notch

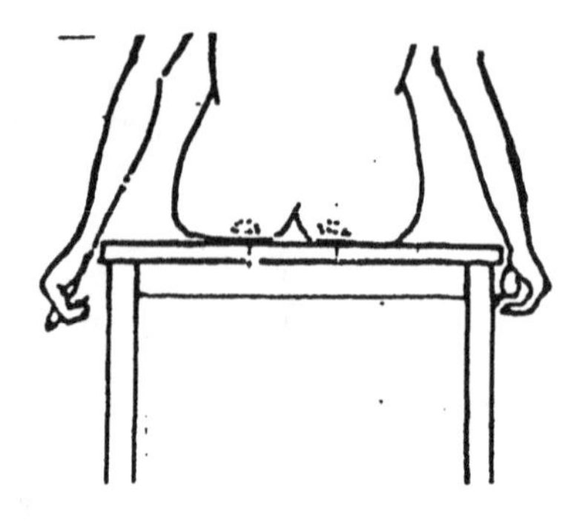

Position

The patient sits well back on the bench so that the Creative Healer's index finger can be properly placed without interference from the bench; the Creative Healer sits behind.

➧ **Step 1: Positioning.** We describe the right side. Place your right forearm just above the wrist on your own right leg, above the knee. Your elbow is free and upper arm is straight below the shoulder. The palm of your hand faces upward for the correct placement of the index finger, the tip of which accomplishes the lift. Place your index finger under the buttocks between the hipbone and the tailbone so that it will clear the bench when it moves upward.

➧ **Step 2: Locate notch.** Locate the notch with the index finger under the buttock and vertically beneath the upper side edge of the tailbone. If the finger encounters the tailbone or hipbone, release the pressure and reposition the finger. If the finger slides backward, move it forward and try again.

Press straight up very slowly

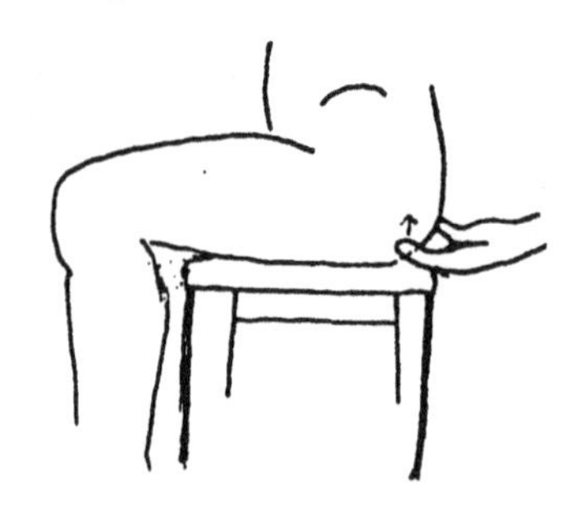

➧ **Step 3: Press nerve into notch.** The tip of the index finger will press straight up, parallel with the spine, with the aim of lifting the tissue into the highest point of the notch. The pressing is applied with a slightly arched finger, steadily, firmly, persistently, of long duration and must not be hurried. The shoulder is pressed downward and acts with the forearm and stiff wrist in a lever like action to allow the index finger to move slowly upward and lift the tissues that will replace the nerve into its natural position. The pressure is slow and straight up and parallel to the spine. When the finger ascends very slowly, the muscles will begin to relax with its penetration upward. It is amazing how easily this is accomplished as the index finger, in the correct location with slow and steady pressure, reaches the highest point of the notch between the hipbone and the tailbone. Release the pressure smoothly and slowly, and repeat the treatment on the left side of the body.

To further strengthen the muscles in the floor of the pelvis, the bed wetting spots may also be treated. See page 5–51.

Diarrhea

Diarrhea, to Mr. Stephenson, meant loose bowels arising from an infestation of parasites in the small intestine. In contrast, he said if the loose bowels are of the ordinary type, they result from the effort of the body to eliminate material that it cannot handle (indigestible food, wrong combinations, etc.) and this elimination should not be suppressed. Unlike the condition of ordinary loose bowels, which are over in 2 or 3 days, diarrhea continues beyond the third or fourth day. This condition begins to seriously weaken the person, and may persist for an indefinite length of time, if not treated. Treatment for diarrhea is not applied until the third or fourth day, or until it becomes apparent that the person is definitely being weakened.

The treatment is based on the use of natural apple cider vinegar, which contains a "mother" and has not been pasteurized. If loose bowels are of the diarrhea type, the treatment, applied too early will fail, so it must be applied after 4 days, in exact amounts given for each age group.

➤ ➤ ➤CAUTION: This treatment should never be employed if the patient has a sick stomach or if the abdomen is sore and sensitive to the touch.

Dosage to be Taken Once an Hour Until Results are Obtained

Age	Proportion
• 6 to 10 years	1 part vinegar to 3 parts water
• 10 to 18 years	1 part vinegar to 2 parts water
• Over 18 years (adult)	1 part vinegar to 1 part water

The vinegar and water are mixed according to proportions indicated above and taken one swallow at a time between meals during the course of one week; replenish the solution as needed. The swallows should always be small enough and the time intervals between them long enough, to prevent any sensation of nausea from developing. The time will vary by individual.

The treatment applies to any kind of loose bowel caused by parasites that are lodged in the walls of the small intestine. Thus, it applies to amoebic dysentery, or any type of recurrent dysentery, and to recurrent malaria.

The effect of the vinegar is twofold: It kills off the parasites and it thickens and generally enhances the lining of the bowel.

➤ ➤ ➤CAUTION: It is vital that the treatment not be applied before the fourth day of the loose bowel condition or before the patient really begins to weaken. At that time, the parasites have reached the height of their activity. They are flourishing, and out in the open, and therefore most vulnerable to the effects of the vinegar, which kills them. Applying the vinegar at an earlier stage would merely drive them back into the walls of the intestine where they would hibernate to become active again later. The heat of the intestine stimulates the same action in the vinegar that originally caused the "mother" to grow. This is the action that thickens and enhances the lining of the bowel. In order that the bowel may fully benefit from this action, the vinegar is taken during an entire week, though the actual diarrhea will have stopped several days before the week is up.

Chronic Bleeding of the Bowel

Check the spine for cord-like formations that may extend from between the vertebrae and continue parallel to the ribs. Such formations may be present on either side of the body. These cord-like formations emanating from the spine may be detected by palpating, though frequently not apparent to the eye or discernible to the superficial touch. An effective means of palpating is the scissors treatment, page 3–5, applied from the sacrum to the base of the neck. These formations are usually detectable for 2 or 3 inches following a course parallel to the ribs, then buried at its end in the tissues.

Position

The patient sits; the Creative Healer sits behind.

➧ **Step 1: Quarter twist.** To correct such formations start at the end of the cord near the spine. Bury the cord in the tissue by repeated quarter twists. Proceed in this manner as far out from the spine as you are able to replace the displaced substance. Alternate the quarter twists with stroking away from the spine, parallel to the ribs in the areas beyond that of the quarter twist. Apply the breaking up movement in the area beyond that of the quarter twist. By alternating these three movements, the whole formation can be made to disappear.

➧ **Step 2:** Apply digestive and bowel treatments if deemed helpful.

Colitis

Colitis is a condition in which the bowel is in a continual state of inflammation because its lining is so thin and weak that it sheds away. The colitis patient may pass long strings of what appears to be mucus but is actually strips of the lining of the bowel. The lining then becomes even thinner and weaker. To obtain relief, the patient must adopt an appropriate diet, avoiding all scratchy foods that irritate the bowel. This includes whole grains because the body cannot digest the grain hulls. Under ordinary circumstances they act as roughage and do no harm, but in the case of colitis they act as serious irritants, aggravating the already inflamed condition. Bran is one of the chief trouble makers because it is frequently taken as an aid against constipation. Brown rice and sweet corn, when the whole kernel is taken, become irritants because their hulls cannot be broken down by the digestion no matter how long they have been cooked.

A bland diet should be followed and in extreme cases a short term bland diet of steamed white rice may be an aid (see vomiting, page 5–17). When a proper diet is followed, a digestive tuneup, page 5–14, would help the consistency of the digestive mixture. If the lining of the bowel needs additional strengthening, the vinegar treatment (see diarrhea, page 5–38) will thicken the lining of the bowel. When this is achieved, a reasonable amount of roughage may again be used in the diet. Also apply the constipation treatment if needed, page 5–34.

Diverticulosis: Diverticulitis

Diverticulosis is a condition in which the walls of the colon bulge with stretched and distended sections or sacs, especially in the sigmoid flexure, where the distended portions act as pockets for accumulation of deposits. As long as these deposits remain, the muscles of the colon cannot regain their strength or ability to contract, creating a blank spot in the successive waves of normal peristalsis. At the same time, the narrowed sections of the colon have been overburdened. Their state of permanent contraction (smaller diameter) obstructs the passage of fecal matter and creates an additional block in the successive waves of peristalsis.

Even with a certain amount of food entering the body each day and a proportional amount leaving it, too much is retained. So, the excess contents within the bowel must be removed.

Diverticulitis is an inflammation of one or more of the bulged distended sections of the colon. During periods of inflammation the patient will experience crampy pain, particularly over the sigmoid area, and fever.

Step 1: High enemas. Mr. Stephenson considered high enemas the most desirable method in assisting to dislodge unwanted material. A high enema uses a thin, soft rubber tube, about 18 inches long, for the average adult. In the hands of one proficient in its use, it offers no likelihood of injury to the colon.

Step 2: Abdominal wall treatment. After the enema, apply breaking up movements over the descending and ascending bowel. They are performed best when the person lies down with knees bent. The action of these circular movements penetrates the abdominal wall and loosens and propels fecal matter on its natural course.

Loosen the muscles of the abdominal wall and the internal muscles by curling the fingers around the front of the hip bone as though to reach along the inside surface of that bone and lift up and clockwise on the left side of the descending colon. To do this, the abdomen must be flat and empty of excess matter.

Step 3: Spine treatment. Treat laterally between the vertebrae of the lumbar region of the spine on either side using the quarter twist to replace substance.

Step 4: Groin treatment. See crippled leg, page 7–4.

Step 5: Abdominal support. All of these treatments, to take full effect, demand that the muscles of the abdominal wall be in good condition or be assisted by a proper abdominal support. It is particularly important that such a garment does not pinch and must not constrict at the waistline. Rather, it must lift from below. The pelvic girdle at the floor of the pelvis roughly represents a funnel. The tissues must be lifted and not jammed into the bottom of the funnel. See protruding abdomen, page 5–29.

➧ **Step 6: Eating habits.** To completely overcome diverticulitis the patient must modify eating habits. See eating suggestions for colitis, page 5–40.

Mr. Stephenson observed that women frequently cross their arms in front of the body, resting them on the abdomen. They even carry packages and babies in this position. These habits tend to press everything into the floor of the pelvis causing sag and shutting off the flow of action of many vital functions.

Kidney Treatment

The two kidneys are situated in the back part of the abdomen one on each side of the spinal column, embedded in a mass of fatty tissue. Together with this tissue, they are enclosed in a sheath formed of a membrane of fibrous tissue. This membrane is attached to adjacent similar membranes above and behind the kidneys and are supported rather insecurely, held in position partly by their attachment to the neighboring membranes and partly by their relationship to other organs. The right kidney is slightly lower than the left because of the liver above it. The kidneys are rugged organs but at the same time very delicate organs and they will not tolerate any violence or heavy treatment.

The function of the kidneys is to cleanse the blood stream and if they do not function properly, one may feel sick and miserable all over.

The kidneys can be dislodged from their natural position if torn loose from their support. This can happen when the body is subjected to great violence such as an auto accident, a high fall or a blow in the unprotected region of the back beneath the ribs and just above the hipbones where the lower portion of the kidneys are not shielded by bony structure. Such a blow can dislodge or bruise the kidneys and cause serious injury. A dislodged kidney is also called a floating kidney.

People can overload their kidneys by drinking too much or too little liquid or by introducing unnatural substances into the body. When overloaded, the sweat glands have to help and profuse perspiring may be the result. Such perspiring may be an indication that the kidneys require treatment.

A kidney problem is sometimes indicated when a person holds his/her left or right hand or both hands over the unprotected area between the ribs and the hipbones on the back and complains of aching in that region. This indicates that the kidneys need more nerve life. If they are not fed enough nerve life through the spinal column to nourish them, they will not be able to cleanse the blood stream as they should.

A person with kidney problems must sit erect as much as possible. It may help to place a small pillow in the kidney region so that one can move firmly against it and keep the back in position. Synthetic fibers worn next to the body can cause the kidney function to slow down. A person with a chronic problem and exposed to extreme temperatures should wear an insulating band of wool flannel around the body, next to the skin and over the kidney region, for protection.

When a person is not ambulatory, enforced inactivity slows down the functioning of the kidneys. Things to avoid are a sagging bed, plastic or rubber sheeting against the body, a heating pad used over the kidney area, and sheets or clothing worn next to the skin made of synthetic fibers.

When the kidneys are locked: no urine is present in the bladder and none is descending from the kidneys, which seem to have stopped functioning, the Creative Healing kidney treatment is invaluable. The patient may ask to void the bladder during the administration of the treatment.

The kidneys have great capacity and many people live successfully a long, normal life with only one kidney. One is adequate if it is kept functioning properly.

The nerve center that governs the flow of nerve life to the kidneys is located at a space between two vertebrae on the back. A displacement of cartilage or a contraction at this kidney spot or in the surrounding region above and below, can slow down the flow of nerve life to the kidneys.

A treatment to restore the kidneys to normal functioning will replace the displaced substance or release the contraction at the kidney spot and in the surrounding region. This will allow the nerve life to be fed through to the kidneys. The second part of the treatment will restore normal temperature, and finally a drainage movement channels surplus secretion of the kidneys into the bladder. All three parts of the treatment stimulate the activity of the kidneys.

This is an easy treatment to administer and it can produce amazing results. Because it is done so gently with nothing but the hands covered with a little olive oil, it is pleasant to receive, easily given, and can have nothing but positive results.

Position

The patient sits on a bench throughout the treatment; the Creative Healer sits behind.

➧ **Step 1: Locate the kidney spot.** To locate the kidney spot, place your palms over the area between the lowest rib and the hip bone so that the lower edges of the hands rest on the hipbones. The fingers point to the sides of the body as the wrists are brought together to touch at center back. Swing the thumbs up together at the center line. The pads of the thumbs will rest at the approximate location of the kidney spot between two vertebrae. The exact spot may be sensitive or painful, may give off heat and show obvious displacement of substance. The spaces above and below may give the same indications. In some cases it may be necessary to check the spaces from between the fifth lumbar vertebra and the sacrum, all the way to the uppermost of the spaces described. Sometimes there is an obvious stress or pull along the spine and within the muscles on either side that converge in the kidney spot area. The relief of this condition must be included in the kidney treatment.

Location of kidney spot

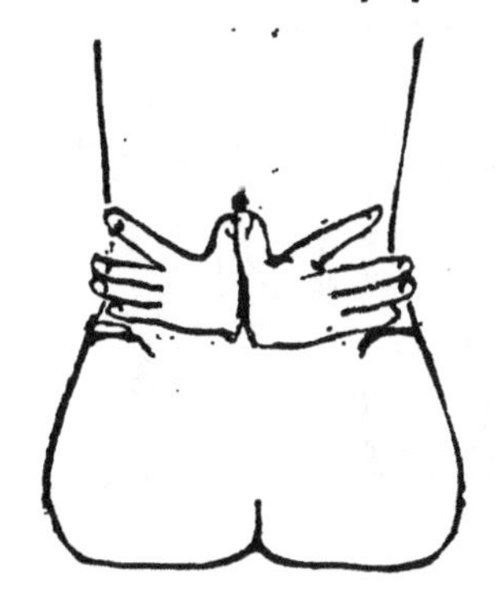

Quarter twist at kidney spot

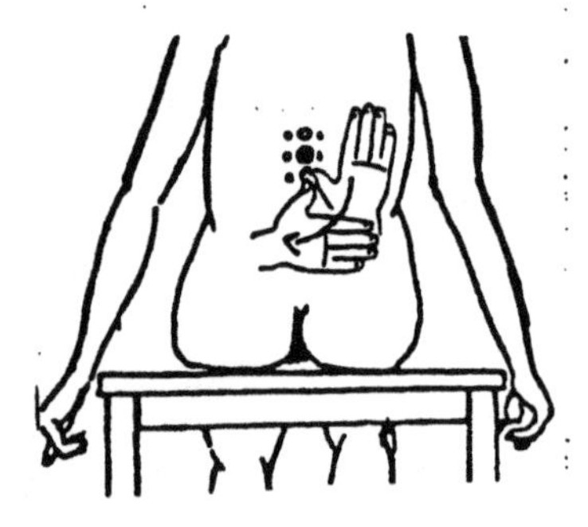

➧ **Step 2: Replace substance.** Place the thumb horizontally with its pad in the space between the vertebrae and slowly rotate it to a vertical position. Work gently with this quarter twist on the center of the kidney spot and to the left and right of it, as well as the center and both sides of the vertebral spaces above and below. While centering the substance your mind is thinking strongly of restoring the nerve life to nourish the kidneys.

➧ **Step 3: Remove heat.** The kidneys must be brought to normal temperature and for this, use the palms of the hands. Treat both sides at the same time by placing both hands (well oiled) on the patient's back so that the palms are at the level of the kidney spot. Hold your fingers and thumbs together as a unit and point upward. Begin with the right and left thumb beside each other at the spine. With very light strokes bring the hands downward in a slightly curved diagonal to the sides of the body. The base of the palms moves just above the crests of the hipbones. At the end of the stroke the palms are opposite each other on either side of the body on the fleshy area between the ribs and the hip bone. Repeat the stroke until the region feels at normal temperature.

Remove heat with light strokes

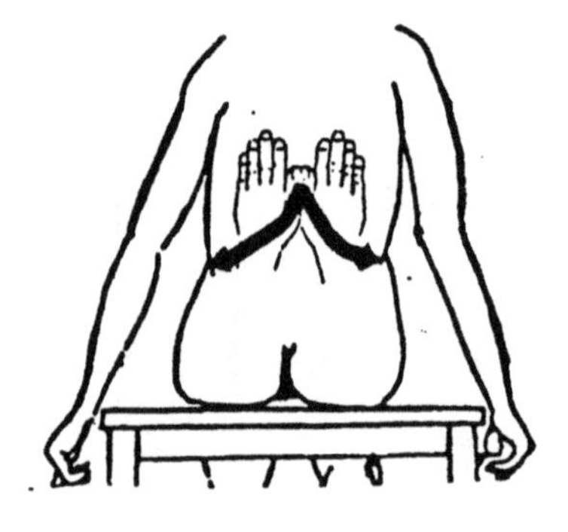

Even though the kidney area may feel cool and clammy when you begin this cooling treatment, you may find a redness appearing on one or both sides in the shape of the kidney that is in trouble. A few strokes may also bring out heat. Continue this very light withdrawal treatment using both hands, one following the other over that side until the redness disappears and the temperature is normal. As the heat is withdrawn from the kidneys, the nerve life flows strongly into them from the feeding spot that has been repositioned. When the temperature of the kidneys has been brought to normal, proceed to the drainage movement.

Step 4: Drain the kidneys. The drainage movement is always performed over both kidneys simultaneously, even if only one kidney is affected. Both palms are placed slightly above the level of the kidney spots on the patient's back, the thumbs vertical and together at the spine. The fingers are held together as a unit and extended toward the sides so that the first and second fingers are on a level with the tips of the thumbs but wide apart. Draw your hands downward in this configuration until the fingertips rest in the soft, unsupported tissue just beneath the ribs. Then move your hands horizontally to the sides of the body, creating a double vacuum with the thumbs following the finger unit but still held wide apart. This double vacuum draws the surplus secretion of the kidneys into the bladder.

Draining movement

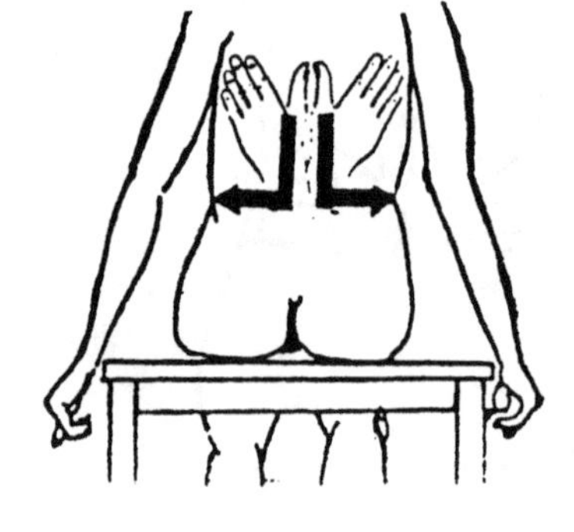

If, after the drainage treatment, heat has returned to the kidney area, repeat step 3 for heat removal and follow it with step 4. Repeat these steps as often as necessary. The kidneys will then do their work of cleansing the blood stream.

As mentioned in the sciatica treatment, the kidneys are at fault in some of the cases in which the sciatica treatment does not bring relief. In such cases, it is not sufficient merely to treat the kidneys. Seepage may be occurring from the kidneys into a triangular region deep within the groin (the scarpus triangle) so that the groin treatment (see page 7–4) is later needed in order to drain out this seepage. (This scarpus triangle, being a natural sump, is also a region where pus may gather in cases of tuberculosis of the spine.)

Mr. Stephenson did not speak of the adrenal glands, but many Creative Healers treat the adrenals with the kidney treatment. The two adrenal glands are located one on top of each kidney.

➤ ➤ ➤CAUTION: The kidney patient is warned against the use of local heat either in the form of a heating pad or lamp. See the sciatica treatment and heat, page 3–21, for a full explanation.

Frequency
One treatment may be sufficient; if not, administer once a week.

Do not be alarmed if a patient faints during a treatment. The release of energy that has been blocked will cause this reaction sometimes. Allow the patient to rest a little and continue the treatment. Mr. Stephenson was very clear about this.

Examples from Creative Healers

1. After sitting for several hours at a desk in a chair that gave no support to the upright spine, the woman attempted to get up, got half-way and could not stand erect. Her back was frozen with pain. Step 3 of the kidney treatment was given, the soothing and smoothing out action to the nerves: very lightly. In a few seconds the nerve spasm was relieved.

2. A tall California man who did a lot of driving could not find a comfortable car seat because of pain in the kidney area of the back. He could not believe the pain was coming from his kidneys until he finally tried the wool flannel band. The pain was relieved.

3. After receiving the Sciatic Treatment for a chronic back pain, the patient dressed and reported that the area was still hurting. He was asked to disrobe again and was seated again on a bench to receive a kidney treatment. The Creative Healer put her hands on the patient's hips, brought the heels of the hands together and raised her thumbs to the kidney spot. The patient's skin began to feel clammy and he fainted and at the same time urinated all over the floor. He came to after being relieved and wondered what had happened. The need for the rest of the treatment was obvious.

Floating Kidney

A kidney that is dislodged from its natural position is called a floating kidney. This condition may happen when the body is subjected to great trauma such as an auto accident, a high fall or a blow in the unprotected region of the back above the hipbones where the kidneys are not shielded by bony structure.

A floating kidney can, in some cases, be felt underneath the abdominal wall in the front of the body. With the patient lying on the back, the Creative Healer, using a gentle oscillating movement of the hand can guide the kidney deeper into the abdomen until it disappears from the touch. Since a dislodged kidney tends to sag, the direction in which to guide it is slightly upward as well as inward towards the spine. Another way in which a dislodged kidney may become apparent is when the hands are placed in position to find the kidney spot. Normally the shape of the body fills the operator's hands but, on the side of the dislodged kidney there is a concave shaped hollow in the fleshy area between the rib and the hipbone. If this is the case and the dislodged kidney cannot be felt on the forward side of the body, no attempt is made to position the kidney.

➤ ➤ ➤CAUTION: In all cases of floating kidney, only step 2, replacing substance, the feeding part of the kidney treatment, is given. When the kidneys are not in position even the gentle contact of the diagonal stroke or the drainage movement would be too much and might further dislodge them. By repeating the feeding at regular intervals once or twice a week for several weeks the dislodged kidney will come back into position, because of the increase in nerve life.

If the muscles of the abdominal wall are not strong enough to properly support the abdominal organs, a floating kidney will not come into position by administering the feeding treatment. In such cases an abdominal support may be needed. See abdominal support in the protruding abdomen treatment, page 5–29.

Kidney Stones

According to Mr. Stephenson, kidney stones are frequently caused by particles of earth that were not removed from vegetables when they were washed. Such particles can pass through the walls of the intestines into the blood stream and be lodged in the minute cavities of the kidneys where urine is formed.

If kidney function is poor, slime may be present in these cavities because of sluggish action, which, together with the particle of earth, can produce a hard, flinty formation as it is acted upon by the acids and alkalis eliminated from the blood stream. The shape of the stone will conform exactly to the cavity in which it is formed. Some people have kidney stones for years, even until they die, without ever being aware of them. A kidney stone may be as small as the head of a pin and can still cause great pain. Its sharp projections may abrade the walls of the ureter causing a swelling, which blocks the passage of the stone.

The kidneys have great capacity. Many people live successfully with only one kidney, which is entirely adequate for a long, normal life, if it is kept functioning properly. From all that precedes, it is clear that neither kidney stones, nor even a totally missing kidney, need prevent a person from living a full life.

➤➤➤CAUTION: If they are causing trouble, kidney stones should be removed surgically. No attempt should be undertaken to make them pass.

If, however, during a treatment, the patient should experience a sudden, strong pain in the unprotected region of the kidneys, below the ribs or further around toward the front and lower in the abdomen, he/she may be passing a small kidney stone. If this is believed to be the case (such a patient has usually had the same experience before) apply step 4 of the kidney treatment, the drainage movement (repeated below).

Always perform the drainage movement over both kidneys simultaneously, even if only one kidney is affected. Place both palms slightly above the level of the kidney spots on the patient's back, the thumbs vertical and together at the spine. Hold fingers together as a unit and extended toward the sides so that the first and second fingers are level with the tips of the thumbs but wide apart. Draw your hands in this configuration until finger tips rest in the soft, unsupported tissue just beneath the ribs. Then move hands horizontally to the sides of the body creating a double vacuum with thumbs following the fingers (not joining thumb with fingers), which draws the surplus secretion of the kidneys into the bladder.

Have the patient sip water or other liquid more or less continuously during the drainage movement. Persist with the drainage movement and the patient's sipping of liquid until the stone has dropped into the bladder and the pain has ceased. The drainage movement, combined with the liquid, helps to draw the stone through the ureters.

If things are kept in motion with the drainage treatment and the sipped liquid, the stone may be prevented from irritating the tube through which it is passing. This will prevent the tube from seizing the stone and developing a swelling which might cause a blockage.

Should a kidney treatment be needed, it is safe to give it to a patient known to have stones. The gentleness of the treatment should reassure the patient and the Creative Healer of the safety of the treatment in these cases.

Other Kidney Problems

Locked Kidneys

Inability to urinate may result from locked kidneys. When the kidneys are locked, no urine is present in the bladder and none is descending from the kidneys. They appear to have ceased functioning. When this is the condition, the kidney treatment is invaluable. It may, at times, be even spectacular. The person may, during the second step of the treatment (removing heat), ask to be excused in order to void the bladder.

Inability to Urinate

If the inability to urinate is not due to locked kidneys, but is of a more emotional nature, prolonged attempts to bring about urination often result in no response. This is because the person is too upset by the attempts to be able to relax sufficiently. In this case, have the person stand or kneel in a tub of warm water and lift the water and let it flow over the abdomen, genital area and legs. The sound of the flowing water and the vacuum that draws upon the urethra as the water flows down over the penis or vagina, enables the person to begin the flow of urine. Results can be obtained in 15 to 20 minutes. This is true in cases where there is already an extreme distention of the bladder.

Dribbling of Urine

Dribbling of urine is usually caused by the valve of the urethra not shutting off. Treat the bed wetting spots, page 5–51. It may also be due to a fallen bladder or injury in childbirth.

Overloaded Kidneys

When the kidneys function poorly and their capacity is reduced, they are not equal to the load imposed upon them by the body; we can say they are overloaded. The overloading of the kidneys may also be caused by unwittingly followed practices, such as drinking too much or too little. When the kidneys are overloaded, the sweat glands may have to augment their function—profuse perspiration may set in. Such perspiring may be an indication that the kidneys need treatment.

Kidney Problems and Posture

A person with a kidney problem should sit erect as much as possible. It may be helpful to place a small pillow in the kidney region, so that the person can move up firmly against it and keep the back in position for any considerable length of time.

From the writings of Joseph B. Stephenson

Mr. Hamilton told me on my first visit to him, "My doctor said 'well, Barney, you are a healthy man but your kidneys are all shot. They are breaking up and your urine test shows matter and blood. I am afraid we can't do anything for you.' "

"Then this is when I call Mr. Stephenson," said Hamilton, "so I had my wife call you this morning."

Hamilton was suffering acute pain so I gave him a short treatment and promised to come and stay up with him all night as his case called for a gentle treatment to relieve the pain and take the inflammation out.

I sat up with him three nights. He had no more pain but I gave him 10 treatments in all. I had just started on the tenth when the doorbell rang. He said, "I believe that is the doctor. Go into the den and wait there." So, I did.

The doctor came up the stairs and said, "Well, Barney, I have great news for you. Your urine test proved that your kidneys are all healed up and your urine is 98% pure. It is a miracle and a great discovery for the medical doctors. That new medicine I gave you last week seems to be just the thing."

Then Mr. Hamilton called me in and said, "I want the doctor to meet the medicine that has made me well."

I walked into the room, got a sickening shake of the hand from the doctor who said to Mr. Hamilton, "Did you take the medicine I gave you?"

"Open that cupboard door, doctor." There was the bottle. The cover had never been removed. The doctor put it in his pocket and turned to me.

"Stephenson, you have saved this man's life but how you do these things is a mystery and we doctors don't like it."

All I said was, "I'm sorry, doctor, but this man has too much to live for to die at age fifty."

Hamilton said, "Send me your bill, doctor; I think I will be able to go to work soon."

That doctor never spoke to me again.

The Bladder

One function of the bladder is to act as a cooling system for the body. When a person is not able to void the the bladder completely, urine is retained and the bladder heats up. When there is severe burning, pain, or bleeding when passing urine and especially when the person is middle-aged or elderly, there is frequently a sagged condition of the tissues of the abdomen, marked by a slightly curved crease on the surface of the abdomen, 1 or 20 inches above the pubic bones. This sagged condition results in a kinking of the urethra, which does not allow the bladder to empty completely. The heat of the body then works on the retained urine and makes it much stronger than it would normally be. This may be the main or even the sole cause of the discomfort.

Teach the patient to use the tips of the four fingers on one hand to stroke upwards along the middle line of the body from the pubic bone to below the navel while voiding the bladder. This lifting stroke done repeatedly will overcome the kinking of the urethra and enable the the bladder to empty completely. It may also take the distressing aspect away from what is referred to as a bladder infection. The stroking described above may also be helpful in some prostate conditions.

When the bladder heats up above normal temperature, the urine changes color and organisms develop that are not usually present. Urination may be accompanied by a sharp burning sensation and the patient may suffer pain and discomfort in the entire abdominal region.

There are three different methods of treating an inflamed bladder.

Method 1: Cooling Treatment Without Touching

Move your slightly cupped hand about 1 inch above the heated area at the rate of 40 to 50 strokes a minute, tracing circle-like paths. As the hand moves off the inflamed area, let it relax. Stroke with the thought of drawing the heat out of the inflamed abdomen by creating something like a cooling breeze. Though this action is compared to a cooling breeze, it has nothing to do with fanning but is carried out in long uninterrupted strokes that extend over the entire area in whatever direction they are performed. Continue the strokes until the goal is achieved and the bladder area, when gently contacted, feels normal. This may take 20 minutes of stroking. When completed, stop all further treatment for that session. If, after two applications of the cooling treatment, (see cooling treatment, page 8–27) the abdomen is still inflamed, recommend that the patient see a physician.

Method 2: Milk

The patient is asked to drink up to 1 quart of milk replacing one of his meals, drinking only as much of the quart as possible, without forcing. The mucous forming properties will cool the walls of the bladder and reduce the inflammation, while the extra amount of fluid taken will bring about additional urination, flushing the bladder and effectively cleansing it of the irritating substances that have formed in it.

Method 3: Treating the Bladder Spots

This method may be used except when there is a fever.

Location of bladder spots

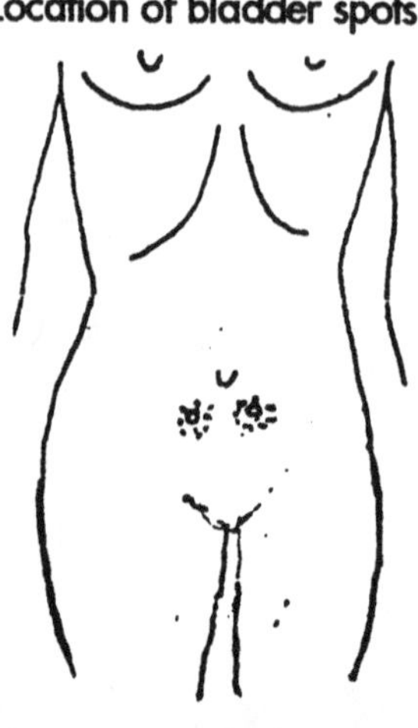

➧ **Step 1: Locate bladder spots.** To locate the bladder spots on an average-sized adult, place the heel of your hand just above the pubic bone, and the thumb and the middle finger on the lower abdomen at a distance of 4 1/2 to 5 inches apart. The thumb and finger will lay on the centers of the bladder spots. These spots are actually to be thought of as small areas.

➧ **Step 2: Create vacuum.** Begin vacuum-type movements on the lateral-most positions on the spots, proceed to the uppermost central position, then draw nearly straight downward and release. Your finger and thumb carry the surface tissue with them all through the small movement except at the release. Even then the contact with the surface is not broken. The movement is small because the spots are areas of only about 3/4 of an inch square. It might be thought of as describing a circle but more nearly approximates a semi-circle. The intention of the Creative Healer is to gather and feed the natural secretions to the wall of the bladder to cool it.

➧ **Step 3:** When treating the bladder also press the bed wetting spots, below.

Sensitivity in the Region of the Pubic Bone

Sometimes when there is a bladder or groin condition or hernia, the region above the pubic bone is sensitive. The condition may be relieved by rolling the fingertips in an upward lifting movement that glides over the edge of the pubic bone in a horizontal direction toward the groin area. When comfort is obtained, proceed with whatever treatment is appropriate.

Bed Wetting

Bed wetting spots in a man

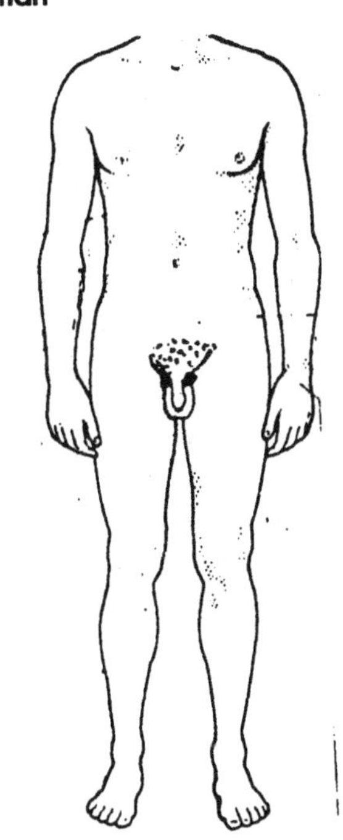

Bed wetting, or any involuntary form of release of urine, is caused by improper functioning of the sphincter muscle that acts as a valve for the control outlet of the bladder. This valve functions hydraulically by gravity. That is, the proper weight of blood or pressure flow must get in and around the sphincter muscle to give it the strength to fulfill its valve function without fail.

For a child less than 5 years old, it is reasonable to give the child the benefit of the doubt. The child may not be trying to control the bladder. But after that age a genuine mental effort is made to effect that control. If unsuccessful, it is generally caused by a failure of this sphincter muscle to function properly. The same is true for bed wetting in the case of adults. Bed wetting, or any other involuntary release of urine that may occur when one gets excited or frightened or laughs very heartily, is generally caused by a malfunctioning of this valve.

The sphincter muscle valve is restored to proper functioning by pressing two spots Mr. Stephenson named the bed wetting spots. This treatment is important whenever there is a dribbling of urine because the valve of the urethra does not completely shut off even though there may be no conspicuous prolapse of muscles, bladder or other organs affecting the bladder by pressing on it. These spots are found in the same location for both male and female.

Position

The patient lies down; the Creative Healer stands at the right side.

➧ **Step 1: Locate spots.** To locate them on a male, place your left hand on his right shoulder and place the palm of your right hand on his lower abdomen. The fingers are extended toward his feet, and the axis of the index finger is parallel to the spine. Curl the index finger over the pubic bone next to and to the right of the penis. The first depression or cavity encountered is the right bed wetting spot. The left one is found in the corresponding manner.

Bed wetting spots in a woman

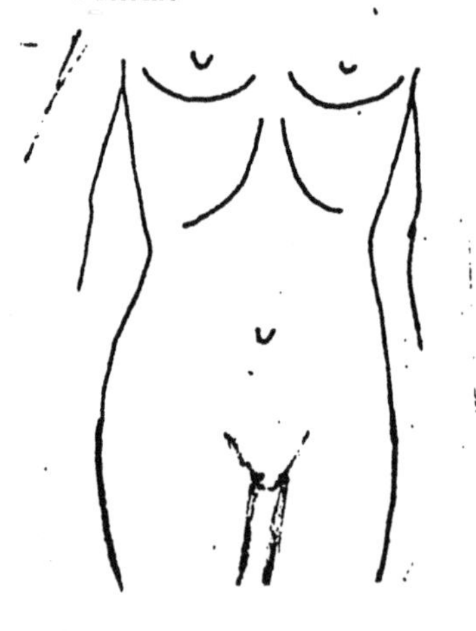

In a woman, the spots are located as in the male, allowing for the separating width of a penis.

➧ **Step 2: Press to restore muscle control.** When the index finger has contacted the cavity, pause for a moment to make sure that the person is relaxed. Then press quite firmly, toward the head, parallel to the spine, using the pad of the index finger. Release at once. The pressing almost always causes a sharp sensation that produces an involuntary recoil within the body. This recoil is what is desired as it causes the muscles to be drawn up and reestablishes their control. When repeated on the left side, the recoil is anticipated by the patient so ask that a big breath be taken and wait until the exhalation is almost complete, then be ready to press the left spot. This action affects not only the muscles surrounding the sphincter of the bladder but also other muscles on the floor of the pelvis and the muscles fanning out from there on each side into the abdomen. With this in view, one can understand the effect of pressing the bed wetting spots in cases of female disorders.

If needed, these bed wetting spots may be treated in conjunction with the pressing of the spots for bearing down pain, in order to further strengthen the muscles in the pelvic floor. The sharp sensation caused by pressing usually subsides within 1 minute or so. On the rare occasions in which the pain is still felt 5 minutes after the initial pressure, press the spot again, this time sustaining the pressure. This will cause the painful sensation to vanish.

With a male it is possible that the cords extending from the testicles into the body lie across one of the cavities. Be sure to push them aside before applying the pressure.

When treating a child, apply only half the pressure employed when treating an adult.

Frequency

The treatment is usually applied only once. It may be repeated within 1 week or even sooner if necessary. In some cases of female disorders, repeated applications may be indicated.

Do not overlook the value of treating the bed wetting spots when there is a possible but not conspicuous prolapse of the muscles, the bladder, or other organs affecting the bladder. These spots are of vital importance whenever there is dribbling of urine caused by the valve of the urethra not shutting off completely.

Chapter 6 ♦ The Arms and Hands

When considering treatments for arm problems, we begin to appreciate a basic truth about the functioning of our bodies because in the arms we can easily see the consequences of obstruction to the flow of blood and nerve life (life force).

Pain in the arm is known by many more specific names depending on the location of the discomfort and the parts involved but pain or lack of power in the arm is caused by interference with the flow of life to that arm. When life force to the arm is obstructed, the arm will cry out in pain to be "fed" or nourished. Something needed for normal functioning is missing in this extremity.

We may or may not know the specific causes of pain in the arm, but bodies are created in such a way that we can find the places where obstructions occur and resolve the problem by using our hands in the correct way for that location.

Arm treatments always include the general treatment because this gives attention to the muscles parallel to the spine; the basic arm treatment aims to restore the flow of life. In traditional massage techniques, the arm stroke is upward toward the heart; Mr. Stephenson believed that this is not necessary, therefore arm stroking in Creative Healing is downward toward the hand.

Arm Treatments

Basic Treatment for Pain in the Arm

This basic arm treatment is given first in every arm problem because its aim is to restore the flow of life. If this treatment does not relieve the problem, the blockage is further down the arm and other subsequent treatments will be in order.

Always begin with the general treatment (see page 1–8) and give attention to the muscles parallel to the spine. These muscles have much to do with the strength and energy needed to use the arms. The filter areas are cleaned to insure the flow of blood to the arms. The basic arm treatment is described for the right arm. For the left arm, substitute left for right, counterclockwise and clockwise, everywhere in the description.

Position

To start, the patient sits with hands relaxed in the lap. The Creative Healer sits behind.

Breaking-up movements

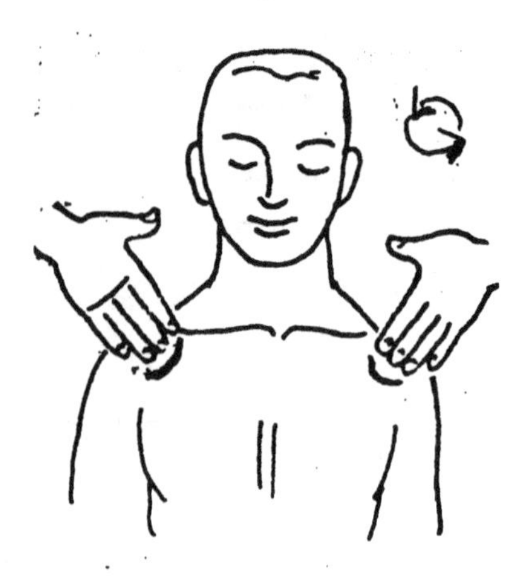

Step 1: Breaking up movement. Place one hand on one shoulder for support and, with the oiled middle fingers of your other hand, perform a gentle, clockwise, circular breaking up movement over the painful area. It lies just inside the most prominent surface of the shoulder joint on the front side. If there is any congestion at this spot, it will be sensitive and hot. Congestion here is responsible for much of the pain. Sometimes there is an epaulette-like calcium deposit over the patient's shoulder. This will be dissolved and the repeated application of the basic arm treatment allows the circulation to carry the deposit away. If the circular massage is too painful for the patient, do step 2 first. Continue it until the congestion in the shoulder spot can be broken up without the patient suffering.

Creating a vacuum

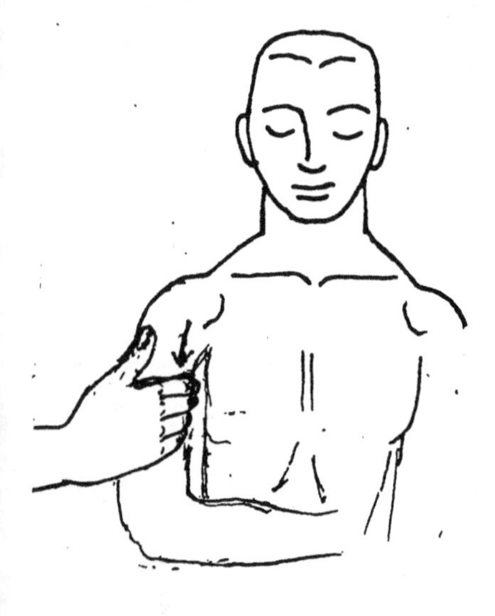

Step 2: Create a vacuum. Still seated as before, your right hand is in position to create a vacuum down the front of the upper arm (a little toward the inside). Your palm moves down on the outside of the arm while your cupped fingers create the vacuum toward the front of the arm. The middle finger plays the major role; hold your thumb perpendicular to the hand so that the arm will not be squeezed.

Step 3: Break up congestion. An obstruction about half the size of a pea might be found part way down the arm, lodged in the muscle. It may feel like a string of beads. Break up the obstruction with the circular motion, directed downward, of the index or middle finger. Alternate this circular breaking up movement with the vacuum movement. The first aims to dissolve the obstruction, the second, to stimulate the arterial circulation and flow of life down the arm.

Reposition cartilage

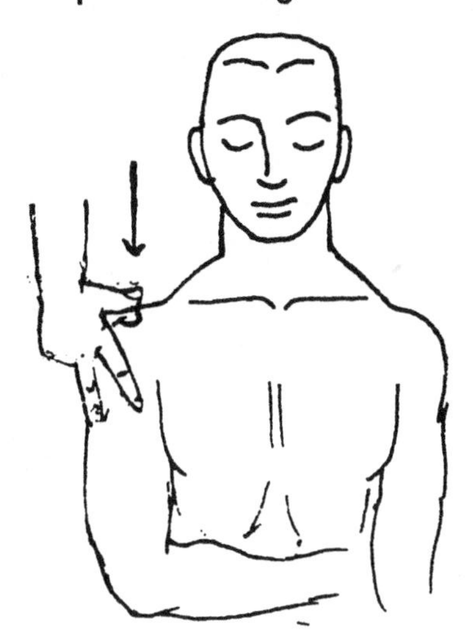

Step 4: Reposition cartilage. If, in addition to the pain, the patient has difficulty raising the arm above the head, the cartilage on top of the shoulder is out of place. Thc flow of life force is restored through a nerve center located at the first flat surface at the edge and top of the arm. This spot is toward the front of the body from the extension of the shoulder ridge that forms one boundary of the filter area in the general treatment. If in doubt about the correct position for the thumb, have the patient raise the left arm (assuming this arm is normal) so that the elbow is higher than the shoulder. When the arm is moved horizontally and vertically, the center in question will be recognized as a neutral point, from which the arm pivots.

For treatment the patient's arm should lie relaxed with hand in the lap. Stand toward the right of the patient with your left hand on the left shoulder. Form a tripod with the thumb and the index and middle fingers of your right hand. Place the tripod so that the thumb is on the nerve center, the index finger is to the front and middle finger is to the back of the patient's arm. Your right arm should be held so that the wrist is straight and the elbow is considerably above the hand. Support your right hand by pressing your body against it. With your left hand draw the patient's body firmly against your body. Now press straight down with your thumb, gently leaning the weight of your body on your hand. When you feel the spot yield under your thumb pressure, ask the patient to gradually relax the shoulder, lowering it, but still keeping the forearm in place and the body straight (don't lean). Follow through, increasing the pressure until the shoulder is fully relaxed and lowered, offering no resistance, and you feel that the yield has come to completion.

The treatment will have replaced any displacement of cartilage and any contraction that may have been present will have been relieved. The pressure applied in this repositioning of cartilage is the heaviest exerted in any of the Creative Healing work.

Step 5: Scissor-like massage. To bring circulation where the pressure was applied, massage with the thumb and fingers in a scissor-like motion all around the spot.

Step 6: Patient raises arm. Instruct the patient to bend the arm at the elbow with the palm facing the front of the body, then fully extend the arm upward without any help, to an erect, hand-above-head position, the upper arm in contact with the ear. The head should not be tilted. This act of raising the arm is part of the treatment. When the raising can be accomplished, it is evidence of the effectiveness of the treatment in having restored a strong flow of life and circulation through the regions treated and into the arm.

Frequency

In extreme cases, like bursitis, it may be necessary to treat once a day for 3 successive days. Then space the treatments at longer intervals, to avoid causing an irritation to the regions treated.

From the writings of Joseph B. Stephenson

It was about 9:30 when the phone rang. I said, "Hello," then the voice at the other end said, "Stephenson, this is Doctor X. I have a pain in my arm and have not slept one minute in three days. Are you still busy?"

"No," I said, "the last one has just left so you can come. No one will see you."

"It's not that, but I will be there in 15 minutes." He was, and I started to treat him.

Then I said, "By the way, Doctor, this is what you call arthritis?"

He said, "Yes."

"Then why come to me? You doctors say that."

About 15 minutes later, he told me I was getting results.

"Oh, yes," I said, "I have cases like this every day. I have had as many as 19 in one day."

"And you give everyone the same relief as you are giving me?"

"Yes, it's my work. You see, Doctor, I do know my work, don't you think?"

"I am sure of it and you hurt so little."

Just by this time I was ready to put the cartilage back in place, so I got set to put my thumb on the spot, told the doctor to lower his arm slowly, and I pushed and pushed. I felt him wilting but the cartilage went right home.

"Feel sick, Doctor?"

"Yes, a little sick at the stomach."

"Just lie down for a few minutes."

He did and I brought him a glass of water. Soon he felt better.

So I said, "Well, Doctor, raise your arm."

He did and when he got it up so far he could not hide his emotions any longer. The tears came into his eyes and rolled down his cheeks. "To think I can use my arm again. We tell people that they will never get the use of their arm and here you fix the whole thing in a few minutes."

"Well, you see a man can only accomplish according to the capacity of his brain. You see no help; I see help quickly, because the pain makes the biggest men shed tears just as you did the night you were kept awake."

"How do you know I did?"

"Oh, just because I did. I had it for three months once until I increased the capacity of my mind to know how I should do for myself what I had done for others. I found a way."

"I want to tell you, Stephenson, I tried everything before I made up my mind to come to you."

"Yes, I know you would not want your medical friends or your patients to know that you had come to me. But Doctor, you have nothing to be afraid of; a Creative Healer never tells who his other patients were, or who they are, or what they came for."

Added Treatment for the Arm that Cannot be Raised

Check the spine for a cord-like formation that may extend from between the vertebrae and continue parallel to the ribs on the side affected. These cord-like formations emanating from the spine may be detected by palpating, though frequently not apparent to the eye or discernible to the superficial touch. An effective means of palpating is the scissors treatment (see page 3–5) applied from the sacrum to the base of the neck. These formations are usually detectable for 2 or 3 inches following a course parallel to the ribs, then buried at its end in the tissues.

➧ **Step 1: Quarter twist.** To correct such formations start at the end of the cord near the spine. Bury the cord in the tissue by repeated quarter twists (see page 3–3). Proceed in this manner as far out from the spine as possible to replace the displaced substance. Alternate the quarter twists by stroking away from the spine, parallel to the ribs in the areas beyond those of the quarter twist. Apply the breaking up movement in the area beyond that of the quarter twist. By alternating these three movements, the whole formation can be made to disappear.

Frequency

Repeat this treatment as necessary. In addition, break up any contraction in muscles high up under the arm between the shoulder blade and the ribs. A painful residual contraction is often found in this region and may be relieved by the treatment for contraction of muscles around the shoulder blade, page 3–15.

Forearm Nerve Treatment

If there is pain in the forearm, or if, after the basic treatment for arm pain, the circulation in the forearm still seems slow, the following treatment may be appropriate. This description continues to deal with the right arm.

Position

The patients sits. The Creative Healer sits to the right side of and facing the patient.

➧ **Step 1: Hand placement.** Place your right hand, palm upward, beneath the patient's elbow, whose arm is partially flexed, with the thumb side up. Your thumb will rest just above the process of the ulnar bone on the inner side of the elbow.

➧ **Step 2: Stimulating a nerve.** With the outside edge of your thumb, at its last joint, perform a quick pressing movement upward away from the ulnar process, and then immediately make a hook-like movement turning an angle of about 90° toward the patient's hand. The turn of the angle is made where a nerve is crossed. The crossing of this nerve causes the patient to feel a sharp, stimulating action.

Stimulating a nerve in patient's right arm

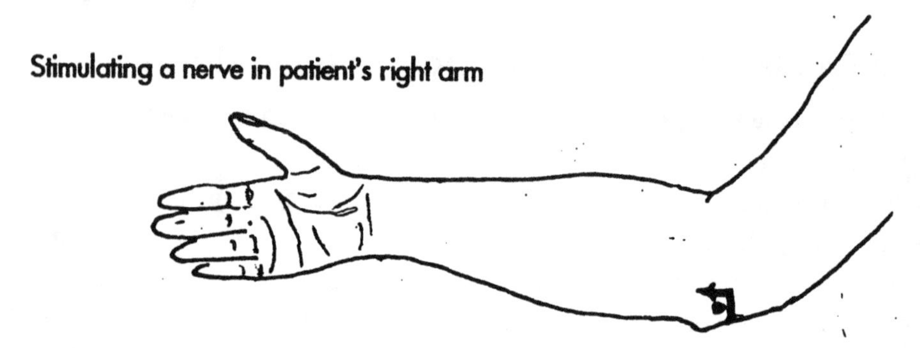

➧ **Step 3: Vacuum stroking.** To encourage circulation, support the edge of the patient's hand, thumb upward, in your left palm and create a vacuum by placing your right palm over the upper (radial) surface of the forearm and stroking from the elbow downward. Let your thumb and fingers contact the arm in a natural manner. Your fingertips point toward the patient's elbow. Be sure to finish out the vacuum movement, to bring circulation through the wrist into the hand.

Vacuum stroking

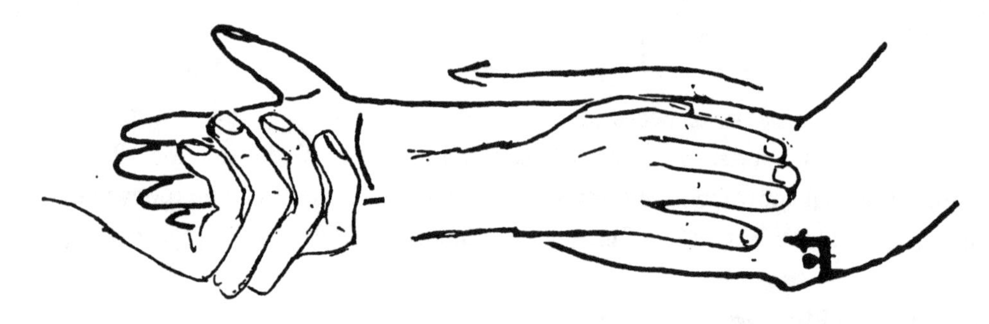

Frequency

In extreme cases, it may be necessary to treat once a day for 3 consecutive days. After that, space the treatments farther apart, to avoid causing an irritation to the regions treated.

Carpal Tunnel: Middle and Lower Forearm

Position

Patient sits; Creative Healer sits in front, facing patient. To work on the middle and lower regions of the forearm, support the patient's forearm, palm downward, with your left hand.

➧ **Step 1: Clearing the tunnel.** Several inches above the wrist, the tendon crosses to the radial bone; if the area is congested, it is as though the nerve passes through a blocked tunnel. This spot can be very tender and sore until it is cleaned out. At the spot, clear out any obstruction beneath the tendon using the thumb or fingertips of the right hand in a downward movement toward the hand.

➧ **Step 2: Stroking.** Stroke with the flat sides of the fingers of your right hand, down over the tunnel area and out to the patient's fingertips, to encourage blood flow into the hand and fingers.

Carpal Tunnel Syndrome

Many people today have repetitive action problems in their arms, wrists and hands. Many are diagnosed as carpal tunnel when the median nerve is not truly being compressed by the carpal ligament and other tissues.

Whatever the cause, the treatment is as follows:

➧ **Step 1:** Administer the basic pain in the arm treatment, at the beginning of this chapter.

➧ **Step 2:** Apply a medium-to-firm breakup massage first to muscles along spine and shoulder blade, then to muscles on the back of arm just above elbow, and finally to the muscles just below elbow on thumb side of arm.

➧ **Step 3:** On the top side of the arm, apply firm strokes with the thumb, starting ~5 inches from the wrist and ending at a "vee" an inch or two above the wrist.

➧ **Step 4:** Administer the wrist treatment, page 6–12, then the wrist filter area pump action, step 2 on page 6–13.

➧ **Step 5:** Apply the breakup massage to web between thumb and hand, to the heel of the hand, then to all of the hand.

➧ **Step 6:** Apply the vacuum stroke down the forearm from elbow to hand.

Ganglion

A ganglion is best understood by realizing that a displacement of tissue has taken place in the area beneath its location. This displacement causes the visual aspect of ganglion as a lump or puff or protrusion often seen at the wrist but occurring also at other joints and usually of a fluid nature.

Position

Patient sits; Creative Healer sits in front, facing patient.

➧ **Step 1: Placement of thumbs.** Place the thumbs, one on top of the other, on top of the protruding ganglion sustaining a firm positive pressure.

➧ **Step 2: Wrist circumduction.** While maintaining the pressure, circumduct the wrist and the ganglion will disappear as though it had burst. The protrusion of cartilage will have been corrected at the same time or it will be corrected by carrying through an additional circumduction of the wrist while the pressure contact is firmly sustained.

➧ **Step 3: Breaking up circles.** In cases where the arm is used in rough work and a ganglion has been ignored for some time or perhaps repeated surgery has been employed only to have the ganglion recur, and the first two steps are unsuccessful, use breaking up circles as for breaking up adhesions* and ask the patient to refrain from hard, heavy straining of the wrist. This may allow the tissues involved to soften and then the full treatment might be successful.

If the repositioned tissues do not strengthen or stay in place, the person should avoid extreme dorsal flexing. In addition, a coin covered with tape, centered over the area and bound firmly to the wrist may furnish the needed support.

*Breaking up movements for adhesions and ganglion should be tiny, gentle circles carrying the skin with your fingers or thumb. Deep heavy movements might cause a reinforcement of the problem. These movements should be around the edges, mainly working toward the center.

Exercise for Extended Arms

When shoulder muscles have been stretched outward by overusing the arms in activites such as hedge clipping or long hours at the computer, pulling the shoulders back 5 or 6 times as though coming to attention in the military, will allow these muscles to be stretched in the opposite direction and give relief. (See also pillow relief, below)

Arm Problems: Pillow Relief

Many daily activities require extending the arms in front of the body; this tends to pull the shoulder blade from its proper position in the back of the body toward the side, and the shoulder blade becomes dislocated. This is compounded by sleeping too long on either side with the arms extended forward. Such positions will not let adequate circulation get to the muscles and the night's sleep does not allow a sufficient recovery.

A pillow can help a person with arm troubles achieve the best sleeping positions. The pillow should be large, but not too firm and used as follows: Lie on the back and hug the pillow to the chest with a portion of the pillow extending above the shoulders. Roll over on the pillow onto the stomach. Bring the affected arm along the side of the body. Roll slightly onto the affected side so that the weight is borne by the front side of the affected shoulder. That shoulder is pressed against the bed with sufficient pressure to push the shoulder blade toward the back where it belongs and slack is provided for the tissues beneath and around the blade. This slack allows for increased circulation to reach the affected muscles.

The upper portion of the pillow can be adjusted so that the neck and head extend in a straight line with the trunk. The unaffected leg and arm can be drawn up into a most restful position. The body appears to be draped over the supporting pillow.

Arms that Cannot Rest at Night

A person may suffer from extreme discomfort, numbness, uneasiness or pain in the arms, preventing rest at night. The condition causes much movement of the arms from one position to another. People who use their arms and hands a great deal in their daily activities, such as electricians, carpenters, painters and housewives may suffer from this condition.

To correct such a condition, check the bottom edge of the deltoid muscle on the outer side of the upper arm. There, you will find a little knot or convulsed spot in the muscles. This denotes a muscle-bound condition.

To treat the condition, bring your curled index finger down over the arm from above so that the curled part of the finger strokes through and beyond the knotted spot. Do this until the knot softens and reduces somewhat in size. It will become less sensitive. Clean out and open up the surrounding area.

The person can be shown to self administer this treatment, and instructed to do it at night before retiring.

Throwing the Arm Away

This problem is caused by throwing an object that is too light to correspond to the forces of momentum generated. In the throwing motion the arm is forcefully and swiftly extended and if this motion does not carry a heavy enough weight, the sudden stopping of the arm at the end of extension is so abrupt that it can dislocate the arm. A similar problem can happen when the arm is jerked forward suddenly such as when a water skier is pulled up out of the water.

The dislocation occurs at the shoulder attachment where the motion is most sharply opposed by the inertia of the body. The trouble spot is found at the innermost edge of the scapula (shoulder blade), just above the spine of the scapula. The muscles there will be crossed and overlapped.

To relieve this condition, use the thumb to press inward and downward just above the scapula. Repeat these gliding motions until you feel the muscles lie smooth and parallel and no longer crossed. Once this has been done, the recovery is rapid. See also pillow relief for arm problems, on page 6-8.

Elbow Treatments

Elbow Problems

Arm, showing bones and joints

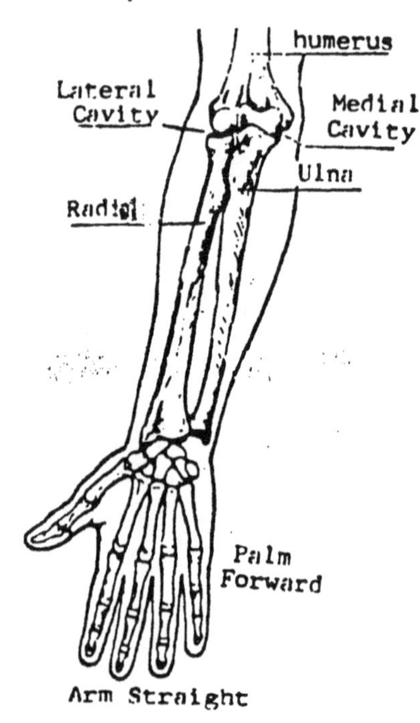

The Elbow: Lateral Side

Visualize the arm hanging straight down with the palm forward. Two cartilages are situated in the elbow, one on the outside (lateral side) and one on the inside (medial side) between the ulna and the humerus bones. These sometimes get out of place and cause arm trouble. This first treatment applies particularly to an arm that cannot be fully flexed or extended; this explanation refers to treating the right arm.

Position

Patients sits; Creative Healer sits facing the patient.

➧ **Step 1: Replacing cartilage.** To treat the outside (lateral) cartilage, place your right hand, palm upward, under the patient's elbow; patient's arm is partially flexed, thumb side up. Then, place the bony tip of your index finger in the cavity between the ulna and the humerus, where the cartilage to be replaced is located, and press on this cartilage. At the same time, oppose that pressure with the thumb, placed in lengthwise contact, at the junction of the ulna and humerus on the inside (medial side) of the elbow.

➧ **Step 2: Extend and rotate arm.** At the same time as the pressure of the right index finger is gradually increased at the elbow, extend the patient's arm with your left hand rotating the arm as you extend it counterclockwise. You will feel the cartilage move into place as the arm is fully extended.

The Elbow: Medial Side

This second treatment applies where there has been severe interference with the circulation and the flow of nerve life through the forearm to the hand. If this interference is prolonged the forearm and hand may develop a high fever and cause peeling or shedding of the skin in the affected areas or the arm and hand may appear withered, the skin drawn tight and white, and the muscles atrophied. In these cases this elbow treatment is highly valuable.

➧ **Step 1: Pressing and rolling**. To treat the displaced cartilage on the inner (medial) side of the elbow, your right hand should, again, be under the patient's elbow. The patient's arm must be extended. The index finger opposes the thumb pressure in the position it held in the treatment for the lateral cartilage. The pressure is exerted with the bony tip of the thumb in a slightly rolling motion in and slightly up in a groove.

Step 2: Flexing and repeating. After you feel the cartilage yield, have the patient flex the arm. It may be necessary to repeat the whole procedure several times to encourage circulation and the feeling of life and strength returning to the forearm.

Tennis Elbow

A person with tennis elbow will feel a general incapacity in the use of the arm and/or feel numbness and tingling and cannot get into a restful position either in waking or sleeping. There may be snapping and cracking when the shoulder blade is circumducted and erroneously ascribed to a bad joint. But there is no joint connecting the shoulder blade with the body skeleton except where the shoulder attaches to the collar bone (clavicle). Otherwise, the shoulder is completely suspended in muscle and a muscular contraction in this region can have a distorting effect. The person may have stiff and contracted muscles above the shoulder blade that lead upward into the neck, and have difficulty turning the neck when backing up the car. There may also be stiffness in muscles below the shoulder blade that encircle to the front of the body over the ribs. The shoulder blade will often be carried more to the side of the body than to the back where it belongs. The area between the shoulder blade (scapula) and the ribs, high up toward the back of the armpit is where residual contractions in the muscles will cause trouble. The person is usually not able to point out this location when describing the pain.

Position

The patient sits and the Creative Healer stands next to the patient's unaffected side, facing the patient's shoulder after performing step 1.

Step 1: Clear circulation. The pain in the arm treatment is administered first to insure good circulation to the entire arm (see page 6–2).

Step 2: Relief action. To treat the right arm, place the four fingers of the right hand under the patient's armpit toward the back and gently but persistently circumduct the shoulder, using the left hand merely to assist. Circumduction is accomplished by carrying the shoulder up toward the head then toward the spine. The right hand fingertips press inward and high up under the armpit between the shoulder blade and the ribs toward the spine. The patient may find this painful at first, but proceed positively once or twice and then let it rest so that circulation can enter. When the circumduction is begun again, it will be much less painful.

Frequency

The treatment may have to be repeated at another time and should be continued until all contractions disappear and the cracking and popping has stopped. The muscles will again lie smooth. It is possible to achieve this in 1 treatment.

Treating Tennis Elbow on a Muscular Person

Ask a heavily muscled person to lie on the unaffected side and rest the troubled forearm on the hip, with head to the foot of the couch. The circumduction can then be done with both hands. Place your 4 fingers in the same place and place the tip of the other thumb high up toward the back of the armpit. Both hands can assist in the circumduction, carrying the whole structure around by grasping the front of the shoulder joint with the cupped palm. This pressure stretches the muscles. Continue the pressure with the heel of the hand gliding downward over the shoulder blade toward the spine. This breaks up any remaining contraction. The muscles actually change their shape so that the shoulder blade can once again resume its natural position.

Wrist Treatments

The Wrist

Sometimes the wrist, with its eight small bones, is painful and lacks the power to pick up an object. This could be caused by displaced cartilage, which leads to obstructed circulation and stiffness, or restricted motion.

Position

Patient sits; Creative Healer sits in front, facing patient.

Checking for displacement

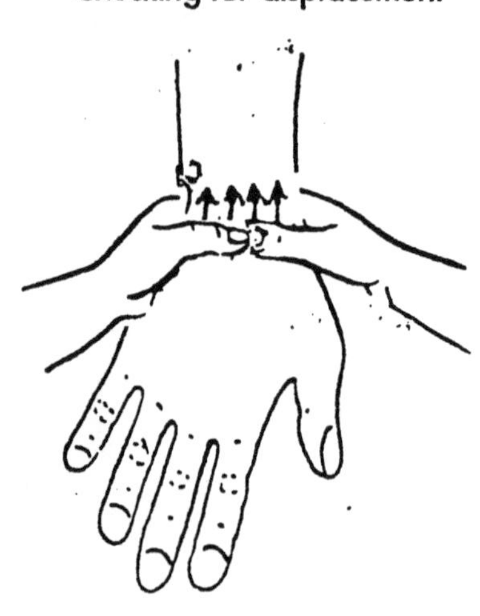

➧ **Step 1: Check for displacement.** Place the patient's wrist, with the hand palm down (pronated) limply on your two abutted index fingers. Roll the wrist over your fingers by stroking upward over it with your thumbs toward the arm. Under this stroking action, the moving joints (articulations) within the wrist will move freely if they are unobstructed. At the same time, this action permits the detection of any obstruction, if the wrist motion is limited. Such an obstruction is most often caused by displaced cartilage.

➧ **Step 2: Thumb placement.** If in the stroking action you detect a stiff or unyielding spot between the bones, place the tip of the nearer thumb on it. Then, grasping the patient's hand between yours, without changing the position of your thumbs and index fingers, move the patient's hand downward, and away from the point of contact. At the same time, press on the spot with your thumb. This movement of the hand down and away from the spot provides the greatest possible opening of the space between the bones. This is the same principle used in replacing substance in the cervicals of the neck by moving the head away from the thumb pressure.

➧ **Step 3: Stretch and circumduct.** Continue the pressure by superimposing the second thumb on the first, clasp the patient's hand, and stretch the arm by pulling on the hand, to put the wrist in tension. Stretch the wrist and arm until the arm is fully extended. Then circumduct the hand until it is fully extended and in line with the arm. As you do this, you will feel the cartilage yield and move into position. Then, after releasing the hand for a moment, flex it back (dorsally) upon the forearm.

To test for regained strength ask the patient to use the hand in a firm handclasp with yours. The weakness should have disappeared.

Wrist Filter Area

Position

Patient sits; Creative Healer sits in front, facing patient.

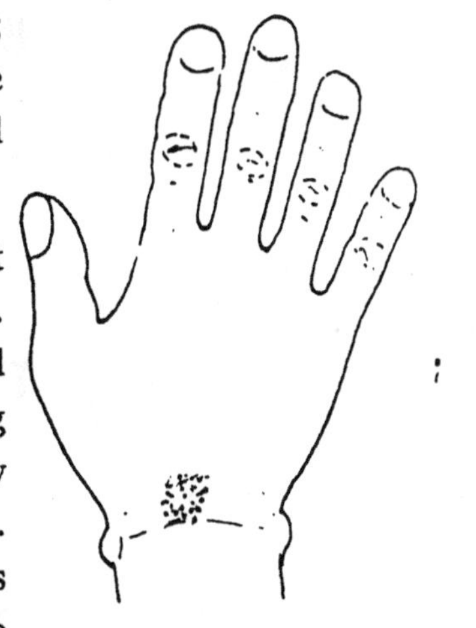

Wrist filter

➧ **Step 1: Locate the cavity.** A special depression is located on the back (dorsal side) of the wrist between the bones slightly to the thumb side of the center line; it is the wrist filter. The wrist filter regulates the deep arterial flow of blood to the hand and fingers. Regulation of flow is achieved by a combined breaking up and pumping movement.

➧ **Step 2: Breaking up and pumping movement.** The patient's hand (start with the right hand) is extended, dorsal side up, and supported on your left palm. Place your right index finger in the center of the cavity described above and perform a pumping movement down toward the patient's hand. This pumping movement is a circle with pressure exerted on the downward movement only without lifting the finger on the upward movement but also without pressure. Release the pressure and return your finger to the original position. Repeat this action making certain to carry the surface tissue along during the entire downward movement. The circulation to the hand will be stimulated by the downward, pump-like displacing stroke. This treatment is applied whenever circulation to the hand and fingers is impaired.

➧ **Step 3: Stroking the hand.** With the person's hand still supported by your left hand, use your right hand with fingers extended to stroke lightly from the wrist to the tips of the fingers bringing in better circulation. This stroking is downward only.

Hand Treatments

The Hands

Position

Patient sits; Creative Healer sits in front, facing patient.

➧ **Step 1: Stroking.** If the hand lacks circulation and if the fingers are white and the skin feels taut, place the patient's palm on your left palm and stroke with your right hand, from wrist to fingertips. Your hand is at right angles to the patient's hand, with your thumb leading. Alternate this stroking with the treatment of the filter area on the wrist (see above).

➧ **Step 2: Roll, rotate and twist.** To loosen the taut skin on any finger and relieve its whiteness, take that finger between your thumb and fingers and work on it gently, with a rolling, rotating, and slightly twisting motion taking the surface tissue along. The movement is toward the fingertips. There may be a particularly tight spot on one (or several) of the phalanges. This spot is usually near the center of the bone, on the dorsal side. Such a spot will require special loosening up by the circular breaking up movement.

When circulation is fully restored to the hand and fingers, the fingers will be pink to the tips and beneath the nails.

Bent Fingers from Shortened Tendon

Hold patient's hand, palm down and slightly cupped in both your hands. Work gently on palm on each side of the tendon simultaneously to break up on the sides of the tendon. The person can be taught to work on the tendon. If done often the fingers will begin to straighten and the tendon to disappear.

The Fingers: Non-Systemic Arthritis (Osteoarthritis)

Arthritis is essentially a disease of the joints. Mr. Stephenson thought it occurred in two forms, systemic and non-systemic. Systemic is at large in the system and can attack any joint. This he called rheumatoid arthritis. Non-systemic is more localized and is commonly called osteo or wear-and-tear arthritis and can be due to traumatic injury.

The development of cartilaginous protrusions at the finger joints is largely due to repeated chilling of the joints, i.e., with sudden changes from hot to cold water. The trouble is found most frequently in women and can be very painful.

Repeated chilling starts an inflammation within the capsule of the joint. This causes internal swelling and expansion of the tissues. The resulting pressure extrudes the cartilage out of the joint and tears loose the ligaments that reinforce the fibrous capsule of the joint. Nature in its effort at compensation, deposits bony tissue at the extremities of the affected joints. This is done to, once again, provide tuberosities into which the ligaments can insert themselves. If much bony tissue has been deposited, it will not be possible to mold the cartilages back into place. As long as the swollen spots are still red and painful, the cartilage will yield to the treatment because the bony tissue has not yet hardened.

People with swollen finger joints often exercise their fingers by forced flexing with the idea of preventing the stiffening of the joints. This will only add to the pressure already present in the capsule and increase breakdown of the capsule.

Actually, if joints with protruding cartilages of this type are not treated, they will normally not become immobilized (ankylosed). They may become disfigured by swelling and restricted in freedom of motion, but they do not suffer deformation.

Position

Patient sits; Creative Healer sits in front, facing patient.

Replacing cartilage

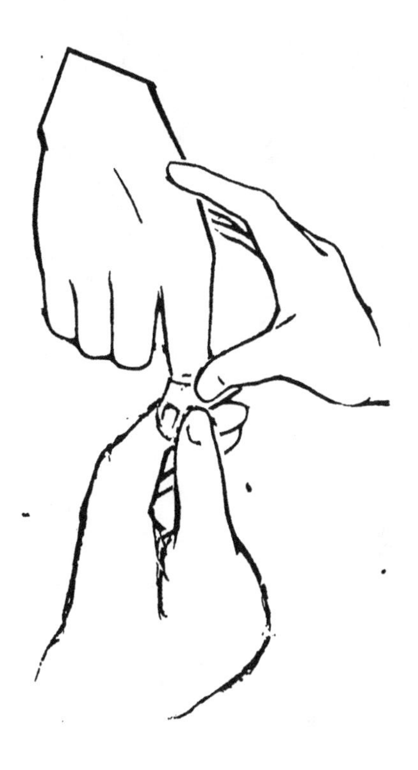

➧ **Step 1: Replace cartilage.** Protrusions at the finger joints can occur only on the two sides of the joint and slightly toward the upper surface. Imagine two plane surfaces, one horizontal on the top of a flat finger joint, and the other vertical up the side of the joint. The protruding cartilage is located on the part of the joint between these two surfaces. Place the problem joint over your right index finger and flex the patient's finger at the joint, downward to the right or left: opposite the side of the protrusion. This opens the space into which the cartilage is to be returned. Then press on the cartilage with the bony tip of your right thumb until the cartilage warms and moves back into the joint.

➧ **Step 2: Extend, press and flex.** When the cartilage has gone into place, alternately flex and extend the finger slowly to insure proper articulation and remold the cartilage within the joint.

➧ **Step 3:** Massage the joint with your thumb on one side and index finger on the other. Movement is circular with pressure on downward (toward fingertips) stroke only. Carry tissue with your fingers.

Restoring finger joints for better circulation can be self-administered.

Example from Creative Healers

For six months I have used a teaspoon of brewers yeast in the juice of half a lemon each morning before eating anything else for stiff and achy fingers, wrists and shoulders, with good results.

Jammed Finger

When the finger is hit on the end and pushed back into the hand as in sports, do the cartilage replacement at each knuckle. Pull the finger straight away from hand (traction) and work up into hand around the base of the finger with breakup movement.

Hand or Nail Fungus

If hands are badly affected by fungus, the problem may penetrate to the nails and the roots of the nails, threatening to destroy them. In stubborn cases, results have been achieved by soaking them in a solution of black tea. The tea may also be used for the feet. The tea bath must be made from English black tea, Pekoe or Orange Pekoe varieties. Bathe affected part in drinking-strength tea at comfortably warm temperature for 12 to 15 minutes. Repeat as needed.

Chapter 7 ♦ The Legs

Creative Ability to Combine Treatments

The Creative Healer's work, particularly on the legs, rests on combining and applying previously learned principles, intuitively followed. By the time treatments have been completed on weak or incapacited legs, the Creative Healer will realize the importance of her/his intuition in obtaining results both expected and unanticipated.

The practice of combining and applying various treatments fosters creativity in the Creative Healer's power to visualize her/his intentions. This is one of the greatest powers with which mankind is endowed, a power just waiting to be developed. The Creative Healer may begin then to understand the true significance of the name "Creative Healing," given to this work. What is stated in the groin and leg treatments applies also to treatments for any part of the body. A good example of treating a condition by combining various treatments is in treating allergies. See page 9–16 for this discussion.

A crippled leg, defined as either partial or total loss of leg function, could be the result of a condition in the back or the hip joint or in a ligament running under the thigh up to the groin. It could be caused by a sprained or dislocated groin, or could be a consequence of polio.

The upper sciatic nerve, as it leaves the groin, descends on the median side of the thigh where it lies deep within the flesh. It passes through the popliteal space under the knee between the hamstrings on the median side, continues on the median side of the calf down to the foot and finally to the great toe and the one adjacent to it. This nerve is important with reference to the back, the thigh, the lower leg and the foot. A weakness of this nerve may contribute greatly to a severe rocking inward of the foot.

Similarly, if the lower sciatic nerve is not intact, it can cause complete incapacity to move the leg forward so that it is merely dragged. In this condition the hipbone seems incapable of moving freely.

To treat many problems in the legs one must understand the important role the sciatic nerves play and be able to combine any and all leg treatments pertinent to the case.

Mr. Stephenson's Concept of the Sciatic Nerves

A nerve harness fits over the rump of the human body, a harness that conforms roughly to the pattern of an inverted candelabra with a stand or trunk and paired branches to either side. In this human "candelabra," many collateral branches extend between the basic ones, and the entire nerve network converges principally into the great sciatic nerves that descend down the legs. A horseman knows that if the harness on the rump of a horse is out of position, distorted or asymmetrical, or if the single tree (pulling bar) is crooked, it is obvious what should be done to correct the situation. It should be just as obvious to the Creative Healer what should be done to correct the nerve harness on the human body when it is out of position.

The sciatic region is the main distribution center for power and life going to the legs. Mr. Stephenson understood this and further described what he called the upper and lower sciatic nerves. He saw that long-standing interference with these nerves creates a sagged condition extending the full length of the leg, causing obstruction and contraction of the muscles controlled by the sciatic nerves. The discomfort in moving the body imposed by this condition can be likened to that suffered by a woman wearing a long skirt and standing with her heels on the hem of the skirt—attempts at bending over are constrained and uncomfortable. Here again, it is obvious to the Creative Healer that sciatic nerve constraint must be released, unlocked and freed up throughout the length of the leg. This is accomplished by working on the muscles and freeing the sciatic nerve paths.

The upper sciatic nerve descends through the groin and feeds the front and inner (anterior and medial) aspects of the leg down into the foot. If the nerve sags, it can be compared to a puppet that cannot be controlled because the string has too much slack. Again, it is obvious that the slack or sag must be taken out. This is accomplished by the treatment at the groin as described in the upper leg treatment and pertains particularly to the area from the knee to the groin.

According to Mr. Stephenson's experience, a person may be 80 years of age, have suffered from sciatica for 10 years and yet can be completely and permanently healed of this trouble, possibly in 1 treatment.

From the writings of Joseph B. Stephenson

The Doctor with Sciatica

About 9:30 one night the doorbell rang. I went down to answer. I saw Dr. X standing at the door. He said, "Stephenson, I am sorry I came late but I have such pain down my leg. I wonder if you would give me relief."

I said, "Come in. I never turn down anyone who is suffering pain."

I took him upstairs and had him get ready for his treatment. In a few minutes I said, "Stand up." He stood slowly.

"No," I said, "stand up." Naturally he sat down then stood up.

"Why, the pain is all gone except a little above the ankles."

I put my hand down, used a little pressure on the seat of trouble. "Now," I said, "how is that?"

"Why it feels all right," he said.

"Stand up and stoop down, Doctor," I said.

"You know me then?"

"Doctor, a man who has done as much for me as you did could never be forgotten. You may have forgotten me but me forget you, never. I am glad you came to me, but no one will ever know you were here if you don't tell them."

"Stephenson, you know you have a mysterious power over people. You were always a mystery to me."

"Well, Doctor, it if hurts, come again."

But he had no reason to come again.

Next morning he was in the hospital walking around as if nothing happened. The other doctors kept saying to him, "You must have been to Johnstown last night."

But all he would say was, "Mind your own damned business."

Whole Leg Treatments

The Filter Areas

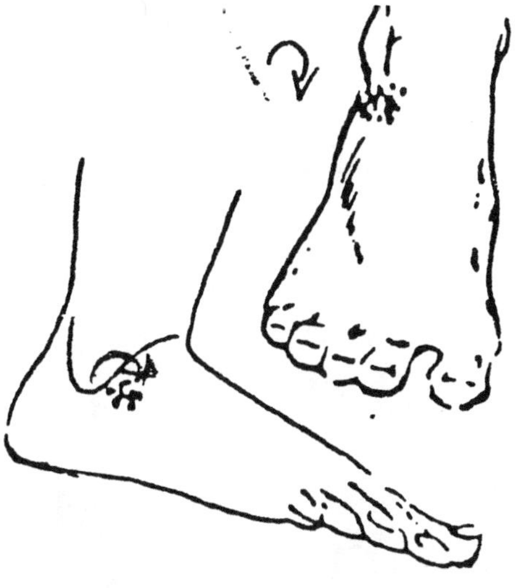

Each of the three filter areas (at the neck, wrists and ankles) acts not only as a regulating center but also in a more specific and localized manner as a distributing center. This fact is most apparent in the ankles where eliminating the circulatory disturbance caused by congestion is more obvious. At times, the ankle filters display an unusual degree of sensitivity and/or swelling. Working on the filters for 1 or 2 minutes regulates the deep arterial flow into the toes so that the blood can then return through the natural channels. This restores normal circulation and the sensitivity disappears.

Filter areas for the feet

The filters' regulatory function is more comprehensive than the redistributing function. While the filter's redistributing function is temporary—when normal circulation is restored, this function ceases—the regulating function is continuous. However, the filters have another vital function, that of "sizing" the blood stream to accommodate blood flow into both large and small vessels in the body. Blood flowing through the more minute vessels of the fingers and toes or through the larger muscles and more massive tissues of the arms and legs must be "sized" accordingly. Thus, filters in the ankles and wrists act not only as regulators and distributors but also break down the blood stream so that it might enter the more minute vessels.

A filter area in the body acts like an oil filter in a car. It will not allow the blood to pass unless it has the right consistency and is free of clots or other thickened elements. Such elements accumulate behind the filter until they are sufficiently broken down to pass through it. The filter automatically stands as a safeguard against clots that could be a threat to the heart or other areas of circulation and restores normal functioning by helping to break down thickened blood to normal size. Thus, the filter areas are both a safeguard against improper blood and a mechanism for imparting to such blood the proper consistency. In this way circulation through these areas is restored to normal functioning.

➤ ➤ ➤CAUTION: Varicose veins on the medial side of the lower leg 6 inches up from the ankle bone should never be massaged.

Crippled Leg: Groin Treatment for the Upper Sciatic Nerve (Thigh)

This treatment concerns a crippled leg that is totally or partially paralyzed, not because of polio but because of a condition in the groin. There is a distinction but the two cases are often confused. The crippled leg discussed here is caused by a sprain or dislocation in the groin. The groin massage frees nerve life and permits circulation in the leg.

The groin injury is often brought on when footing gives way, such as stepping into a gopher hole or on a board that breaks, or may be caused by trauma suffered in a fall or car accident. The problem can also be the consequence of overdoing a physical activity. A groin sprain or dislocation can cause trouble ranging from a slight incapacity to complete paralysis of the leg. Also, a weakness of the upper sciatic nerve in connection with the back, the thigh, the lower leg, and the foot can contribute to a severe rocking inwards (pronation) of the foot.

In crippled leg cases, check the groin first. Sciatica is a case in point even though the sciatic treatment is adequate for most cases. If the sciatic treatment does not remedy the condition, the problem might be in the groin. If, for example, after the sciatica treatment the patient can raise one leg easily but the other only with difficulty, this is an indication to check out the groin. The groin treatment plays the role of a continuation of the sciatica treatment, when needed.

When the groin treatment seems to be appropriate, it is useful to compare both sides of the groin area. This will often help you to discover what is needed.

The treatment is described for the right leg. The changes to be made when the left leg is treated, are indicated later.

Position

The patient lies on the back. The Creative Healer sits to the patient's right.

Massage upward

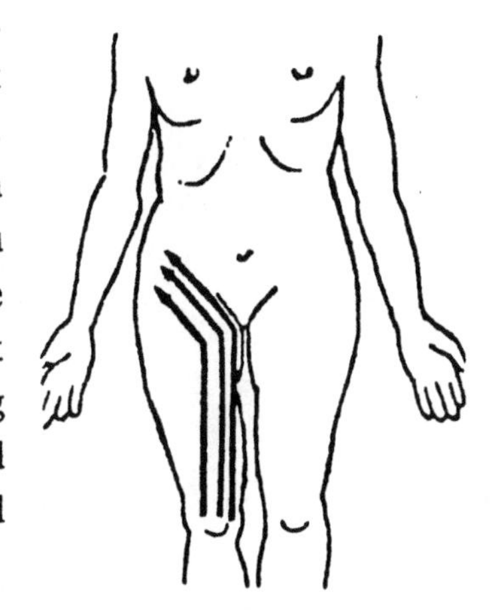

➧ **Step 1: Massage upward.** Massage with medium pressure upward from the knee to the groin over the inner (median) and front (anterior) sides of the thigh. Hold your hand in flat contact with the tissue, generally with the thumb adjacent to the fingers. Massage upward with the fingers leading and the palm following. The entire movement, especially that part approaching the groin, must be slow in order to give the tissues time to respond. If during the upward massage you encounter swelling, inflammation or heat, draw out the heat and relieve the inflammation and swelling with light strokes of the palm while the fingers effect the drainage. As the hand reaches the groin, move it laterally outward following the natural fold of the groin. The massage must have this upward and outward direction, because tissues that slip out of place in the groin will move downward and toward the median line of the body.

➧ **Step 2: To find a kernel.** Next, the massage follows the extension of the upper sciatic nerve ascending from the knee up to the groin. As you perform this massage, you might encounter a little below the fold of the groin a formation that is harder than the adjacent tissue. Mr. Stephenson called this a kernel. In the less severe cases, when there is no kernel, there will have been a slight dislocation or sprain and the massage will restore the use of the leg in one treatment. If not, repeat the treatment at weekly intervals, continuing until all heat and swelling are gone and the tissues feel completely normal.

Replace the kernel

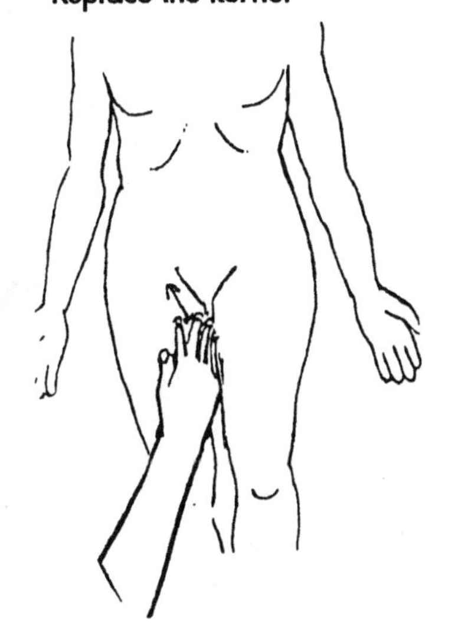

➧ **Step 3: Replacing the kernel.** When there is a kernel, massage the upper leg using medium pressure until swelling and heat are removed. Then continue to massage, but with more pressure, letting the hand follow the path of the upper sciatic nerve. Place the hand more specifically so that the index and middle finger are precisely over the nerve path. The discovery of just where this nerve path lies within the thigh will come about as you continue to work with actual cases. It will be evidenced largely by the degree of sensitivity registered by the patient and is more toward the medial than the anterior of the thigh. As the hand moves toward the groin, the kernel will be caught in the space between the index and middle fingers. Enough pressure must be exerted, especially by these two fingers, to get the kernel to yield. As it does so, it will move upward and then appear to move outward, away from the median line. Allow it to do so and follow it on the path it wants to take. As stated earlier, the massage movement must be very slow as it approaches the groin so that tissues can move back into place. Once the kernel has yielded, it will no longer be felt. It will have dropped into place, flush with the adjacent tissues.

➧ **Step 4: Strengthening massage.** Continue to massage from the knee to the groin much as before to allow life and circulation to pour strongly into the leg. The only difference from the previous massage is that the hand is now held so that the thumb is separated from the fingers to span the front of the thigh. Use medium pressure. This strengthening massage is administered for 10 to 15 minutes after the replacement of the kernel, which releases the flow of life and circulation into the leg. If needed, apply the massage to the lower part of the leg also from the foot to the knee. The thumb again spans the front of the leg over the shin.

It is important to stress that while the massage for the upper front of the leg (when considering the groin) is always performed in the upward direction, the massage for the path of the lower sciatic nerve is performed in the downward direction on the back of the leg. Both of these movements, however, encourage the flow of life force and circulation.

➧ **Step 5: Drawing the leg up.** After having performed the strengthening massage in step 4, as described, ask the patient to draw up the leg, flexing it at the knee and letting the foot drag on the surface on which he is reclining. In severe cases, as the leg is drawn further upward, the patient will lose control and the leg will fall outward, away from the median. If this occurs, place the leg down and massage it additionally with the strengthening massage for about 10 minutes. If the patient's control of the leg is still not sufficient to hold it in position, have the patient return at weekly intervals as needed. If the leg, when drawn up as before, now holds its position, the patient is ready to stand and use the leg.

Frequency

Repeat the treatment at weekly intervals, as needed.

Treating the Left Leg

The principles of the treatment are the same for the left leg as for the right, the only difference lies in the use of the hand.

When treating the right leg, trace the path of the nerve channel with the index and middle finger, and the kernel is caught in the space between them. In treating the left leg, trace the nerve path with the thumb, and catch the kernel in the notch on the inner side of the end bone (distal phalange) of the thumb.

Weak Legs and Feet

"Slack" in the Nerve Path

There are instances in which attention to the groin is needed, but no apparent problem can be found, even when comparing the right and left groin. These problems may have been caused by long-standing interference from the back or lower back, evidenced by what is found when the treatment for sciatica is given. They may be cases where more obscure incapacities are indicated, perhaps by an asymmetric response of the body in certain situations, or cases where the need for a groin treatment rests almost entirely on intuitive insight. All these somewhat indefinite cases may be due to "too much slack" in the nerve path from knee to groin. These cases may be compared to the puppeteer who cannot get the arms and legs of the puppet to respond properly because there is too much slack in the strings and, just as the puppet strings have to be shortened, so must work be done on these leg cases to take the slack out of the nerve path in the thigh and groin.

Position
The patient lies on the back. The Creative Healer sits at the patient's right.

➧ **Step 1: Upward massage.** Stroke upward toward the groin as though there is a kernel present (see crippled leg, groin treatment, page 7–4). Remember to always work upward and lift very firmly up the nerve channel in the thigh through the groin all the way to the notch just below the anterior superior spine of the ilium. Perform this work, guided only by the thought of removing the downward sag in the nerve channel, a sag which, of course, can only be visualized but not felt.

This massage will often restore the capacity that you, the Creative Healer, intended. Other limitations that you had not anticipated nor even been aware of, may be helped also. For example, a patient may report being now able to climb stairs two steps at a time with equal power in both legs, or that a long-standing numbness in some part of the thigh or leg has disappeared, or being able to again kick a football.

As mentioned in the sciatica treatment, the kidneys are at fault in some of the cases in which the sciatica treatment does not help; see sciatica treatment, page 3–23. In such cases, it is not enough to do the kidney treatment. Seepage may be occurring from the kidneys into a triangular region deep within the groin (the Scarpus triangle) so that the groin massage is later needed in order to drain out this seepage. (This Scarpus triangle, being a natural sump, is also a region where pus may gather in cases of tuberculosis of the spine.)

The Lower Sciatic Nerve (Thigh)

The path of the lower sciatic nerve passes just behind the lateral-most projection of the head of the femur (greater trochanter). When the patient sits or lies down, the path of the lower sciatic is just under the leg, not on the side. The channel retains its slightly posterior position as it continues beneath the lateral hamstring tendon, approximately a hand's breadth above the joint of the knee. Remaining on the medial side of this tendon and close to it, it passes through the space behind the knee and descends through the lower leg, extends through the foot and connects with the three outer toes.

Freeing adhesions to the bone

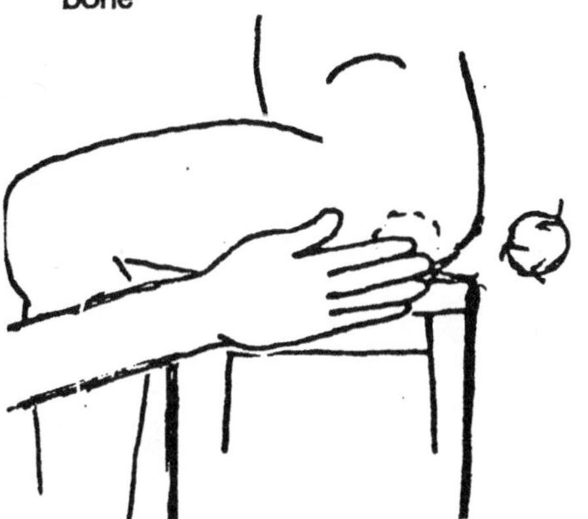

Moderate to severe incapacity of the leg can result from obstructions in this channel. At times, a large and firm lumpy obstruction will be found in the region at, or just behind and lower than, the trochanter. Such an obstruction must be broken up and then followed by downward stroking, performed by the middle finger, over the narrow channel of the lower sciatic nerve.

Position
The patient sits. The Creative Healer sits facing the patient.

➧ **Step 1: Downward stroking to detect obstructions.** With mainly the third finger, stroke downward along the lower sciatic nerve channel all the way down to and through the popliteal space behind the knee. This may reveal chain-like, beaded or knotty formations along the channel. Break these up and clear them by downward stroking with the hand. If it seems that the nerve has become attached to the bone, work with the specific intent of freeing it from this adhesion. Such adhesions occur mainly in the upper half of the channel. The person who suffers from this condition may find it difficult or even impossible to bear any weight on the leg without the support of a cane. When shifting weight onto the afflicted leg, the patient will flinch and say that the leg is painful and can't bear the weight. This all results from the apparent adhesion of the nerve to the bone, although such an obstruction or adhesion never seems detectable by x-rays. The condition is progressive and especially incapacitating to the elderly.

The leg can often be restored to normal function in a single session. Sometimes repeated treatments may be necessary.

➧ **Step 2: Treatment lying down.** In some cases, when there are many lumps in the region of the trochanter, have the patient lie prone (face down) in order to give a very thorough breaking up treatment to the obstructed area. Along with this, give a thorough stroking over this area. Perform the stroking in an upward direction except for the narrow channel of the lower sciatic nerve over which stroking occurs downward only.

➧ **Step 3: Follow-up for slack nerve.** When the obstructions are sufficiently cleared, ask the patient to be seated again and administer the downward stroking with the middle finger along the channel as far as needed.

Apply these steps to the condition along the nerve channel that appears like the puckering caused by the pulling of a thread in a piece of material. This trouble is frequently caused by prolonged sitting or sitting on unsuitable supports.

➧ **Step 4: Another check for restrictions.** Another way to check for restrictions caused by the lower sciatic nerve is to ask the patient, when lying on back with legs extended, to rotate the feet and legs inward one at a time, so that the medial sides of the feet are lying fully on the surface of the bed. This position will reveal to the patient any tight or sore areas.

If assistance is needed to do this, lift upward from beneath the trochanter to help in the rotation. In doing so you can determine what else needs to be freed for the patient to be able to do this movement independently.

Mr. Stephenson saw the vital importance of the sciatic nerves for controlling the motion of the legs.

The Sciatic Nerves in Lower Legs and Feet

In the treatments for upper and lower sciatic nerves, the paths of the two sciatic nerves through the lower legs and feet were outlined. The upper sciatic nerve feeds principally to the big toe and the one next to it while the lower sciatic nerve feeds principally to the three outside toes. The sciatic nerves are contacted by the Creative Healer along these paths in certain places. A patient with sciatic trouble may have pressure so great in one or both legs that sitting down is impossible or difficult. Work on the ankle filters (see page 7–27) to reduce the pressures so that the patient may sit with reasonable comfort to receive the treatment

The sciatic nerves in the legs and feet

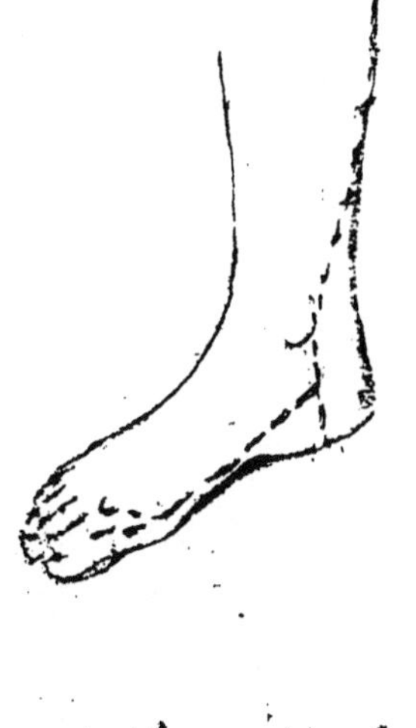

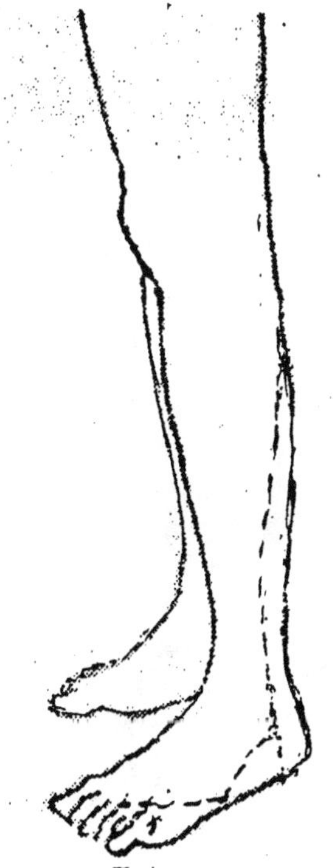

Upper Nerve Path

➧ **Step 1: The upper sciatic nerve.** The path of the upper sciatic nerve is traced down the medial side of the calf into the foot. Treat the nerve indirectly by massage to the calf muscles and other tissues at the nerve center midway down the calf, and again at the ankle spot.

➧ **Step 2: First specific contact.** The spot to be treated is on the medial side of the heel on the line joining the center of the malleolus (ankle bone that protrudes) and the center of the plantar surface beneath the heel, slightly upward from the midpoint of that line. According to Mr. Stephenson, a nerve and artery pair embedded in a common sheath descends from the calf to this point and fork there apart from each other into two paths, which then proceed, one in a more downward, the other in a more forward direction of the foot. The forking point becomes congested and has to be cleaned out. This is done by a stroking movement with gentle pressure. Start the stroking at the upper side of the forking point and follow a line directed toward the toes midway between the horizontal and vertical direction. It can also fan out to follow the two paths. If the spot appears extremely sensitive continue to work in the indicated direction but more gently until the sensitivity decreases and the congestion is cleaned out.

➧ **Step 3: Second specific contact.** A small notch is located on a promontory on the end near the heel of the first metatarsus (medial foot bone), midway between its lateral side and its base. This is near the base of the large toe. Here the nerve may become displaced and must be centered up in the notch. With the edge of the first or second phalange of the index finger, not alongside and not underneath, but midway in between, draw from either side of the notch, to center the nerves and arteries involved in the notch. The tissues here will always be sensitive to any but moderate pressure.

Lower Nerve Path

➧ **Step 1: The lower sciatic nerve.** The path of the lower sciatic nerve is on the front of the lower leg to the outside of the bone (tibia) on the center. It is located in the groove between the tibia and fibula (closer to the fibula).

➧ **Step 2: First specific contact.** About 4 inches above the ankle filter spot for the adult will be a sensitive ridge-like tendonous formation. The action here is to stroke down in a vertical line. The nerve over which you are stroking passes beneath this tendon through a tunnel formation and it is here that a sensitive obstruction occurs. Stroke down over this line with the thought of breaking up the obstruction and feeding life on through the tunnel.

Sometimes the nerve has adhered to the fibula and requires loosening with the edge of your index finger before the whole region can be softened up. If the front part of the patient's foot goes down prematurely while placing the heel to the ground in normal walking and the patient cannot prevent this from happening, an adhesion of the nerve to the fibula is likely. Such a person may be unable to raise the front part of the foot while standing, as long as the heel is on the ground. The correction for this is made at the place described above except in cases of stroke. However, even then the spot might be successfully worked on in the latter stages of recovery.

➧ **Step 3: Second point of contact.** This point of contact is on the outer side of the heel (opposite step 2 of upper sciatic nerve: first specific contact). This area is more toward the back of the foot than the upper sciatic area.

Here again stroke halfway between the vertical and horizontal and use more of a positive pressure and less of a stroking movement than on the medial side. While on the medial side we want to accomplish a gentle cleaning out, here we want to give a few sharp contacts or gentle spurt-like actions. Sometimes just one spurt-like action will suffice. Both on the medial (upper sciatic) and the lateral (lower sciatic) side, the areas in question are recognized by their sensitivity.

Adductor Muscles and Tendon

Frequently the adductor muscles that draw the legs together and the tendon by which they are attached to the pubic bone need attention because they may be very sore. The tendon may be particularly sensitive at the place where it inserts into the pubic bone.

Position

The patient lies on the back. The Creative Healer sits to the patient's right.

➧ **Step 1:** Stroke upward over the muscles and tendon on the front of the upper leg with medium pressure until the tissues begin to feel more natural.

➧ **Step 2:** Grasp the tendon, at its insertion into the pubic bone, with the thumb and the first two fingers. The fingers should surround the tendon at this place and the fingertips should make breaking up circles; alternate this movement with circumducting the tendon itself. This clears out accumulated obstruction so that full circulation can again reestablish itself and the soreness will disappear.

The patient may self-administer this treatment, especially as it refers to treating the tendon at its insertion into the pubic bone.

In lingering cases, when trouble in the leg persists, it may be necessary to check out and treat the sciatic nerve channels, the groin and even the kidneys. When the kidneys faulty functioning results in seepage, the effects extend far downward.

From the writings of Joseph B. Stephenson

The Lady who had not Walked for Eight Years

This woman was a nurse who married and had a baby. After the baby came, she and the doctor found that she had lost the use of her legs. Why the doctor did not know the reason is more than I can understand. Why he could not see that her back did not go into place and that the life lines were pinched and why didn't she feel the pinch and tell the doctor?

Anyhow, her husband's mother was sick with a heart ailment. He brought her to me since the heart is one of the easiest things for me to help. I soon had his mother doing her own work again. So, seeing what I had done for her, he talked to his wife.

"What can that man do? The doctor specialist can do nothing; I don't believe in these kind of men," she said.

But one day he took her out for a ride, stopped in front of my house and said, "Now, you are going to see Mr. Stephenson," and he just took her in his arms and carried her in and upstairs.

I went into the room and told him how to get her ready. Then I gave her her first treatment for about 15 minutes and said, "Stand up."

She said, "I cannot. I have not stood up for nearly eight years."

I said again in a sharp voice, "I said stand up; do as I tell you."

She did and she stood for about three minutes then she said, "I feel sick in the stomach."

I said, "You must stand every day until you get tired. The more you stand the sooner I can make you walk."

"You are going to make me walk again?"

"Yes, if you are not too stubborn."

The next time she came she never spoke a word but took her treatment like a lady. "So your mind has improved a little since last week?"

"I don't care what you say; you cannot spoil the joy I feel because I have improved so much since last week. I too, know I am going to walk again and you don't know what that means."

"Oh yes, I do. You see I could not walk for four years myself."

I had her walking a little but I had to leave town for a rest so I set the time when she would get the full use of her legs, on my birthday.

"Where will you be that day?" she asked.

I said, "In California. On the 12th of June, from noon until 12:30 keep your mind on me and watch the clock. As the clock strikes twelve get ready to stand up. At 12:30 you will walk."

She did and when I returned home she came to show me how well she could walk.

Wonderful? No. Just knowing how to keep the blood stream running smoothly with great anticipation.

Inguinal Treatment

When all other treatments have been given in the area of the groin and it still does not feel right, the inguinal treatment may resolve the problem. The patient may experience a difference when climbing stairs or, after the femur has been repositioned to the hipbone, there may remain a crunching or clunking sound in the hip when the leg is lifted up or set back down. This is usually more of an annoyance than a source of pain.

Position

The patient stands. The Creative Healer sits facing the patient.

➧ **Step 1: Positioning.** If the right leg is to be treated, use the right hand with the thumb outspread, separated from the finger unit. Place the hand on the patient's thigh so that the thumb rests in a long line of contact parallel to, and just below, the inguinal ligament. (The inguinal ligament extends from the top of the hip bone to the pubic bone.) The tip of the thumb rests just below the midpoint of this ligament, taken lengthwise. Extend the fingers around the leg on its inner side, just below the groin area. Rest your elbow on your own leg to effect a firm support.

➧ **Step 2: Action of patient.** Ask the patient to place his/her right hand on your right shoulder for a solid, steady support. Ask the patient to relax the right knee, allowing it to bend slightly. As this happens, the weight of the body descends on your thumb, so that the thumb "bears up" the soft tissues that lie in the inguinal channel. It bears these tissues up in such a manner as never to override them or move above them but will always remain below them so that any movement will carry them upward. The amount of motion needed to obtain the desired result and restore normal function is very slight, although the action itself has to be carried out in a firm and positive manner.

To treat the left leg, interchange right and left everywhere in the preceding description.

Frequency

The treatment can be repeated if necessary at the same session, after the patient has moved about to test the lifting already done.

Upper Leg Treatments

Posterior of Thigh: Dull Legs

The Strumming Treatment

A feeling of numbness or a feeling of lifelessness as though the leg were going dead characterizes a problem we have called dull legs. There may also be pain and the trouble may extend down the entire leg but the problem is mostly in the thigh. The cause is usually not in the great sciatic nerve that descends down the center line on the back of the thigh. Mr. Stephenson saw that the cause was in the ligamentous, tendonous or muscular tissues and the nerves adjacent to the sit-upon bone (ischial) that run down the backside of the thigh to the popliteal space under the knee. There is a disarrangement of these tissues that obstructs the flow of life and blood to the leg, due mainly to the compressive forces received when the body is in the sitting position.

For the legs to function well, the muscles of the thigh must be normalized and toned up with massage to the front and back, mostly in the upward direction, with the one exception of massaging the lower sciatic nerve channel on the lateral back of the thigh.

An important element in ongoing numbness and slow progress in recovery is inadequate seating arrangements such as sitting too long or sitting on a faulty surface that exerts a higher unit of pressure at particular spots. Seats should be on the firm side. Too soft will allow the legs to sink in and the tissues will be pressed up around each side of the bone, throttling the circulation. If the ischial bones and the buttocks sink in and the hips rotate backwards, the circulation to the muscles of the back can be affected and that would disturb the natural curves of the spine and affect the legs. In severe cases of leg problems, attention to seating habits must be given.

Several different massage techniques may be used for specific problems, i.e., after completing a sciatic treatment, when the patient is asked to bend over as part of the treatment, constraints or pain is felt in the thighs.

Position

The patient lies on the back. The Creative Healer sits to the right of the patient.

➧ **Step 1:** Hold the four fingers together and use them as a unit; reach toward the medial side of the back of the thigh, the hand covering the entire area to be treated, beginning just below the bone. Curl your fingers to give a positive grasp. From this position move the hand horizontally and quickly across the back of the thigh to the opposite side.

➧ **Step 2:** This motion is described as "strumming" (such as across the strings of a bass violin) because one feels cords and strings being drawn at first. As the fingertips glide over them one can feel them being released. This random release will effect the rearrangement of the tissues in their normal position and will open up the flow of life and circulation into the leg. Continue this strumming downward as far as the sensitivity and the obstructions extend.

For less severe cases, for example, when the patient performs the bending over motion after the sciatic treatment and has discomfort in the back of the thigh, the strumming can be applied as the patient stands with the side of the body facing the seated therapist.

Strumming Plus Massage

This treatment is given in more severe cases when the use of the leg is lost.

Position

The patient lies prone or face down. The Creative Healer stands next to the patient.

➧ **Step 1:** Alternate the strumming, as described above, with a massage of medium pressure upward on the back of the leg.

➧ **Step 2:** If thin or bulged spots in the muscles are encountered, apply a circular breaking up and cleaning out movement and then return to the massage. The treatment is ended when the tissues feel uniformly soft and warm and pliable and the patient reports a feeling of increased strength.

Frequency

Length of time per treatment will vary according to the need and treatments are spaced not more than a week apart.

Strumming to the Inside of the Leg

This treatment is given in cases where the patient cannot extend the legs at night in order to lie comfortably and must keep them drawn up.

Position

The patient lies on the back. The Creative Healer stands next to the patient.

➧ **Step 1:** Administer the strumming as described above except the hand reaches from between the legs to the far side of the thigh, and the fingers are curled to grasp and strum as before but toward the medial side of the leg.

Massage

This treatment is given when the legs are simply heavy and sluggish and have lost their agility.

Position

The patient lies prone or face down. The Creative Healer stands next to the patient.

➧ **Step 1:** Massage the thighs, singly or together, with the hands moving upward and spanning the entire back area of the thighs. This kind of massage takes out the sag and provides a general lift and the sensation of dullness and heaviness disappears.

Severe Anterior Contraction of the Thigh

There are cases of leg trouble in which intense contraction of the muscles in the anterior of the thigh has resulted in serious incapacity and often severe pain. A person in such a condition may be unable to extend the legs and so is forced to walk in a crouched, knee-bent position. Such a state of contraction is most frequently caused by severe chilling, but may also be caused by prolonged wearing of wet garments over the front of the thigh.

Position

The patient lies on the back with legs flexed. The Creative Healer stands next to the patient.

➧ **Step 1: Raking movement.** The first movement consists of an upward stroking with mostly the tips of the extended fingers. It might be called an upward, inverted raking. The fingertips lead and the fingers are separated about a finger's width. Perform this movement with the thought of breaking up the contracted or adhered separate bundles of muscle fibers. These fibers are not in their normal position of being smooth and parallel and therefore prevent the large muscles from fully extending.

With continued application of this movement, the legs will gradually be able to stretch out. As they do so and the patient can lie more comfortably, begin the second movement and then alternate it with the first.

➧ **Step 2: Kneading movement.** The second movement consists of kneading the anterior of the thigh, from the knee upward. Hold your fingers flat, as a unit, with the thumb stretched out. Place your hand on the patient's thigh, just above the knee and perform a slightly compressing action, filling the palm with tissue. In the kneading motion, the hand first partially closes and then opens again. However, these closings and openings are limited to the bases of the thumb and fingers, which do not curl but remain extended. This successive opening and closing of the hand, performed by the bases of the thumb and the fingers, results in an alternating compression and suction, which thoroughly intermingle the fluid tissues with the solid ones.

Begin at the knee and work all the way up to the groin with a succession of kneading motions. Work with the intention of loosening the contracted and adhered tissues. When this is completed, retain the hand in its position and now carry out the kneading movements on the thigh in the downward direction, all the way to the knee. On this downward path, work with the intent of drawing circulation and fluids that lubricate the sheaths of the muscles and tendons downward along and over the already loosened tissues.

➧ **Step 3: Repeat and alternate.** Repeat this up and down kneading and alternate it with the raking movement until the muscles are entirely freed from any binding influences.

Frequency

Relief can often be accomplished in a single session if the condition has not lasted too long.

Twisted Hip

A twisted, rotated, or tilted hip may be caused by improper lifting, a fall or an automobile accident or even a muscle contraction. It frequently results in uneven length of the legs.

Position

The patient sits on a bench with a firm surface. The Creative Healer sits behind the patient.

Thumb pad spans joint between sacrum and hipbone

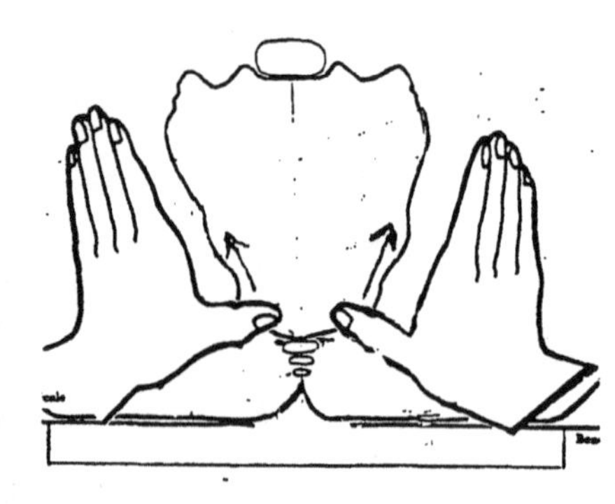

➧ **Step 1: Placement.** The patient sits on a firm treatment bench so that the weight of the body can help in realigning the hips. The pressure of the patient's weight bears more heavily on the flats of the ischial bones and less on the legs (as in the normal sitting position). Sometimes the hip has slipped so far out of its normal position it seems folded under as though being sat on. Draw the patient's leg outward just before sitting so that he/she sits more squarely on both hips.

➧ **Step 2: Check the symmetry.** By placing your fingertips on the crests of the hipbones and your thumbs on the joints connecting the sacrum with the hipbones on the two sides of the body, you can feel the extent of the twist, rotation or asymmetry of the hips. Where the sacrum and hipbones join, the surfaces feel uneven, like little hills and valleys. But these bones are securely fastened together by the strongest ligaments found at any joint in the body. Creative Healing works with the ligaments.

➧ **Step 3: Thumb movement and lifts.** To treat, place well-oiled thumbs, tip facing tip at the level of the top of the tailbone, with the tip of the thumb pad resting on the sacrum and the middle part of the pad spanning the joint between the sacrum and the hipbone. Starting at that elevation, let the thumbs glide slowly and smoothly upward together with a firm, forward pressure, while the elbows are supported by the knees (similar to the hemorrhoid treatment, page 5–35). The part of the thumb that moves on the sacrum exerts a heavier pressure than the part that spans the joint. The thumbs are in a similar position as for hemorrhoid treatment but farther apart.

If you encounter protrusions of cartilage, release the pressure and remold the cartilage by using the quarter twist; see page 3–3. Resume the lift below the level of the protrusion and continue the upward lifting to the top of the sacroiliac joints. Return to the starting position and repeat the process. Occasionally, reseat the person to a more favorable position and continue the lifts as long as changes are taking place. Changes can be limited by swelling, inflammation or disruption of circulation. Sometimes a release of circulation will be felt as pressures are equalized. It is proof that the treatment is effective and the circulation increase will feed and repair as the asymmetric parts are realigned. Alignment automatically occurs through the effect of gravity when the tensions and unequal pressures are released. Also, many other disturbances pertaining to the area are corrected simultaneously when the twisted hip is treated.

Note: Even if only one hip is tilted, the treatment is applied symmetrically to both sides of the spine. Note also, that although bones are repositioned, the intent is always directed by the mind to the softer tissues of the body and when the tension in the ligaments is released, realignment will take place.

This treatment applies when the sacrum seems wedged too far down between the hipbones, appearing too prominent to the posterior. This causes a stress and cross-pull across the sacrum, which is relieved by the lifts.

Frequency

Repeated treatments may be necessary and may be given 3 times a week. In severe cases, a 5-day interval gives the treatment more time when vascular healing is needed yet does not let too much time elapse before it is reinforced. If there is pain when you cross the area of the sciatic nerve, stop and do the sciatic treatment first; see page 3–23. Also check the kidney spots and the back.

Repositioning the Femur

There is another case when the hip is said to be out of place, as in twisted hip above, but where actually the leg bone (femur) is out of place with regard to the hipbone and the head of the femur does not fit correctly into the cup-like socket of the hipbone. If this condition is suspected, use either or both of the movements described below. Both of these movements affect the repositioning of the femur, as well as that of the surrounding tissue, by utilizing the muscles of the body.

First Movement

Position

The patient lies on the back with legs well flexed, but not under any strain. The Creative Healer stands next to the patient.

➧ **Step 1:** Place the patient's feet next to each other, in straight alignment with the median line of the body. The pelvis should rest flat and squarely on the supporting surface and the whole body should be symmetrically aligned.When this position is achieved, gently separate the knees and guide them to the widest angle of repose. Don't use force or push the knees apart but merely allow gravity to work. If it is not possible to spread the legs in this manner, do not persist. Instead, check the groin and the sciatic nerves for the cause of the constraint and treat accordingly. The legs should then be able to spread without actual pain, possibly just with a little discomfort arising from stiffness. At this time, it may be necessary to reposition the feet (they are now lying on their sides). Soles must be facing each other at the median line. One leg might relax into a much lower position than the other; the non-relaxed leg could be out of position with respect to its socket in the hip, indicating a need for the repositioning treatment.

➧ **Step 2:** Place a hand on each knee. Keep a hand on the unaffected leg to steady this leg in its spread position. Place the other hand on the leg to be treated and grasp the knee gently. Place the fingers on the outer (lateral) side and the thumb on the inner side. Swing the knee toward the median line of the body through an arc of about 4 to 6 inches. From this point, using your thumb, push the leg in the opposite direction that gently yet positively flips the knee back toward the widespread position. Just before giving the flip, check to see that the feet have remained in position, sole to sole. The flipping action does not impose any trauma to the leg. It does, however, impart a velocity that is sufficient to generate a force of momentum within the leg. The momentum of the leg will carry it outward to the point at which it is suddenly arrested by the extreme extension of the muscles. This action serves to "drive" the ball of the femur into its socket in the hip, and automatically positions the joint and the surrounding tissues.

The whole performance is gentle and should be acceptable within the most reasonable bounds of comfort. It can be repeated at the same session after the legs have been extended for a short period of rest. Obviously, the repositioning action cannot take place unless the person is relaxed and can allow it to happen.

Second Movement

Position

The patient lies face down or prone with toes extending over the end of the support. The Creative Healer kneels next to the patient.

➧ **Step 1:** Glide one hand from the inner (medial) side, under the thigh that is suspected to be out of position. Place the hand three-fourths of the way down from the groin to the knee. The leg rests on the palm of the hand and is free to rotate in the hand. The patient's position, with toes extending over the end of the support, allows the leg complete freedom to rotate.

➧ **Step 2:** Now use your other hand to rotate the leg into position. Place the heel of this hand on the thigh behind the projection of the greater trochanter. By an abrupt movement, push it downward, giving it a slightly inward (toward the median) and upward (toward the head) orientation. This orientation is necessary in order that the hand can follow through and complete the movement without sliding out of position. The hand remains, during the whole rotary movement, as originally placed, behind the trochanter. The movement is applied with sufficient force to impart a degree of momentum to the rotary motion of the leg. The momentum will reposition the ball of the femur in its socket in the hip by way of the muscles, as in the first movement.

The preferred position of the hands, to treat the right leg, is to have the left hand support the leg and the right hand impart the motion. To treat the left leg, reverse the above directions.

Knee Treatments

Displaced Cartilage of the Knee

When weight is placed on the knee when stepping down and the knee acts like a trick or football knee and fails to hold up the person, the semilunar cartilages in the knee are separated. Weight on such a knee has the tendency to force the two cartilages further apart. This explains the often experienced sharp, unexpected pain in a trick knee under the strain of compression and weight. If the knee is not too badly injured, without congestion in the popliteal or surrounding space, or if the ligaments are not too badly torn, and there has not been time for fluid to collect so there is no swelling, inflammation or obstruction, it is entirely possible to reposition the cartilages immediately. After the repositioning, the person can go on as though nothing had happened. An example of this is a football player returning to continue the game.

Position

The patient sits on a bench. The Creative Healer sits facing the patient.

Position of the leg

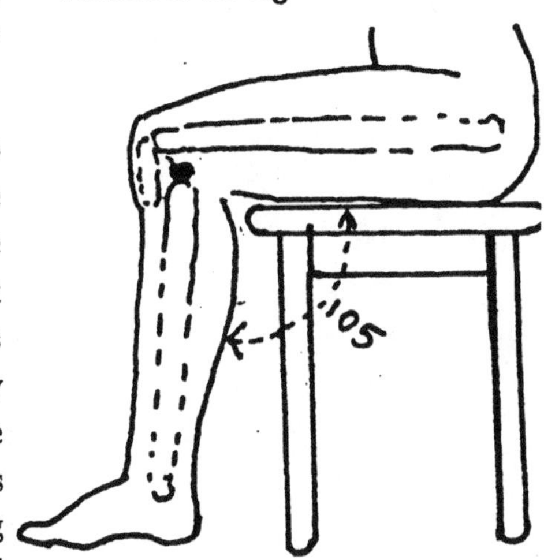

➧ **Step 1: Placement.** Position the patient's foot on the floor so that the lower leg makes an angle approximately 15° wider with the thigh than the normal 90° sitting angle.

➧ **Step 2: Locate depressions.** When the knee is in this position, there are two natural depressions or cavities, one on each side of the knee. This is where the tibia and the femur meet to form the articulation of the knee joint. These depressions are most easily discerned in this position and present their widest open aspect. The depression on the lateral side is tiny, that on the medial side is larger. These depressions, easy to locate when the knee is in good condition, may be more difficult to find when the knee is in trouble, when the entire area may be swollen. In such a condition, however, the depressions may be recognized as spots having a considerably higher degree of temperature than the surrounding tissue, when the palms are drawn across them. When the depressions are pressed with the fingertips, they are more sensitive than the surrounding tissue.

➧ **Step 3: Testing.** If the right knee is the injured one, place your right hand so that the end of the index finger is presented to the medial cavity and the thumb is placed in the depression beneath the kneecap (patella) on the opposite side. Place your left hand correspondingly, with the index finger in the lateral depression and the thumb on the medial side of the kneecap. The relative position of the two depressions, with respect to one another, will vary from patient to patient. Sometimes they will be directly opposite one another, sometimes one will be considerably lower than the other. This relationship will determine which thumb should be above the other for the most comfortable position. To steady the hold on the knee, rest your forearms on your thighs.

To test the condition of the knee: With the patient's leg and your hands in the positions described above, exert an even, inward pressure with both index fingers. Direct the pressure along an imaginary line that joins the depressions and runs directly through the knee joint. Sustain a firm and constant pressure at first then increase the pressure from one index finger while holding the other steady. Return the pressure of the first index finger to its original level and increase that of the second. If the knee is in perfect condition, you will feel a direct contact from one index tip to the other along the line through the knee joint. The semilunar cartilages of the knee are located along this line. In the perfect knee, they act as though they abut each other, and it will feel as though there is a solid rod or dowel in contact with the fingertips. When the pressure increases are alternated rapidly, there will seem to be a movement like quicksilver between the fingers; this indicates that the cartilage of the knee is in order and needs no attention.

If this responding movement is not felt, the cartilage needs to be treated. In such cases, the contact between the tips of the index fingers will be recognized as slack, indirect or spongy. This indicates separation of the semilunar cartilages and possibly fluid in the space, resulting from their separation. Separation of the cartilages and presence of fluid in the space between them, is always associated with congestion behind the knee in the popliteal space and an abnormal increase of pressure within the capsule of the knee joint. A long-standing congested condition in the popliteal space causes this abnormal increase of pressure that keeps the semilunar cartilages separated and the space between them filled with fluid.

➧ **Step 4: Remove any congestion.** To proceed with the work of restoring normal function to the knee, congestion in the popliteal space must first be removed. This congestion presents the biggest single factor preventing the knee from being restored to normal function. To decongest the popliteal space, the whole area extending from a few inches above the turn of the knee to about midway down the calf must be thoroughly decongested. This is accomplished by two movements: a breaking up and a stroking movement. If the knee is very painful and has developed considerable heat, start with the stroking movement.

➧ **Step 5: Stroking movement.** With the patient's leg positioned as described earlier, both hands contact the thigh at the upper boundary of the congested area. The hands are curled around the thigh, fingers together, fingertips touching on the under side. The palms are in full contact with the tissues on each side of the knee. Stroke downward with a gentle drawing action to where the fingers reach a point about halfway down the calf muscle. Release the hands at that point and place them on the top side of the leg at the same elevation from which they started. This time, the heels of the hands touch, while the thumbs and fingers are held together as a unit and the palms are in full contact with the tissues. Again stroke downward, but now over the front of the leg about the same distance as before. Throughout the treatment, these two stroking movements are used alternately. They form a pair and neither one is performed without the other.

In this stroking, heat and inflammation are drawn out as by suction, by the palms. Any swelling that may be present will recede and the pain felt by the patient will decrease. This stroking treatment is always welcome to the patient as a soothing and pleasant experience.

When the acutely painful and inflamed condition of the knee has been relieved by the alternating strokes, add the breaking up movement. Throughout the treatment, continue to alternate the stroking with the breaking up movement as necessary.

➧ **Step 6: Breaking up movement.** The breaking up movement is directed mainly to the area behind the knee in the popliteal space. It is performed by either hand and is a circular movement in which the fingers carry the surface tissue with them. The fingers are used in flat, full length contact rather than curled. The mind directs the broken-up material downward.

If varicose veins are encountered in the popliteal space (the projecting veins are easily detected by a light brushing movement of the fingers) do not massage or press upon them. Learn to direct the breaking up movements from alongside such a vein so that they penetrate, when needed, to the region that lies beneath the vein. For this purpose, you may have to use some breaking up with the fingertips, instead of the flat fingers.

To replace cartilage, brace elbows on knees

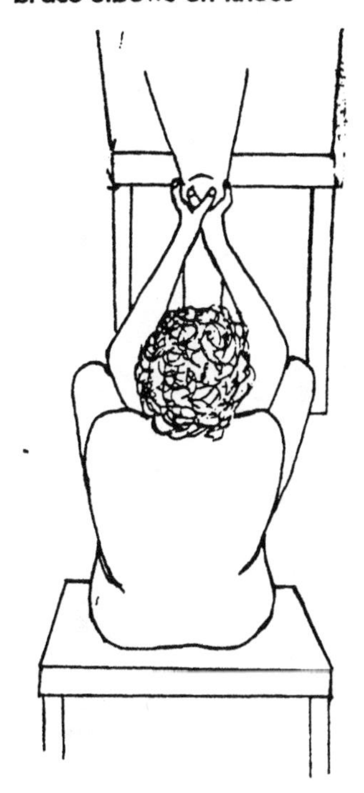

In using the breaking up movement in the popliteal space, the intent is not only to break up the obstructing material but also to cause the broken up material to move downward. To realize this intent, the breaking up movements should have a downward feeding character to them, as well. This, together with the stroking, will serve to thoroughly decongest the popliteal area and to move the broken-up material down into the calf circulation.

The importance of moving the broken-up material through the region of congestion is significant because the knee is a bottleneck, a natural obstruction to the downward flow of life and circulation.

A cross-section of the knee is largely comprised of bony tissue with relatively little space for the functioning of other tissue. Speeding up the flow through this region will greatly relieve any heat and inflammation and consequently reduce any pressure within the capsule of the knee. That is why the downward stroking, which effects this speeding up, has such a beneficial effect.

➧ **Step 7: Replacing cartilage.** When the decongestion is completed, return to the cartilages and work to replace them. The tips of the index fingers are placed in the two cavities as described in step 3, and the thumbs are placed at the sides of the kneecap, crossing each other like scissors. Your forearms rest on your thighs. Apply a steady pressure along the same line used to test the condition of the knee. Gradually increase the pressure until the cartilages are felt to yield. Be prepared to continue the pressure for 3 to 4 minutes or even longer. When the yield feels complete, push with both index fingers in a final follow-through pressure.

It is important to sustain the level of pressure by the grip of the thumbs and fingers, using the back-up support of the thighs to the forearms. This steadies the arms and allows the arms to increase pressure as the thighs are drawn together. If the index fingers feel tired, give them support by pressing on their nails with the tips of the middle fingers.

➧ **Step 8: Test again.** When you feel that the cartilages have been pushed solidly together, reapply the test used in step 3, to determine whether the cartilages abut each other. The time required to reposition the cartilages depends on the degree of their separation. When there is fluid present, it depends on the time it takes this fluid to move away.

➧ **Step 9: Massaging ligaments.** The cartilages are held in place by the ligaments belonging to the capsule of the knee joint. These ligaments must be strengthened once the cartilage has been replaced. The strengthening is accomplished by a massage performed with the thumbs. To massage, cradle the knee in both hands. With the thumbs, direct short, arching strokes from the perimeters to the centers of the cavities; these strokes cover an area 1 to 2 inches in diameter on each side. This brings in circulation drawn mainly from above. The purpose of this massage is to increase the pressure of circulation to the weakened areas, so that the sustained feed will strengthen the ligaments and enable them to hold the cartilages in position.

Reconstructing tissues and eliminating wastes can be accomplished only by the blood stream and its adjuncts. Circulation will be inhibited as long as an imbalance of pressure exists in and around the capsule of the knee joint. When treatment has established an evenly balanced, natural pressure field within the capsule, circulation is free to perform its job.

➧ **Step 10: Walking instructions.** It is important that the knee function only as a hinge joint until it is fully healed, especially in the more severe injuries. Any lateral or twisting forces that impart a cam-like action within the knee are to be avoided. Instruct the patient to walk in a straight-ahead direction over the injured knee. To change direction while walking, place the weight of the body over the other foot and spin on the ball of this foot to change direction. Then place the foot of the critical leg so that the direction of motion of the body is once again straight ahead over that leg. While standing, change direction by spinning on the balls of the feet only. This is most pertinent if rubber or cling soles are worn.

Frequency

It may be necessary to repeat the treatment within 5 to 7 days.

Water Below the Kneecap

Water below the kneecap may be the result of kneeling on hard or rough surfaces for a long time or by a blow that drives the kneecap upward toward the head such as falling on a stone. In either case the kneecap is pushed upward. The cause for the gathering of fluids below the kneecap, according to Mr. Stephenson, is the dislocation of cartilage located beneath the common tendon just above or within the capsule of the knee joint. The fluids are not synovial fluids, but more watery, clear, yellowish types, such as are connected with the lymph circulation or as separated out from the blood stream. He warned against the use of heat because this would draw more fluids.

Position

The patient sits on a bench. The Creative Healer sits facing the patient.

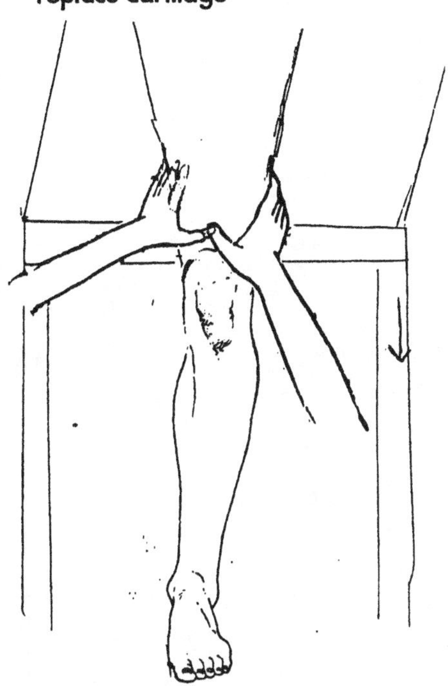

Pressure treatment to replace cartilage

➧ **Step 1: Pressure treatment.** Your hands cradle the leg just above the knee joint to steady the thumbs. One thumb is placed centrally on top of the thigh just above the kneecap and the second thumb is placed on top of the first for added pressure. A firm pressure is directed into the thigh and towards the kneecap by the thumbs. The pressure must be strong to be transmitted through the common tendon to the tissues beneath. You may feel the structure under your thumbs yield and the cartilage shift into place. The pressure treatment is usually necessary once. It can be done after the fluid has been drained off by a physician and no further fluid will collect.

➧ **Step 2: Draining fluid.** The pressure treatment may be done with the fluid present followed by a downward massage to reabsorb the fluid into the circulation. For this massage you would sit next to the patient and use the full length of the thumbs, pointing downward and contacting the leg at the lower edge of the fluid pocket. With the thumbs on an angle, mid-way between the flat and the edge, include a minute portion of the fluid at the lower edge and feed it 3 or 4 inches downward into the circulation of the leg. Use a positive but not a heavy pressure until the circulation has absorbed all the fluid.

Frequency

Perform the draining movement several times daily, 5 or 10 minutes at a time, until the fluid has been completely reabsorbed. The patient can self-administer this treatment. It is also important to keep knees from chilling and to wear loose knee pads to avoid repetition.

Protruding Cartilage at Kneecap

When congestion is removed, protrusions of cartilage may be discovered in the area of the kneecap during the downward massage. These protrusions mean that the compressive forces produced by certain twisting motions, have been great enough to extrude cartilage beyond the rounded ends of the bone. Such extrusion could not have taken place if the ligamentous strength of the capsule had not first failed. Protrusions of cartilage must be molded to where they no longer project beyond the contour of the joint.

Position

The patient sits on a bench. The Creative Healer sits facing the patient.

➧ **Step 1: Thumb placement.** Use the convex surface of the last joint of the inner side of the thumb to remold the cartilage. Place this part of the thumb in the groove where the formation is felt. The fingers lie almost directly opposite to the pressure line of the thumb, to give the hand a firm grasp. The formation will be below the lower edge of the kneecap and may be on one or both sides of the center line. This description is for the right leg. The right thumb is used for the lateral side and the left for the medial side. Reverse thumbs for the left knee.

➧ **Step 2: Extension of leg.** With your thumb exert a pressure strong enough to feel that the cartilage is yielding. At the same time, your free hand grips the patient's calf or ankle and slowly and gently extends the leg. The pressure must be sustained to push the cartilage into place and to follow through to the point when the leg is completely extended. To better trap the cartilage under the thumb, it may be necessary to shift the thumb's point of contact. You may use the end of the thumb or the depression on the side of the thumb near its end. Use whatever point of contact best allows you to feel that the cartilage is yielding and moving in to where it belongs.

Frequency

For any protruding cartilage, the intent is to accomplish the full task of remolding it in one movement, but repetition may need to be made.

Obstructions Around Kneecap

Thumb placement

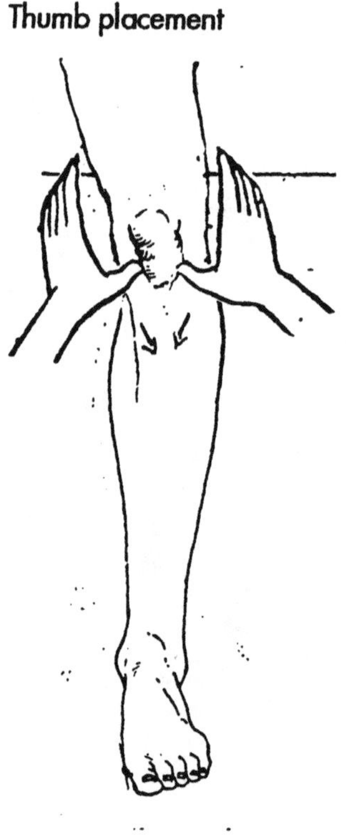

If the cartilage of the knee is in place, and the popliteal space and the space surrounding it is decongested, yet the patient still complains of a constantly painful area just below or on either side of the kneecap, look for obstructions in this region. Obstructions here must be removed and circulation fed into the area.

Position

The patient sits on a bench. The Creative Healer sits facing the patient.

➧ **Step 1: Action.** This is done with a downward stroking movement of the thumbs. Begin at the widest part of the kneecap on each side. From there, two natural grooves follow diagonally downward toward the insertion of the tendon into the tibia bone, a short distance below the kneecap. The grooves in question point right toward the insertion. Stroke with the thumbs along these grooves, massaging always in the downward direction, to slightly below the kneecap.

➧ **Step 2: Teach the patient.** You can teach the patient to self-administer this daily massage. The patient will use the thumbs full length, in a circular massage downward, alternating this with a downward stroking, also with the thumbs, converging at the same point below the kneecap. As the patient performs these movements, the hands should lie alongside the knee. It may be useful to include the base of the thumbs in the massage. This daily massage will nourish the ligaments and ensure proper circulation to the capsule of the joint.

Lower Leg Treatments

Cramping of the Lower Leg and Foot

In knee treatments, all congestion in and slightly above the popliteal space and halfway down the calf must be removed. Congestion in these areas is also responsible for cramping in the lower leg and foot. An important nerve center midway down the calf lies between the two heads of the muscle extending down the back of the leg from the femur to the Achilles tendon and makes up most of the calf. If there is cramping in the lower leg or foot, this nerve center will be extremely sensitive, especially when palpated with pressure. After a severe cramp, the patient may be very aware of the area for several days. This sensitivity is caused by congestion preventing blood and life force from reaching the nerve center. To correct this, and to give relief when cramping occurs, these areas must be decongested; this is accomplished by two movements: a breaking up and a stroking movement. If the knee is in great pain and is hot, start with the stroking movement.

Position

The patient sits on a bench. The Creative Healer sits facing the patient.

➧ **Step 1: Stroking movement (same as step 5 of displaced cartilage of knee).** With both hands, contact the thigh at the upper boundary of the congested area. The hands are curled, fingers together, palms in full contact, fingertips touching on the under side. The palms are in full contact with the tissues on each side of the knee. Stroke downward with a gentle drawing action to where the fingers reach a point about halfway down the calf muscle. Then release the hands and place them on the top side of the leg at the same elevation as that from which they started. This time the heel of the hands touch while the thumbs and fingers are again held together as a unit with the palms again in full contact with the tissues. Again stroke downward, but now over the front of the leg about the same distance as before. Throughout the treatment, these two stroking movements are used alternately. They form a pair and neither one is performed without the other. In this stroking, any heat and inflammation that may be present are drawn out, as by suction, by the palms. Any swelling that may be present will recede and the pain will decrease. This stroking treatment is always welcome as a soothing and pleasant experience. When the painful or inflamed condition of the knee area has been relieved by the alternating strokes of the first movement, add the second, the breaking up movement. Throughout the treatment, continue to alternate the stroking with the breaking up movement as often as appears necessary.

➧ **Step 2: Breaking up movement (same as step 6 of displaced cartilage of knee).** Direct the breaking up movement to the popliteal space, the area behind the knee. Use one hand only; either hand may be used. This is a circular movement in which the fingers, in flat full-length contact, carry the surface tissue with them. If varicose veins are encountered in the popliteal space (the projecting veins are easily detected by a light brushing movement of the fingers) do not massage or press on them, for this could be detrimental. Direct the breaking up movements from alongside such a vein so that they penetrate, when needed, to the region beneath the vein. In using the breaking up movement in the popliteal space, the intent is not only to break up the obstructing material but also to move it downward. To realize this intent, the breaking up movements should have a downward feeding character. This, together with the stroking, will serve to thoroughly decongest the popliteal area and move the broken up material into the calf circulation. In addition, check for residual contractions in the calf muscles below the nerve center and down to the Achilles tendon. In treating these areas, remember never to press on or massage over varicose veins.

The importance of moving the broken up material through and beyond the congested region is even more significant when considering that the knee is a bottleneck, a natural obstruction to the downward flow of life and circulation. A cross-section of the knee shows bony tissue with relatively little space for the functioning of other tissue. Speeding up circulation through the knee will relieve heat and inflammation and consequently reduce pressure within the capsule of the knee, which is why the downward stroking, effecting this speeding up, has such a beneficial effect. Most importantly, decongesting will avert reoccurrence of the cramping. For quick results, treatments can be given for 3 or 4 days in succession; the patient can easily be taught to self-administer this treatment.

➧ **Step 3: Proper stretching.** Until the congestion is cleared and the nerve center receives adequate circulation, keep in mind that any attempt to extend the foot so that the toes point downward (as one might do in stretching) will most often trigger more cramping. To stretch without causing cramps, extend the heel farthest and pull the toes back in the direction of the head. This kind of stretching may even have a stabilizing effect because it lengthens the muscle fibers causing them to lie more smoothly and parallel. Being able to stretch the toes without causing a cramp, and being able to press on the nerve center without giving rise to pain shows that the congestion is cleared and normal function has been restored.

Shin Splints

Shin splints is a condition of frequently persistent and sharp pain along the front of the tibia, the larger bone of the lower leg.

Position

The patient stands. The Creative Healer sits facing the patient.

Location of treatment

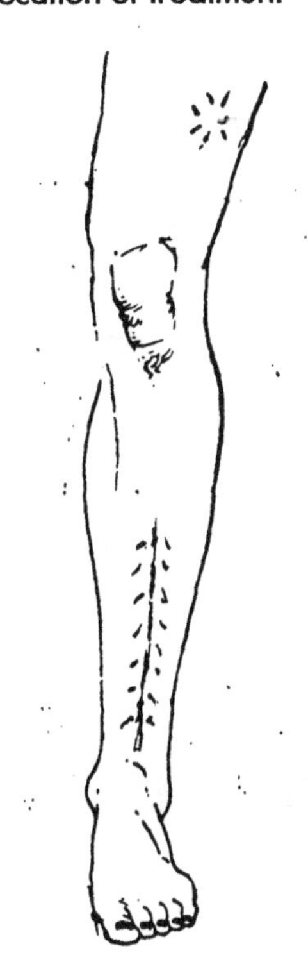

Step 1: Location of treatment. At the lower front of the thigh within the extensor muscles, the treatment spot is situated above the center of the knee cap and slightly outward from the middle of the femur. For the adult, the spot is found about 5 to 7 inches above and 1/2 to 1 inch out from the kneecap toward the lateral side.

Step 2: Replacement on thigh. At this spot, exert a firm inward and downward pressure and repeat, as though to open an obstruction. The spot can be recognized because it is much more sensitive to pressure than any other spot, even immediately adjacent. The treatment can be effective only while the patient is standing.

Step 3: Breakup treatment along shin. Apply small breakup movements up and down the leg on the front and side of the tibia where pain is felt, as needed.

Sprained Ankle

An important cavity is located on the outside of the foot just forward and a little below the ankle bone (lateral malleolus). This depression between the bones is the only such depression on the foot and functions as a filter area much like those in the neck and on the wrist. The significance of this filter spot on the foot is that sediment-ladened blood in the lower extremities requires filtering to move into the narrower blood vessels of the foot. Disrupting this filtering function causes trouble, which is what happens with a sprained ankle.

A sprained ankle, usually brought on by the foot being turned toward the lateral side, stretches, tears or uproots the ligaments, depending on the severity of the accident. This damage displaces the cartilage in the area of the filtering cavity and severely disrupts circulation. If the ankle can be treated immediately with the following Creative Healing treatment, heat, inflammation and swelling will not develop. If swelling does occur, the foot must be treated to remove the heat and swelling first, after which the sprain can be treated. This treatment describes treating the right ankle; to treat the left ankle, interchange right and left in all that follows.

Position

The patient sits on a chair. The Creative Healer sits on the bench or treatment bed opposite the patient.

Position for treatment

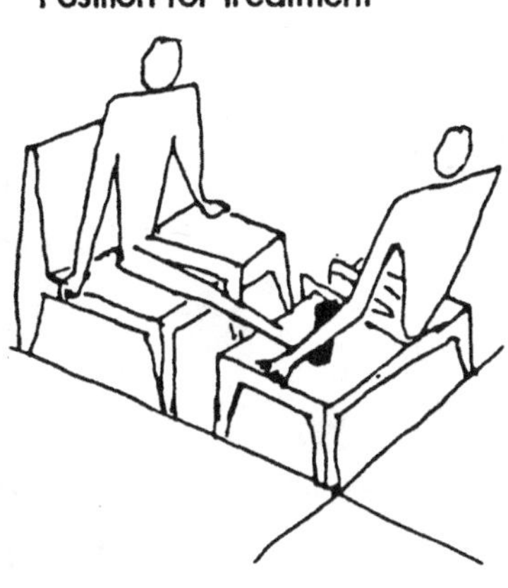

Step 1: Positioning the leg. The patient extends the leg and places the right foot on your left side on the bench. Your left arm extends beyond and below the patient's foot while your left hand rests flat on the surface on which you are seated, fingers pointing away from patient's body. The ball of the patient's foot rests firmly against your left forearm, where it is firmly supported in a upward (flexed) position. Lean the weight of your body toward your left arm and hand; this position can be sustained with ease, giving support to the patient's foot throughout the entire treatment. Any downward or extension movement that

might be imparted to the patient's foot or ankle, because of lack of firm support, would at once cause intolerable pain for the patient. To keep the foot constantly and firmly supported is vital for the patient's comfort, and it is equally vital for the effectiveness of the treatment.

➧ **Step 2: Withdrawing heat and swelling.** To apply the massage that will remove the swelling, heat, and inflammation, use plenty of olive oil. Place your right hand on top of the patient's lower leg, about midway down from the knee. Hold your fingers as a unit on the lateral side, and the thumb on the medial side extended toward the toes. Massage gently downward, very lightly at first. The palm draws out the heat and inflammation, and the fingers act as an extension of this drawing power. As the thumb descends past the malleolus, it glides under the instep on the inner (medial) side of the foot and the fingers pass alongside or just above the outer (lateral) edge of the foot. The thumb and fingers, at this lower part of the stroke, encompass the foot. The long line of contact from the web of the thumb to the tip of the index finger, will work out the lower part of the swelling a little at a time, feeding it into the toes as the congestive material is returned into the circulation.

Continue the massage with gradually increasing pressure. As the swelling leaves, and heat and inflammation recede, your hand will finally be coming down over the patient's leg and foot with a firm pressure. The entire massage has the character of a milking action.

➤➤➤CAUTION: Never massage on the inside of the lower leg from the ankle bone up for 6 inches. Delicate vessels near the surface at that location could be injured. This does not apply to the thumb gliding over the area in this treatment.

Clearing the filter area

➧ **Step 3: Clearing the filter area.** Once the swelling is eliminated, begin to make a downward, toward-the-toes, circling motion in the filter cavity to further clear obstructions. (This is the same pumping movement used on the wrist filter area.) The cavity must be cleaned out sufficiently so that the tip of the index finger can enter into it to a good depth without causing undue discomfort. If the cavity seems extremely sensitive, proceed with a light contact in a circular motion until the sensitivity diminishes and the finger can enter much more deeply without causing any discomfort. Ultimately, the index fingertip can enter the cavity and detect the cartilage that caused the pinch when any weight was put on the foot or the foot was flexed. Repositioning this cartilage is the key to the sprained ankle treatment.The dislocation of cartilage is, in most cases, clearly discernible. All the while, the foot is still firmly supported against the left arm.

➧ **Step 4: Replacing cartilage.** Place the tip of the right index finger deeply into the cavity with the thumb diametrically opposed to it on the inner side of the foot. Grasp the foot with the left index finger and thumb as though they were a pair of pincers. While sustaining this grasp, release the support to the ball of the foot and place the left hand on the bottom of the foot so that the thumb rests along the inner (medial) side along the big toe. The index and middle finger oppose it on the outer (lateral) side of the foot. The curled fourth and fifth fingers provide an additional support for the sole of the foot.

To open the space between the bones within the cavity where the right index finger rests, the left hand carries the foot inward and downward at the same time (inward toward the median and downward from the leg). This is an essentially continuous motion. Complete the circumduction of the foot back toward the center line, then up to the original position. (This method of replacing cartilage is introduced in the neck treatment, page 2–40.) Aided by the pressure of the index finger, the cavity receives the displaced cartilage.

When the circumduction is completed, release the grip of the right hand and, pressing firmly with your left hand against the ball of the foot, flex the foot upward. In this upward flexing the foot must be kept centered so that each point of the foot moves in a vertical plane.

Left hand circumducts foot while right hand index and thumb grasp the filter area in the ankle

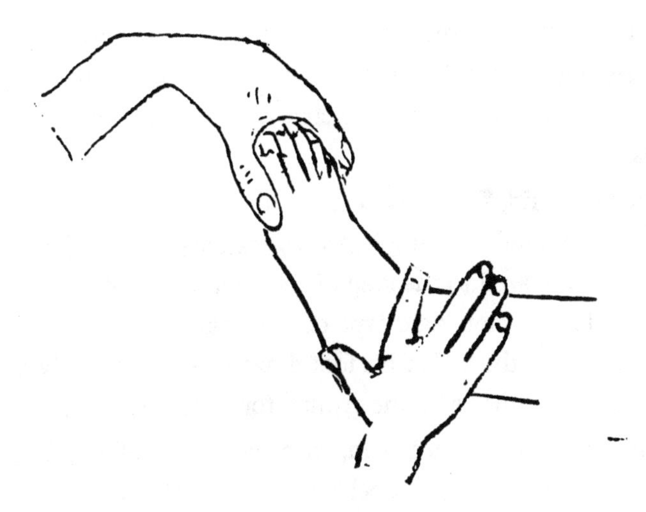

The patient will be able to accept this comfortably. In fact, it will feel good. The patient can now stand on the foot and walk on it, being careful, however, to walk straight ahead without making any attempt to twist or turn until the ankle has had time to heal and strengthen.

The replacement of the dislocated cartilage in the ankle cavity is the key to the sprained ankle treatment. When the dislocation cannot be clearly discerned, still carry through with all the motions as described. Press the index finger into the cavity and carry out the circumduction. This rearranges the tissues in and surrounding the cavity so that the desired result comes about and the sprain, in this case too, is eliminated.

➧ **Step 5: Bandage usage.** If a person is required to stand or walk on an ankle that has been severely sprained so that the ligaments have been very badly affected, the ankle will need bandaging for support. Since the bandage must be applied firmly enough to adequately support the ankle while using it, the patient should notice that the bandage could become restrictive when not using the ankle. Such restrictiveness could be indicated by swelling or discomfort. The bandage then needs to be released so that circulation is not impeded.

If the injury has not been too severe and it is possible to get to the ankle before any swelling has appeared, the dislocated cartilage can be replaced while the foot is circumducted, without any preliminary massage. The person can then immediately resume using the ankle, walking or standing, almost as though nothing had happened.

Foot Treatments

All About Shoes or Why we Have Foot Problems

It is vital for a person to realize the importance of wearing proper shoes. The following considerations are essential when one is working to build up feet that have been injured. Shoes can be a safeguard against further injury when there are foot problems.

Mr. Stephenson said, "When we build a shoe, we need to build a whole shoe properly." To understand Mr. Stephenson's statement, consider how a western person walks, as compared to the step of the American Indian. The Indian wore the moccasin, a flexible, non-rigid type of footwear. This was adequate because, as he walked, he placed the ball of his foot down first. As his body moved over his leg and foot, his heel might touch the ground for a moment.

In contrast, modern western man, in heel-to-toe walking, brings down the heel first, producing a sharp, shocking contact. From this, it will become apparent that it is necessary to build a whole shoe: one with an essentially flat, rigid platform to bridge irregular surfaces such as projections and depressions. The upper should be soft and supple and somewhat porous so that the foot can breathe. However, it must be strong enough to keep the foot centered over the platform at all times. The upper has, at the back, a substantial counter firmly attached to the sole. There should be a lacing at the front. This lacing, in combination with the counter, positions the foot so that the heel is held essentially in contact with the counter. There should be only a very slight shifting of the foot forward and backward in the shoe. This provides a fixed distance from the flex line of the sole to the counter. The flex line lies just beneath the ball of the foot. The distance remains fixed only if the shank of the shoe is sufficiently rigid. It must be able to resist the forces that arise when the heel of the shoe comes in oblique contact with the walking surface. Without sufficient rigidity within the shank, the sole, including the shank, tends to flex. The sharpest flexing occurs where the shank joins the heel. The effects of such a flexing are undesirable for the welfare of the foot.

The counter must be securely fastened to the heel structure. This, along with the face of the insole of the heel and the counter, are the main surfaces presented to the heel of the foot. They form something like a cup around the heel. If there is lack of rigidity in the sole, causing it to flex where the heel joins the shank, this cup structure rotates out of position when the heel is presented obliquely (in a slanted direction) to the walking surface. This sets up unnatural and unreasonable forces within the bones and other tissues of the foot.

The intermittent rotation and release of the counter cup as one walks, imparts a rocking motion to the heel bone, which affects its relationship with the other bones of the foot, causing them to shift. This breaks the essential strength of the arch-like structure of the foot. These shifts disturb the foundation of the arch structure and set up a chain reaction of weakening and disturbing stresses, that extend throughout the foot. The whole foot is affected.

In addition to the ill effects of the rotation of the counter cup, there are other damaging forces present. They arise from the alternate lengthening and shortening of the distance from the flex line (beneath the ball of the foot) to the inside face of the counter. When this distance is shortened, the forward part of the foot is constrained. Little or no forward-to-backward shift is allowed. Thus, the foot becomes jammed into the front part of the shoe by unnatural, compressive forces that affect the whole foot.

To prevent the undesirable effects described, the shoe structure should always include a thin piece of steel to properly reinforce the shank. This steel reinforcement should extend from just behind the flex line, throughout the length of the shank and well into the structure of the heel, bridging the weakest point where the heel meets the shank. In this way, the flexibility of the sole, from the counter to the flex line, is controlled. This construction presents a fixed, and basically rigid, platform from the ball of the foot to the heel. This platform can properly resist the stresses, set up by the oblique contact of the heel with the walking surface, which are inherent in heel-to-toe walking. The effect of these stresses is then properly absorbed within the shoe and not transmitted to the foot.

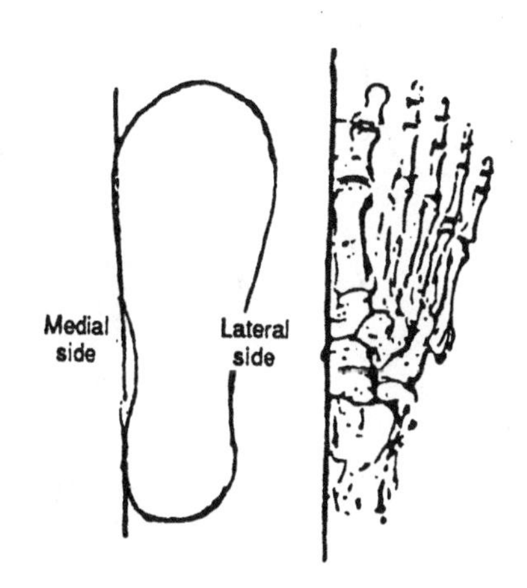

Right foot

In addition, the shape of the whole shoe conforms to the natural form of the foot. In its forward part, the medial outline should deviate only a little from the extension of the straight line represented by a ruler laid against the medial side of the heel and the most medial part of the sole. Any considerable deviation from this line, in the sense of curving toward the lateral side of the foot, will force the big toe to deviate from its natural position. The part of the shoe covering the toes should be snug, but not binding. Allow length room for the foot and toes to extend, as the foot will frequently lengthen toward the end of the day. The insole of the whole shoe is essentially flat on its lateral side. The natural form of the sole of the foot, at its lateral side, is that of a nearly plane surface. This flat contour of the foot can be recognized when the wet foot makes its imprint on a flat surface.

It is important to make sure that the insole presents this essentially flat surface to the foot on its lateral side. This, especially in women's shoes, is frequently not the case. While the curvature of the shank on the medial side might be perfectly reasonable, carrying it through, into the lateral side, gives rise to a surface that is offensive to the natural contour of the foot. Such a bump on the lateral side of the sole presents unreasonable compressive forces, and another whole chain reaction of stresses can be seen to arise within the foot.

Bunions are almost invariably caused by ill-fitting shoes or hose. This is especially true if the hose or shoes are too short or have the toes too pointed. Nylon hose is of such strength that, should it be worn too short, it can deform a foot just like a shoe. It is considered too short if all the stretch is taken out of it when it is put on. It is so unyielding that it does not give as weight is placed on the foot or as the foot lengthens during the course of a day.

Fallen Arches

Physiological (top arrow) and longitudinal (bottom arrow) arches

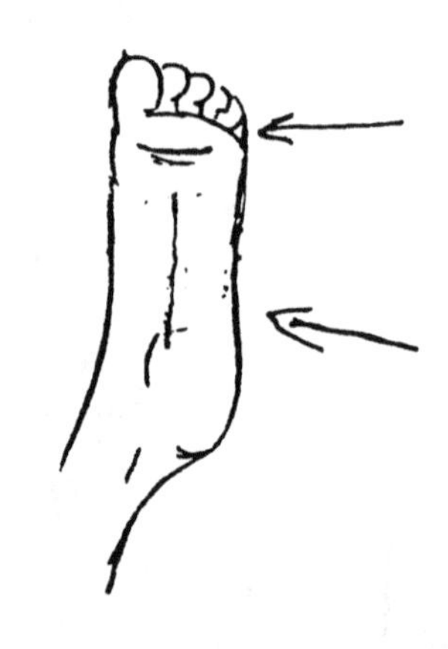

The foot has two arches. The commonly recognized one is the anatomical arch. It lies in the longitudinal direction of the foot. The other one, known as the physiological arch, lies across the foot. It is most pronounced at the ball of the foot.

The area of the foot to be considered is the underneath (plantar) surface of this transverse, physiological arch. Here are found the painful, deep calluses that penetrate upward, nearly to the bone. Here also can be seen a weakened condition of the arch, in which the ball of the foot protrudes downward. This convex position of the arch is the reversed condition of the normal, healthy foot.

When this convexity of the sole becomes fixed, the condition of the foot is precisely the opposite of the ideal one. In the ideal, the physiological arch appears and disappears with each step. When the foot is raised, the normal, concave shape of the arch appears. When weight is placed on the foot the arch disappears. It does so in such a manner that each joint at the ball of the foot bears a proportional share of the weight. The arch is free to accommodate to irregular surfaces.

A frequent cause for the fixed-collapsed condition of the arch, in which all resiliency has been lost, is a shoe with a tramped-down insole or too thin a sole. A sole may lack adequate stiffness from the start. It may also wear down mainly in the center. This is because the strips of material stitched between the sole and the upper (the welts) are thicker and more resistant. Such a shoe offers only a deceptive protection to the foot.

A collapsed condition of the physiological arch will force cartilage and other tissue out of position, most often displaced forward, causing the formation of a wedge with a mushroom-like head. When this occurs between several joints, the ball of the foot can become deformed and held fixed in the convex plantar shape.

➧ **Step 1: Remold cartilages.** To correct this condition, the displaced cartilages must be remolded back into the spaces where they belong. Use the bony tip of the index finger successively at the spaces between two neighboring joints on the underside of the foot. Exert a pressure directed straight upward toward the upper (dorsal) surface of the foot. Steady the hold of the index finger with the thumb of the same hand, placed opposite it on the dorsal side of the foot. Place it on the joint next to the one being worked on from underneath. The other hand supports the foot between the finger unit and the thumb, also from the dorsal side of the foot.

Remolding cartilage; fingers do remolding; thumbs support opposite

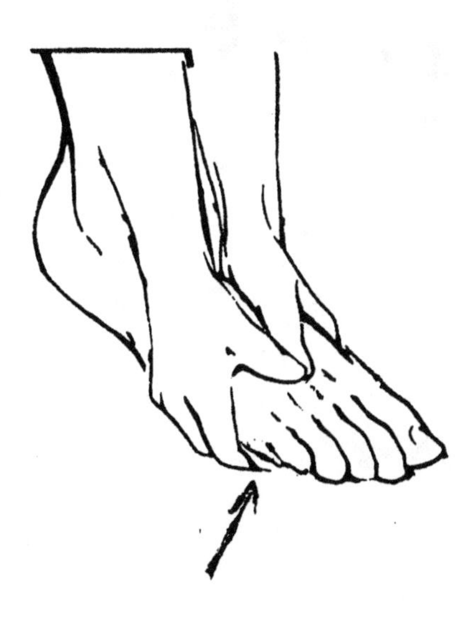

➧ **Step 2: Check for smooth flexing.** When the cartilage has been remolded to such a degree that there is a considerable relaxation of the fixed-collapsed condition of the arch, check the manner in which the ball of the foot flexes. Do this by gliding the curled index finger beneath the ball of the foot from the lateral to the medial side while still supporting the foot, as described, with the other hand. If the remolding is complete, the index finger will be seen and felt to lift each joint in a freely flexing manner, independent of the adjacent joints. If, when one joint is lifted, an adjacent one also rises, further remolding is indicated, either at the same or at later sessions.

Hammer Toe

In a hammer toe condition, the cartilages that have been forced downward also extrude forward (in the direction of the toes). They will first need to be remolded by being pressed backward (in the direction toward the heel). This is done usually with the tip or edge of the thumb. After having been moved back in this manner, the cartilages are moved between the joints as in the treatment for fallen arch.

The metatarsals are the five bones that make up the instep. They are located between the toes and the tarsus (the seven bones of the foot). Sometimes it is necessary to explore the spaces between the metatarsals both on the underside and on the upper side of the foot. Do this by stroking toward the toes to break up any obstruction or contraction there.

It is vital, of course, that the person realize the importance of wearing proper shoes and must not put the foot back into a poorly made shoe that could again deform the foot.

Bunions

A bunion is almost always caused by ill-fitting shoes or hose. This is especially true when the shoes are too short or the toes are too pointed. When nylon stockings are too short or stretched to their limit, the nylon is so strong that it can deform a foot just like a shoe. Nylon is so unyielding that it does not give as weight is placed on the foot and as the foot tends to lengthen during the course of a day. The chief deformity is that the great toe is forced out of line, toward the other toes.

In continuing to walk with such a deformity, it is almost inevitable that the capsule of the joint gives way and cartilage extrudes, forming what is commonly recognized as a bunion. The cartilage protrudes, not on the top of the joint or on its side, but halfway in between. If the bunion can be treated at this stage, the foot can usually be returned to its natural shape without any visual trace of deformity remaining.

If the condition continues to deteriorate, a large reddened area may form. This is partly due to seepage of joint oil into the flesh. Such seepage leads to one of the most painful forms of neuritis. The tip of the bunion will appear in this reddened area, directly at the juncture of the first phalange of the big toe with the first long bone (metatarsus) of the foot. The condition can deteriorate to where the inflamed area becomes very large and the great toe overlies or underlies the neighboring toes.

At first, the situation looks so discouraging that it would appear as though nothing short of a drastic measure, such as surgery, could be applied with any prospect of success. But a bunion can be very effectively treated by the methods of Creative Healing.

Position

The patient sits on a chair with a back rest. The Creative Healer sits facing the patient.

➧ **Step 1: Positioning.** As in the case of the sprained ankle, it is vital to have the patient's foot placed in the correct position for the treatment. The patient extends the leg so that the foot rests between the upper legs of the Creative Healer.

This treatment is described for the right foot. Interchange left and right in all that follows, for a bunion on the left foot.

Hold the left hand with the palm toward the ceiling. With the left index finger on top and middle finger on the bottom, support the foot on the outer (lateral) side so that the metatarsus below the little toe lies between these two fingers. With the third and fourth fingers and the thumb, grasp the big toe, the thumb from above and the two fingers from below. Hold the big toe toward the other toes and draw downward toward the floor, to open the space between the bones into which the extruded cartilage has to be remolded.

➧ **Step 2: Replacing cartilage.** Press gently at first, to keep the pain reasonably tolerable, on the tip of the bunion, using the bony tip of the right thumb. At the same time, hold the great toe over and downward with your left thumb and third and fourth fingers. This opens the joint so that it may receive the extruded cartilage. Increase the pressure gradually, over a period of 4 to 5 minutes. During this interval, the area becomes numb so that you can increase the pressure until it is felt that the tip of the bunion has been pressed into the space where it belongs. When the foot is properly supported, present the bony tip of the right thumb just short of nail contact to the tip of the bunion. The curled right index finger supports the joint diametrically opposite to the contact of the thumb. The backs of both hands rest on the legs, which give needed support during treatment.

Step 3: Flexing and circumducting. Continue to hold the pressure with the right thumb while flexing the big toe up and down with the left hand. Use the same grasp as in the beginning, holding the big toe out of line toward the other toes. Gradually, change the up and down flexing into a circumduction. Let the circle of this circumduction widen to where it meets the straight line extension of the metatarsus, so that the toe swings through its in-line position. (Of course, make no attempt to force the toe beyond this position.)

Flexing/circumducting to treat bunions

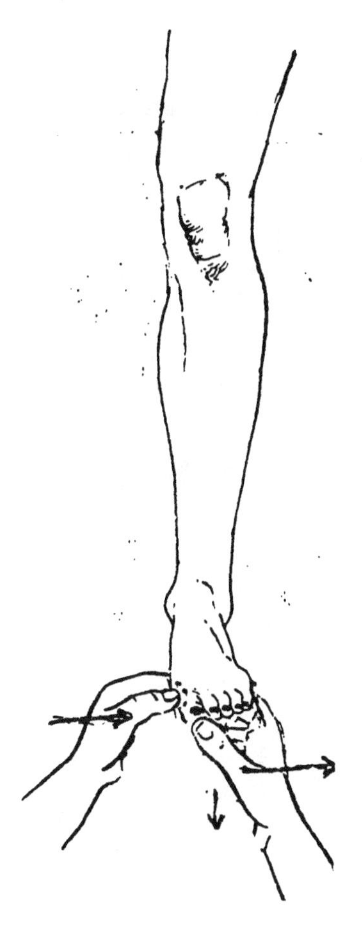

With the pressure of the right thumb, reintroduce the extruded cartilage into the capsule of the joint. These latter movements serve to remold this cartilage, so that it conforms to the joint within the capsule. At this point, conclude the treatment for the time being.

Step 4: Proper shoes. In all cases, once the cartilage has been remolded into the joint, it is important that the patient start wearing shoes that will support the foot on the medial side. It is difficult for the patient to visualize the significance of the abrupt change that has been achieved and to consider wearing shoes that will accommodate the change. The patient must understand that it is at the location of the bunion, where the foot now needs a firm and adequate support to hold the toe in line. The new supportive shoes must allow for the big toe to lie essentially in a straight ahead position. To foster this, a spacer (a pad or cushion) may be used between the big toe and the adjacent one. But such a spacer should never exceed 1/8 of an inch in thickness and should be employed only if the shoe is wide enough so that its use does not crowd the other toes. See all about shoes, page 7–30.

Frequency

In cases that are not too extreme, 1 treatment is often enough. In other cases, it will be necessary to repeat the treatment. Once a week will in general be sufficient until results are obtained.

The Heel

Many people complain about soreness or pain in the heel. The pain disturbs them in walking so that they cannot walk freely. In trying to compensate for their discomfort they change the natural manner of walking, which may set up additional disturbances. Others complain that pain or soreness in the heel does not let them rest properly at night. The discomfort is caused by pressure against the heel, as it lies on the bed.

Such conditions are largely due to a derangement of the soft tissues around the heel bone (calcaneus). The soft tissues are frequently mismolded, with respect to this bone, by the shoe. These tissues are squeezed out from under the heel and pushed around to the side. Once this has occurred, the shoes don't fit any more and that is what causes the trouble. The deranged condition is primarily caused by a flowing or creeping within the soft tissues. This is caused directly by high unit pressures that arise when the heel bone is subjected to excessive shock or high compressive forces. A callus may form where the heel is squeezed into the back of the shoe, which, if very pronounced, has to be removed before treatment is effective. The importance of being attentive to the fit of the shoe is obvious and should hardly need to be mentioned.

Remolding the tissues

➧ **Step 1: Treatment for pain in the heel.** By cradling the heel between the palms of the hands with the fingers interlaced, the tissues can be remolded. Draw the tissue downward and beneath the heel bone. Apply this molding action with the intent of repositioning the tissue to where it naturally belongs. Also it is helpful to mold the loosened tissue with the fingers or by cradling the heel in the palm of one hand. The person may be taught to self-administer this treatment.

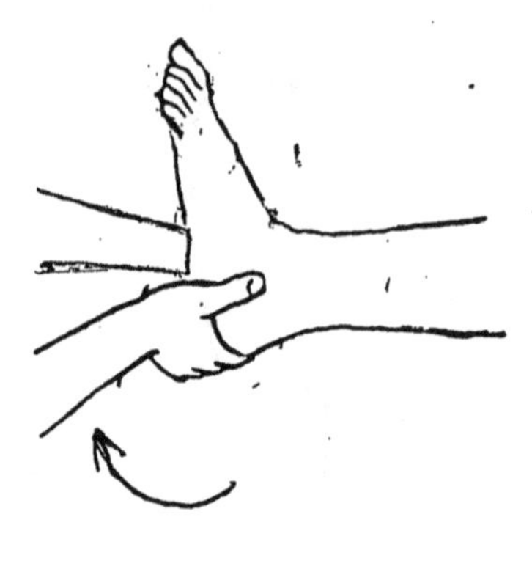

A Spur (Pocket of Fluid) on the Heel

Unreasonable pressure and side thrusts caused by jumping onto a hard surface from some height, or by running hard or kicking hard with the heel may damage the heel tissue and cause bruises (contusions). Thin and worn heel tissue may be torn loose from the bone covering, forming pockets where fluids accumulate, a breeding place for problems. If nothing is done to help the injured area, and if the person continues the problem-causing behavior, nature compensates and frequently a spur begins to form. Such a spur need not be viewed as a mysterious deposit but be considered as a manifestation of nature's own compensation.

➧ **Step 1: Examination by palpation.** In order to determine any possible pocket of fluid, use the technique of palpation (examination by touching). Employ, in a delicate and gentle way, the tips of two fingers (or a thumb and finger) to 2 contact points located just within and on opposite sides of the painful area. In palpating, never break these two contacts. In quick alternation, increase the pressure between the points of contact, first at one point then at the other, retaining the gentle and delicate nature of the contacts.

➧ **Step 2: Locate fluid pocket.** The detection is subtle; the palpation causes any fluid present between the two points of contact to fluctuate. Thus, by adjusting the points of contact, the size of the fluid pocket can be determined. It will usually coincide closely with the area of greater discomfort. Comparison with the other normal heel will also help in establishing the fluid pocket correctly.

➧ **Step 3: Treatment to disburse fluid.** When the fluid pocket has been established, perform very tiny circles around it along the outside perimeter; the circles are centered on the perimeter and sweep in and out of the area. Your intent is that the circles cause the circulation to absorb the trapped fluid in a gradual manner and carry it away. Allow adequate time for nature to do its part. As the treatment continues the perimeter will shrink, gradually coming into the center of the area. This will not necessarily occur in one treatment session.

Finally, work on the center of the fluid pocket. There will be no more fluid, no deposit, no spur left. Derangement of the circulation allowed the spur to form, and reestablishment of the circulation dissolves it. It is carried away and the normal condition is restored.

Continue to work and feed the area until eventually, a fully healed condition is achieved. When this is done there will again be, between the bone and the walking surface, a substantial cushion of tissue that firmly adheres to the bone. It is important, of course, that anything that caused the trouble be permanently avoided.

Achilles Tendon

This tendon can become hardened, shortened, sore and painful in flexing. The trouble can extend from where the sheaths of the separate muscles blend and join in the tendon, down to its insertion into the heel bone.

It is always good to check out the muscles involved with the Achilles tendon even as far up as the area behind the knee. The heel, too, is often involved. The back of the shoe may be too firm and its upper edge may gouge into the tendon; sandal straps may be too rigid. Any such disturbance can cause bulges along the tendon. The connected structure consisting of muscles, sheaths and tendons from behind the knee to the heel can sometimes feel sprained; thus, if the leg isn't considered, the tendon will continue to be sprained and sore. The condition may finally become severely limiting or even incapacitating.

The achilles tendon

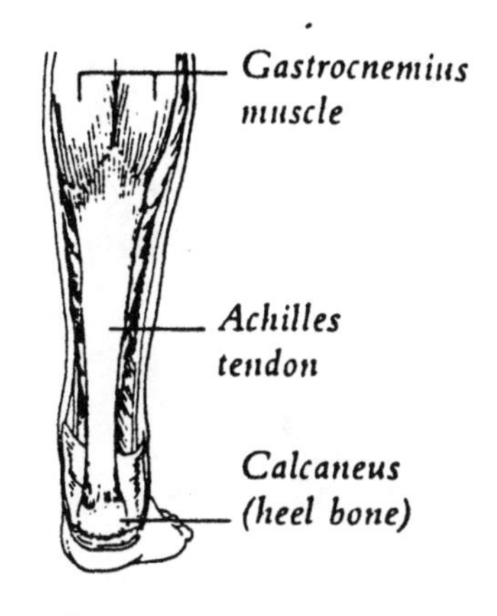

➧ **Step 1:** Massage over the tendon in an upward and downward direction with flat fingers. This movement is like that of softening a leather strap. Use plenty of oil and let the middle finger play the more prominent role. The adjacent fingers should just fit themselves in. Use the breaking up massage on the center and from each side as necessary.

Calluses

Calluses may form on the sole of the foot and around the edges of the sole, or the entire bottom of the foot may become encased in callus. Under the ball of the foot and occasionally under the heel, calluses sometimes take on a cone-shaped form. These can penetrate deeply, almost to the bone. These calluses can all be softened and removed with the help of brown *Octagon* soap or *Fels Naptha* soap. If these soaps are not available, other brown laundry soaps must be tried until one is found that will serve the particular person. The Octagon soap seemed to work for everyone; Mr. Stephenson felt that its pine-rosin content made it such an effective agent. The important feature of this method is that it involves no risk to the living tissue.

➧ **Step 1: Make a paste.** Cut the soap into fine shavings, place them in a jar and add enough water to make a paste. Spread the paste into the mesh of the hose or sock to be worn, so that it will contact the callused area. Apply fresh daily.

No open toe or sandal-type shoe should be worn; rather, the shoe should enclose the foot completely so that the perspiration can work in conjunction with the soap to make a lather that will penetrate the callus and soften it.

➧ **Step 2: Soaking.** After 2 or 3 weeks of this procedure, when the callus has softened and loosened, soak the foot in warm water. Rub back and forth with the fingers, first underwater, and then as the foot is dried; the callus can be raised and actually rolled off the foot. Continue until the foot is completely clear of the callus. Through the soaking, the cone-shaped deep calluses on the ball and heel will also be loosened and these can then be gently lifted out.

Corns

Corns and calluses are brought on both by friction and by uneven pressure on the foot caused by hose or shoes that are too loose or too tight. Excessive pressure on the toes may occur at the center of the physiological arch, caused by tramped down cartilage. These cartilages must be remolded to prevent calluses or corns from forming. See the fallen arches treatment for replacement of cartilage on bottom of foot, page 7–33. Corns, including soft corns between the toes, may also be caused by the wrong shape or fit of the shoe. If these causes are eliminated and proper treatment is applied, the corns will slough off and will not recur once they are removed.

➧ **Step 1:** For a soft corn between the toes, Mr. Stephenson advised placing four thicknesses of toilet paper between the affected toes. These layers of paper break the friction exerted by the toes on one another. The paper also lets in the air. The corn will finally loosen so that it can be lifted out.

Athlete's Foot

The characteristic feature of Mr. Stephenson's approach to athlete's foot is to see it in connection with leather rot. Athlete's foot, according to Mr. Stephenson, simply is leather rot—a transfer of decomposition elements inherent in leather onto or into the human body. Mr. Stephenson pointed out that leather cannot be brought to a stable, inert condition; even tanning the leather cannot destroy the decomposition process. This is seen by placing a good pair of tanned shoes into a dark, damp closet; in a few days, the shoes will be covered with what is commonly called mold—the decomposition effect. Dampness and darkness both generate and accelerate the transfer of decomposition elements of unstable leather to the body; a sweaty foot in a closed shoe is a perfect setting.

Athlete's foot contracted at swimming pools in damp showers is, without exception, caused by a transference of material deposited there by the tread of an infected foot or by contamination carried about by other means. The origin is always the decomposition principle in leather.

Mr. Stephenson also called attention to the possible threat involved in sitting on crumbling or decomposing leather surfaces, such as old chairs. He called attention to the possible threat in wearing leather garments in which the crotch and armpits are particularly vulnerable under sweating conditions. He also added that working in leather factories, where the crumbling dust from leather is allowed to accumulate, may cause leather rot if the dust is in contact with the sweating body. In advanced stages, this condition may appear similar to leprosy.

Athlete's foot is generally considered a fungus attack on the body. A common mistake is often made by trying to kill the fungus by using strong medications, which can burn the delicate healing tissue trying to expel the affected, diseased tissue. If the reconstructing tissue is burned, circulation there will be stopped, and rot will continue to grow.

To self-heal athlete's foot, cleanse the affected parts by bathing them in a mild soapy solution. In a severe case, do this twice a day. Dry by blotting, not rubbing. Finish off by softly and gently blowing the breath over the affected area, from a distance of 12 to 14 inches.

After the bath, fresh socks should be put on; white cotton socks are preferred. Circulation should be preserved and enhanced in every possible way. If the feet are affected and become swollen, wear larger shoes and socks. If the feet or hands are badly affected, the trouble may penetrate to the nails. In certain stubborn cases, striking results have been achieved by soaking the affected parts in the tea foot bath (see foot odors, below). These procedures are the best for care and healing because they favor the delicate reconstructing tissues that are striving to fulfill their vital task.

The Creative Healer will also use the cooling treatment, applied to the affected part without touching as for eczema and will spread the affected toes or the fingers as the treatment is applied.

Foot Odors

Tea Foot Bath

The tea foot bath may be used in many cases to cleanse the system. Certain conditions indicate using the tea foot bath: when the feet have a particularly foul odor; when after removing hose or socks and walking with bare feet on a tile or linoleum floor an uncommon degree of sticking to the surface of the floor occurs; or when, as the feet are massaged, a sticky substance oozing from the pores of the feet clings to the hands.

Sediment in the blood stream is drawn to and settles into the lower extremities. Stickiness of the feet indicated to Mr. Stephenson the presence of a heavier accumulation of sediment than is considered normal. Since the pores of the feet are the largest of the body, he used the tea bath to draw out, through these pores, a goodly portion of this heavier accumulation of sediment. This relieves the overtaxing of the general circulation and eliminative organs.

The tea used for the tea foot bath is English black tea, cured by the fermenting process. The most widely known varieties are Pekoe and Orange Pekoe. Prepare the solution by steeping the tea leaves to the strength ordinarily used for drinking. The temperature should be such that it can be accepted with comfort. Soak the feet until the solution cools and its drawing power is reduced, usually 12 to 15 minutes. If the solution is kept in an enamel pail with a lid, it can be used 2 or 3 times.

Any "improvement" by way of using a stronger solution or a higher temperature would defeat the purpose of the bath because it would burn the delicate tissues that are vital for recovery.

The tea bath is primarily for the feet but is often effective for gout, fungus under the nails (toe or finger) and problems that start farther up in the legs.

Additional Leg Treatments

Restless Leg Syndrome

Persons who have restless leg syndrome find it hard to describe their symptoms. Some descriptions are: crawling sensation, legs have a life of their own, pins and needles feeling, and legs move without instructions.

The treatment for this can be self-taught to the patient to perform at night while sitting or standing.

➧ **Step 1: Strumming.** Perform the strumming to the back of the thigh from the outside to the inner. If this does not work for the individual then strum from inside to outside. For strumming description, see posterior of thigh, page 7–13.

➧ **Step 2: Area near knee.** Clean out with medium pressure an area on the front of the thigh above the knee cap. The area will feel sore and can be contacted only when the patient is standing.

➧ **Step 3:** Also do any of the other treatments on the front and back of the thigh such as raking, page 7–15, to make sure all is well.

Legs of Uneven Length

Occasionally, you will come across a case of legs that are of uneven length. The body needs to function symmetrically in the motions it is expected to perform so when such a condition exists, it is the effect of residual muscular contractions. These may be caused by the state of the muscular tissue crossed by a nerve. The nerve may feel lumpy or taut as a string or it may sag. As these residual contractions yield to massage treatments and the legs are brought back to equal length, the treatments for twisted hip, page 7–16, should be considered.

Work with the intent of molding the softer tissues and breaking up contractions and obstructions. For the legs to function well, the thigh muscles must be normalized and in a good state of tone. Pay particular attention to these muscles.

Position

Patient lies on the back. Creative Healer stands next to the patient.

➧ **Step 1: Massage the thigh.** Massage in an upward direction on the front and back of the thigh, and in a downward direction over the narrow width of the lower sciatic nerve on the back of the leg. In contrast, the direction is always upward over the channel of the upper sciatic nerve on the medial front of the leg. This is stressed in the upper leg treatment.

➧ **Step 2:** Grasp the ankles of both feet, lift them off the bed a few inches and move them together from side to side. It is good to realize that a point may be reached when no further progress can take place unless the body is asked to make the effort for symmetric motion.

➧ **Step 3:** Also apply the twisted hip treatment, page 7–16.

The person must sit, stand or walk in a deliberate way to overcome the problem completely.

One Foot Turns Outward When Walking

It is often useful to determine whether the person, when lying supine with legs extended, can rotate them inward, one at a time, about their own axis so that the medial sides of the feet are flat on the surface on which the person is reclining. If assistance is needed to accomplish this, lift upward from beneath or behind the trochanter to help in the rotation. Seek to determine what needs to be freed up additionally (usually the sciatic nerve) in order that the person will ultimately be able to perform the movement without assistance.

This description shows the vital importance of the sciatic nerves in controlling the motion of the legs. The person must walk in a deliberate way to correct this problem.

Varicose Veins

Most people, prompted by the undesirable appearance of varicose veins, have the idea that the trouble lies with an inadequate return flow in the venous and lymphatic systems. There is, however, an entirely different picture. The immediate cause of varicose veins is a lack of vigor and disruption of the deeper arterial circulation. It follows that as the condition gets progressively worse, the feet always get progressively colder.

Because an interference with arterial circulation lies at the root of the problem, it is exclusively to this arterial aspect of circulation that the Creative Healing treatment is directed. Varicose veins develop because the deep arterial flow coursing down the leg is forced by congestion and obstruction to turn aside and detour through veins that are already over-burdened.

Arterial blood flow should continue down the leg and through the foot. The blood should then return through the much more numerous natural channels that are available to it. Because this does not happen, the feet are affected and become increasingly colder.

The purpose of the healing treatment is to regulate the deeper arterial circulation so that it passes completely through to the feet. Results will be gradual but certain; the patient should not expect day-to-day progress, but a month or two of treatments will show a definite change and improvement. In almost all cases, the veins will be improved to the extent that they no longer protrude above the surface. Without fail, warmer feet will be reported in proportion to other progress. The discoloration, however, cannot always be alleviated.

A person with varicose veins who has to stand long hours, especially on cement, needs support hose of proper fit. But, if the support hose extend above the knee and the person attempts to sit without lowering them below the knee, there is every likelihood that they may cut off circulation and no improvement can be expected. This is because of the stiffness and wrinkling of the support hose and the high unit pressures it may present to the tissues of the popliteal space. Use natural fiber clothing and avoid nylon hose.

➤➤➤CAUTION: It must be emphasized that varicose veins, themselves, must never be massaged or pressed. Direct any massage alongside such a vein so that the action penetrates, when needed, to the region beneath the vein.

Position

Patient sits in a chair and the Creative Healer sits opposite. The patient's right foot rests to the Creative Healer's left side on the Creative Healer's couch or bench.

➧ **Step 1: Foot massage.** Massage as in the sprained ankle treatment, earlier in this chapter, always in the downward direction, but confine the massage to the foot. The foot is not supported at this time. Do not reach much above the ankle. Press downward and into the toes with the intention of speeding up circulation into the foot. During this part of the treatment, occasionally touch the filter cavity on the ankle with a downward-directed, circular movement. Let the finger work like a little pump. This action pumps the blood downward toward the sole and toes as it cleans out the filter, enabling it to again act as a distribution center.

Work on the foot with a downward massage and the pumping at the ankle filter for a total of 3 or 4 minutes.

➧ **Step 2: Protrusion of veins.** Lower the foot to the floor and work on the other foot. Watch to see whether the veins at the surface of the first foot become more flush, carrying more blood. They may stand out, well demarcated, even at the base of the toes. The protrusion of these veins in the foot does not mean that they, too, will become varicose veins. On the contrary, it is a good sign.

The filled filter cavities can be treated with the circular pumping movement both while the foot is raised and when it is on the floor.

➤➤➤CAUTION: As a rule, all the work on the filters should not exceed 2 minutes during any one treatment.

You must be cautious with each case and with each foot, especially with the work on the filters, not to release at any one time too much bad blood into the foot; blood is bad when it has been stagnant and therefore in poor condition. Too great a release might cause congestion in the foot. Do not be too anxious to hurry the progress; for example, do not push to obtain the raised veins but work to feed things in gradually.

➧ **Step 3: Teach filter treatment.** Teach the patient to perform the circular pumping movement in the filter cavities. It should be done twice daily for not more than 2 minutes each time. Also teach the patient to do step 6 of the displaced cartilage of the knee treatment, page 7–21, to clear the space behind the knee of any congestion. The movement is best performed with the foot down. If that is not convenient, the foot may be supported against the edge of a bed. After this pumping treatment, the feet should be set down on the floor. During the self-treatments and immediately afterward, no shoes should be worn.

➧ **Step 4: Raising the legs.** Besides applying the above treatments, the patient will find it helpful at other times, to raise the legs. This will enhance circulation by providing a greater differential of the pressures within the leg.

This treatment attacks the main obstructions in any varicose vein condition but it is more completely effective, without additional types of treatment, if the varicose veins are below the knee. In successive sessions (once a week should be sufficient) gradually work, when necessary, to break up residual contractions in the calf.

From the writings of Joseph B. Stephenson

A woman suffering from varicose veins couldn't be on her feet at all. The veins had erupted into oozing ulcers and threatened gangrene. A doctor had cleaned the sores, bandaged the legs and changed the dressings every three days but they smelled because they were so badly infected; the doctors were talking about amputation.

Mr. Stephenson came to see her and with the bandages still on her legs (he never removed doctors' dressings), he made hand passes down over her legs and feet, never touching her.

"Are you massaging my legs?" she asked. "I can feel what you are doing."

He told her that he was not touching her and gave her several treatments in that manner. After he had come to see her twice more, he taught her how to do the same thing for herself, for "two minutes, twice a day."

"You don't want to do it for too long at a time because you are actually causing the bloodstream to move and agitate. If you overdo it you will be bringing the bad blood back into the circulation too quickly; you will be releasing too much poison into the system."

She did as she was told and in three weeks she was completely healed.

Varicose Veins Above the Knee

To treat varicose veins occurring above the knee, check the groin, the muscles in the thigh, the kidneys, the sciatic nerves and any restrictive garments for the cause of the problem. You may find that pain attributed to varicose veins is actually caused by the sciatic nerves not carrying the full life force they should carry. If they are treated, the pain disappears.

Numbness in the Legs

In conditions of pain and numbness in the legs, particular attention should be paid to seating arrangements. Continued numbness, a feeling of deadness or slow progress in recovery are often caused by sitting too long, or by sitting on a surface whose contour does not provide an equal distribution of pressure but exerts instead, higher pressure at particular spots. Such surfaces should be avoided.

If seats are too soft, the surface will allow the legs to sink into it and there will be a tendency for the tissues to be pressed up around on each side of the bone. From this, a detrimental blocking of the circulation can result. Seating that allows the "sit upon" (ischial) bones and the buttocks to sink into a socket-like support and allows the hips to rotate backward, can readily throw the back into a poor position. This blocks circulation to the muscles of the back and can disturb the three natural curves of the spine and affect the legs.

Seating surfaces should be on the firm side. In severe cases of leg trouble, it is vital for the patient to pay careful attention to seating habits.

With a gentle massage, check the popliteal space behind the knee.There may be kernel-like formations or a lateral ridge in this space that will impede the flow of life and circulation. Break up these obstructions with a gentle breaking-up movement, using the flats of the fingers more than the tips. Do not massage over varicose veins, but direct the movements to regions underneath and on either side of these veins. (See the knee treatment, page 7–19, for details.)

Example from Creative Healers

A woman suffering numbness and difficulty after rising to walk, discovered that each time she sat down she immediately crossed her right leg over her left leg. She never sat with her legs uncrossed or never crossed the left leg over the right. The popliteal space under one knee was puffy and full of lumpy formations. That problem was relieved but it was necessary for her to change her habit of a lifetime to completely correct the problem.

Chapter 8 ♦ Men, Women and Children

Family Members can Help Each Other

The preceding chapters of this book describe the Stephenson Method of Natural Health Care used to restore the natural health of all people. This chapter presents discomforts with applications unique to the differences in male, female and children's bodies. Even with these differences, the underlying Creative Healing concept remains the same: remove the blocks that cause discomfort and facilitate the body's inherent self-healing system.

Because of women's unique physical biology and reproductive cycle, female bodies are more complicated than the male's. Mr. Stephenson has identified and provided treatments for over thirty women dysfunctions, while only twelve for the male body, relatively few distinctive problems according to Mr. Stephenson. All treatments are simple, non-invasive, gentle and effective.

Mr. Stephenson said that even a child twelve years of age with willing hands and a loving heart could do these treatments. These words are appropriate for the material in this chapter of the book because one does not have to know medical terms to understand the treatments; this makes them easy for everyone to do. If only one member of the family learns a few of the more common applications, the entire family can benefit.

Treatments for Men

Mumps in Adults

Mumps is not included in the childhood diseases because it does not produce a fever like the other diseases. Adult men with mumps were treated successfully by an experienced Creative Healer with 3 to 10 grams of vitamin C per day on the advice of a medical doctor. They did not get the sterility side effect that mumps produce in men.

Prostate Gland

Zigzag motion

When a man reaches middle-age, fluids during ejaculation are not expelled as completely and cleanly as in youth when muscle tone and vigor are more pronounced. The left-over secretions coat the walls of the ejaculatory duct, causing obstruction, which spreads, involving more of the surrounding ducts and tissues, reaching eventually the prostate gland. The prostate, located under the pubic bone (symphysis pubis), may then become swollen, inflamed, or abscessed. Because the urethra passes through the prostate, a swollen prostate will restrict urinary flow from the bladder. It is important that circulation moves freely in the region of the prostate; any congestion must be removed. If urinating is difficult or if voiding the bladder takes a long time, the prostate is usually involved.

Position

The patient lies on his back, his legs partially flexed and spread. The Creative Healer stands next to him.

➧ **Step 1: Zigzag motion.** Using the first two fingers or the middle finger and starting immediately forward of the anus at the median line, move the fingers back and forth in a lateral or side to side, partly overlapping zigzag motion. Continue this motion along the median line through the area of the scrotum, up to the base of the penis. The contact should be gentle, never causing distress. On a large man, the zigzag motions should extend about 1/2 inch on either side of the center line. Perform this motion very thoroughly. Slow the advance slightly when encountering thickened tissue, nodules or sensitive areas, to allow the motion to be more effective.

Breaking up movement

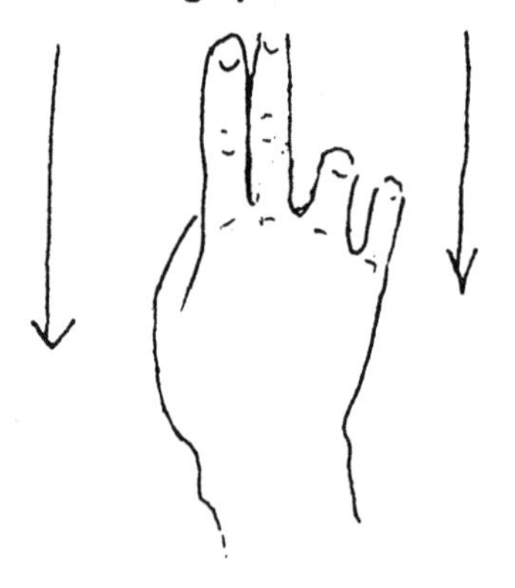

➧ **Step 2: Straight stroke.** When the zigzag motion has been completed, stroke 4 or 5 times along the full length of the same path with the same finger. Repeat the cycle of 1 zigzag plus 4 or 5 stroking motions, 3 times. In all, 4 cycles are performed.

➧ **Step 3: Breaking up movement.** If necessary, treat the prostate gland if congested. The prostate is relatively inaccessible and is treated by gentle circular breaking up movements in 4 places. Two of these are situated immediately above the pubic bone and 1 inch or so to each side of the median line. Use the circular breaking up movements here and direct them beneath the pubic bone toward the prostate. This causes the breaking up action to penetrate to the gland. Work in the same way from two spots similarly located below the pubic bone. Direct the circular movements from the posterior upward under the pubic overlay, again toward the prostate.

A frequent report after one application of this treatment is that during urinating the man observes the passing of a white gelatinous or crumbly substance. This shows the crumbling of the coating and its emission from the body. This process of emission need only be given a good start by the treatment. Nature will then complete it.

Instruct the man to self-administer this treatment. Several applications may be needed if the condition is severe, but advise him to be gentle so as not to cause irritation during the treatment. According to Mr. Stephenson, if a man uses this information and checks himself periodically, he will not need to worry about prostate trouble as long as he lives.

Varicocele

Varicocele occurs usually, but not always, in the left testicle and the ducts issuing from it. It is not known why the left testicle is more prone to this trouble. When varicocele occurs, the ducts issuing from the testicle are sometimes enlarged and lengthened, and sometimes they appear to be all curled up in the scrotum above the testicles. Upon palpation, they may feel like a "nest of worms." A man with such a condition will, at the very least, be aware of a constant disturbance, and can experience mild to severe pain. The usual treatment other than surgery is to wear an athletic support.

Mr. Stephenson felt this trouble is caused when the sexual urge is stimulated but the contemplated act is not carried through to completion. This stimulation begins the secretion of fluids from the testicles but they are not released from the body and remain within the tubes of the scrotum. Any subsequent sexual stimulation results in an enlargement or elongation of the tubes in order to accommodate the fluids generated. This process leads to a distressing condition or even to ill health. The true answer to the situation is, of course, to not stimulate or tease bodily functions unless intending to carry through to the full act. If this stimulation is stopped, the body will eventually heal itself.

To treat varicocele, massage upward through the groins in the usual manner for groin treatment; see crippled leg, page 7–5. Continue the massage further upward over the edge of the pubic bone and over the groin area into the abdomen. The massage must be gentle and directed upward. Before beginning, make sure the bladder is empty. This treatment relieves the stresses in the muscles. The discomfort is further relieved by pressing the bed wetting spots, page 5–51.

Hydrocele

The term hydrocele denotes a collection of fluids within the scrotum. This is most frequently brought on by lifting and straining. The seepage takes place through the weakened area of the bed wetting spots. Doctors can withdraw the fluid with a needle, and it is ideal if the bed wetting spots can be treated before new seepage accumulates.

The treatment consists of applying a molding pressure to each bed wetting spot; see page 5–51. The pressure is directed toward the center of the spot from its perimeter, as though gathering additional material and compacting it into the spot with successive pressings. The intention is that of strengthening the natural forces to block the line of seepage. In minor cases, withdrawing the fluid with the needle may not be necessary.

Frequent Night Emissions

Uncontrolled, frequent emissions may so debilitate the body that the man becomes incapacitated. Such a state may be brought on by injury, excessive masturbation or uncontrolled thoughts. When the body's control mechanism is weakened, lying asleep on the back will cause repeated semen ejaculation. The problem is due to the heating of the mid-lumbar region through body heat when this region is in contact with the bed. Treat with the quarter twist (replacing substance) on the spine at the first space below the main feeding spot for the kidneys, page 5–43. The nerve center located there controls the principal feed of nerve life to the reproductive organs, both male and female. All treatments for reproductive system disorders should include checking this spot and, if necessary, centering and replacing the nerve center.

The body's control mechanism can also be strengthened by pressing the bed wetting spots but until the control is fully strengthened, the man must avoid sleeping on his back.

Treatments for Women

Basic Female Treatment

The vagina puts forth three glandular secretions that may be called glandular oils. One performs a strong cleansing action, one serves to heal possible injuries and the third one lubricates. When one of the glands doesn't function properly, a sensation of burning, a yeast infection or an unbearable itch may develop in the vagina. If the second and third glands don't function properly there may be the pain of a dry vagina. What appears to be an infection of the vaginal tract or a lack of hormones may be eliminated by this simple treatment that balances the three secretions. If the three secretions are balanced, the vagina and other reproductive organs need no artificial cleanser or douches, but will stay clean.

The basic female treatment is not given during the patient's menstrual period except as noted under menstrual pain, page 8–7, and menopause troubles, page 8–16.

Position

The patient lies on her back. The Creative Healer sits at her right side at a comfortable height, high enough to allow the arm to operate freely above the patient without strain. It is comforting and reassuring to the patient if your free hand rests quietly on the patient's arm or the side of her body during the treatment. Liberal use of olive oil from a dispenser close at hand makes these treatments easy to give and to receive. Mr. Stephenson said that natural olive oil agreed with more peoples' skin than any other oil and would act like surgical gloves to protect both parties.

➧ **Step 1: Check abdomen temperature.** Before beginning the treatment, check the abdomen to be certain the temperature is normal; if the abdomen feels above normal do not massage it. The cooling treatment without touching, page 8–27, should be given instead and this female treatment given in another session.

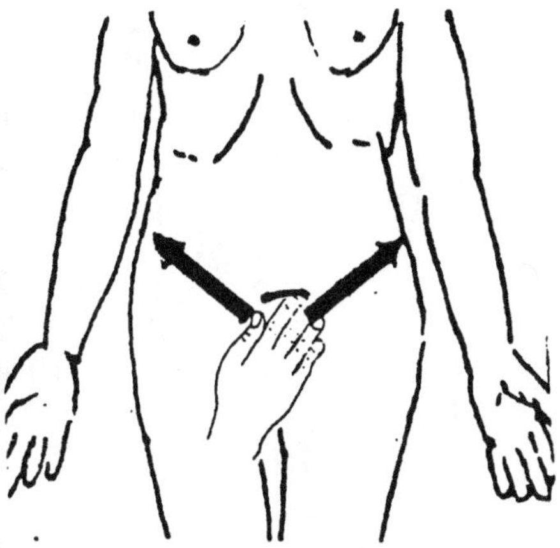

➧ **Step 2: Massage over tubes.** With the fingertips of the right hand, touch the body just above the pubic bone, and as fingers progress toward the side of the body just above the hip bone, the palm and the rest of the hand make contact with the body. Hold the fingers and thumb together. The hand moves diagonally upward and toward the side of the body, over the ovaries, with gentle strokes. The total hand movement is about 8 to 10 inches long. The strokes are so light at first that any small pocket of heat is removed. There is no compression of tissues and even in the most sensitive cases, there should be no pain or even discomfort. As the gentle treatment continues, any sensitivity will diminish and the hand (particularly the middle fingers) can gradually enter deeply into the tissue but never beyond the point of comfort.

Massage and drain

Work on one side until the sensitivity has decreased then do an equal amount of work on the other side. This may require 15–20 minutes of stroking on each side. You can alternate the stroking between the two sides but do not switch too often. It is better to bring one side to completion, then the other. If the abdomen does not gradually soften and yield to the fingers, do not continue the treatment. At a later time, the sensitivity will yield. The patient's sensitivity is always the guide.

➧ **Step 3: Drainage movement.** As you continue with the massage movement and the sensitivity has decreased, the drainage movement can be applied as the fingers enter deeply into the tissue. Depending on the firmness of the abdominal muscles, the fingers may reach a depth of 1/2 to 1 inch. When you have reached this state of the drainage movement, apply a few deep strokes, then treat the other side in the same way.

Centering muscles

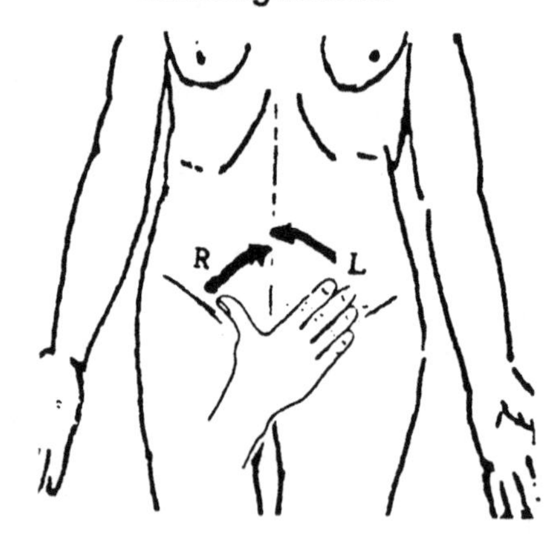

Step 4: Centering muscles. The second part consists of centering the muscles above the pubic bone. With the first 2 fingers, enter the tissue just above the pubic bone on the patient's left side, about 1 1/2 inch from the center line. Move all the tissue toward and nearly to the center line, being careful never to push the tissue beyond it. Repeat over an area extending 2 to 3 inches upward from the pubic bone. Perform the same motions on the right side of the median, using the thumb. The fingers and the thumb, used on the 2 sides, enter the tissue to a depth of at !east 1 inch but must do so without any appreciable discomfort.

If obstructions are encountered during the centering movement, explore the region extending laterally about 2 1/2 inches from the median line and several inches upward from the pubic bone and apply the breaking up movement to the area before completing the centering. The breaking up movement consists of making small circles with the fingers over an area (carrying the skin with the movement) where obstructions are detected. Work inward toward the median over the entire area until it feels uniformly soft and pliable, then center the muscles as described.

Press bed wetting spots

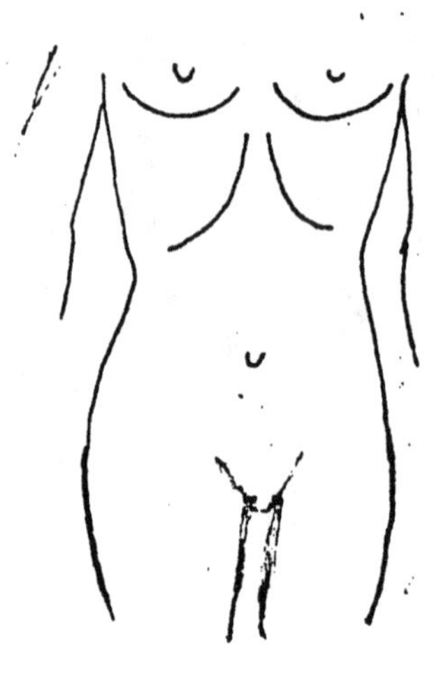

Step 5: Pressing bed wetting spots. To locate the bed-wetting spots, stand at the right side of the patient and place your left hand on her right shoulder. Place the palm of your right hand on the lower abdomen with fingers extended toward the feet. Curl the index finger over the lower edge of the right side of the pubic bone. The first depression or cavity encountered is the bed wetting spot. The left spot is found in a corresponding manner. When the index finger has contacted the cavity, pause for a moment to make sure that the patient is relaxed. Then press quite firmly toward the head, parallel to the spine, using the pad of the index finger. Release at once. Repeat on the left side.

This pressing action almost always causes a sharp sensation producing an involuntary recoil within the body, which causes the muscles to draw up and reestablishes their control. It affects not only the muscles surrounding the sphincter of the bladder but also the other muscles on the floor of the pelvis and the muscles fanning out from there, on each side, into the abdomen. With this in mind, one can understand the effect of pressing the bed wetting spots in cases of female disorders.

The patient must be relaxed for this treatment. This is not always easy to achieve, especially in connection with the second spot. If the patient is tense with anticipation, have her take a deep breath and exert pressure when she exhales. The sharp sensation caused by the pressing usually subsides within a minute or so. On the rare occasion in which a pain is still felt 5 minutes after the initial pressing, touch the spot again, this time sustaining the pressure; the painful sensation will vanish.

In some cases of female disorders, repeated applications may be needed. Pressing these spots is valuable in cases where there is dribbling of urine because the valve of the urethra does not close. To treat for this, only one treatment is usually needed. In addition, give the bearing down pain treatment, page 5–37, to help strengthen the muscles in the pelvic floor.

➧ **Step 6: Centering a nerve.** The final part of the treatment is the centering of a nerve on the lower edge of the pubic bone. On the median line of the lower edge of the pubic bone there is a groove in which the nerve should lie when it is in the correct position. In this, its normal position, it cannot be felt. However, the nerve may be dislocated by as much as 1/2 inch and may be swollen and enlarged, like a thick cord. Use the edge of the forefinger with a scraping movement over the lower edge of the pubic bone, from each side to the center groove, to carry the nerve back into place. This movement is similar to the centering of the nerve in the chin in the pain in the face treatment. If the nerve is dislocated, repeat the centering movement several times during the initial treatment. Even then, it may not stay at center and the centering movement may have to be repeated at later sessions or at intervals that allow time for the swelling to reduce.

The process may be taught to the patient. Then she can treat the nerve herself until it stays at center. This may be done even when there is sensitivity.

Example from Creative Healers

A patient's upper legs were stiff and hard and very painful from the pelvis to the knees. When step 5 of the female treatment was given, the legs softened, the pain decreased and next day the legs were normal.

➧ **Step 7: Check nerve life to the reproductive organs.** The patient sits erect on a bench for this part of the treatment. While sitting behind the patient, place the palms of your hands in the space above the hips on the back. Let your palms cup the fleshy area between the ribs and the hip bone so that the lower edge of the hands rest on the hipbones. Pull your hands to the center line so that your wrists touch and raise your thumbs straight up. The thumbs will be on the approximate location of the kidney spot. The nerve center controlling the principal feed of nerve life to the reproductive organs, for both males and females, is found between the vertebrae just below the main feeding spot for the kidneys. With the thumb, perform a quarter twist at that spot and also in the space above and the space below the identified space. Perform the quarter twist on both sides and on the center of each vertebra to reposition the substance or relieve any contraction.

Menstrual Pain

During a normal menstruation, the cervix opens wide to let the blood flow out freely and then closes again, much like a faucet is opened to let out water and then shut off. The principal cause for dysfunction and pain in connection with the menstrual period is the inability of the cervix to relax and let sufficient air into the uterus to allow the blood to flow out. The comparison is drawn with a bottle such as a ketchup bottle: the contents will not flow out unless air enters the bottle.

Dysfunction and pain can be explained as follows: When the covering on the inside wall of the uterus sheds away in the monthly cycle and bleeding commences, the cervix does not open to release blood through the natural channel. Pressure builds up within the uterus causing pain. Blood is trapped and pressure continues to build forcing the cervix to let out a small amount of blood, which also allows a small amount of air to enter. The cervix contracts and closes tightly again. The heat of the uterus expands the air, increasing the pressure, and clotting the blood, which further obstructs the opening of the cervix. As the pressure increases, becoming more and more painful, the cervix is finally forced again to open slightly and the same cycle repeats. This may go on for as long as 2 or 3 days until the buildup of pressure forces the cervix to open wide and let in an amount of air sufficient for the blood to flow out freely. Then the pain is gone.

To relieve menstrual dysfunction and pain, the full basic female treatment, page 8–4, is applied 1 to 5 days before the start of the menstrual period. One application is often sufficient, but if it does not bring complete relief, repeat it every month as needed. It is effective with every degree of menstrual trouble and at every age.

In giving the treatment, your mind is creating the thought of relaxed muscles around the cervix that will allow air to enter freely when the menstrual period begins. You are creating a vacuum that will draw air into the uterus through the cervix, though it will not actually enter before the menstrual period begins. If the menstrual period has followed a regular pattern before the treatment, it will usually begin 2 or 3 days earlier, after the treatment has been administered. This shows that it had, before the correction, followed a delayed pattern. If, after the menstrual period is over, there continues to be a little show of blood over several days or even a considerable length of time, this means that the cervix is too weak to completely close. It needs the strengthening that another treatment will give.

When treatments have been given several times and perhaps some improvement has been noted but pronounced difficulty with clotting still persists, it may be necessary to treat **once, during** the menstrual period. In this case, give only the first step of the treatment and stroke for 15 minutes. Be guided by the intention of getting more air to enter the cervix, which will cause a more profuse discharge, strong enough to carry the clots away. It is necessary to make the flow increase, even slightly, to have the desired effect of carrying away the clots.

Menstrual Trouble: Tampons

In connection with menstrual trouble, it is important to realize that introducing into the vagina any object that acts as a plug, is contrary to the principle of a free out-flowing of the blood, as the basis of healthy menstruation.

Dysfunction of the Tubes and Ovaries

This dysfunction is usually accompanied by heavy congestion, with possible discharge of pus and other malodorous matter. The menstrual period will often be erratic and involve trouble from heavy clotting or profuse bleeding, with constant discomfort for the patient. Occasionally, there is such extreme pain and sensitivity to jarring motions, that the patient will not walk normally. There may also be such heat in the abdomen that the cooling treatment, page 8–27, has to be applied before any other treatment can be administered.

When the first step of the basic female treatment, page 8–4, is begun, provide a soothing, relaxing touch that relieves the patient's discomfort and pain. Work until you feel a flow or action taking place within the body. It will often be audible and the patient will sense the inner movement. When good action and normal temperature are obtained, do not immediately proceed to the deep drainage movement; it may be necessary to refrain from it for several treatments until the patient can accept it without discomfort. Ultimately, you can apply the entire treatment and all the steps will be helpful. Pressing the bed wetting spots also strengthens the abdominal muscles.

Fallen or Tilted Uterus or Bladder

The habit of crossing the arms and resting them on the abdomen presses internal organs onto the floor of the pelvis. This works in union with gravity to cause sag and to cut off the flow of action of the many vital functions of the organs and muscles. The constricting force of tight elastic waistbands or of hourglass-shaping foundation garments produces the same effect.

Those subjecting themselves to these effects are usually quite unaware of why they do not feel well or why they are nauseated and suffer from poor digestion, constipation and lack of energy. They should be made aware that these troubles will continue unless they change from the restrictive type of foundation garments and elastic bands. This is the only way to enable the muscles of the abdomen to regain their tone. According to Mr. Stephenson, normal clothing marks should disappear from the body within 10 minutes; if they linger longer it is a sign that the clothing restricts the body too much.

The treatment for a fallen womb or bladder is like fallen stomach, although differences will be pointed out as necessary.

➧ **Step 1: Preparatory massage.** Give a 10-minute preparatory massage; see fallen stomach: step 1, page 5–18. If the tubes and ovaries are in poor condition it may be necessary to precede this massage by the complete female reatment, page 8–4, to put the patient at ease.

➧ **Step 2: Patient use of olive oil.** If the uterus or bladder has prolapsed to the outside of the body, ask the patient to cover it with olive oil before you begin the lift. This way the replacement of the organs is accomplished without touching them. **Note:** Mr. Stephenson treated cases in which the entire uterus and bladder were outside the body and the covering mucous membrane would be black from contact with the air.

You may also have a patient get in the knee-chest position to bring the organ closer to its normal position before the lift

➧ **Step 3: Lifting.** When you have finished the preparatory massage, give the patient an opportunity to void the bladder. Then, sit at a distance that allows your arm to be extended full length so that your body weight can assist with the necessary lifting. Hold your thumb and index finger about 2 to 3 inches apart and place them just above the pubic bone. The rest of the hand is held vertically. In contrast to the fallen stomach treatment, the hand must retain the vertical position throughout the entire lift. As the lift proceeds, gradually let the thumb and index finger move farther and farther apart until the midpoint of their span contacts the body. Instead of bringing the whole hand, palm and all in contact with the body as in the fallen stomach treatment, just the leading edge of the thumb and hand establishes and maintains full contact. It may be necessary to make several starts moving the hand only far enough to have the thumb and index finger separate part way, not to their full span. As this initial movement is performed, a vacuum is created under the hand and starts to draw up the fallen tissues.

When you have achieved a real contact below the organ, proceed to the full lift, moving the hand slowly forward each time the patient exhales. This deliberate movement creates a long, strong vacuum under the entire leading edge of the hand. It is this vacuum that draws the fallen organs back up into position. The lift may be repeated until the organs are felt to be back in place.

Arm and hand position for lifting the fallen uterus or bladder

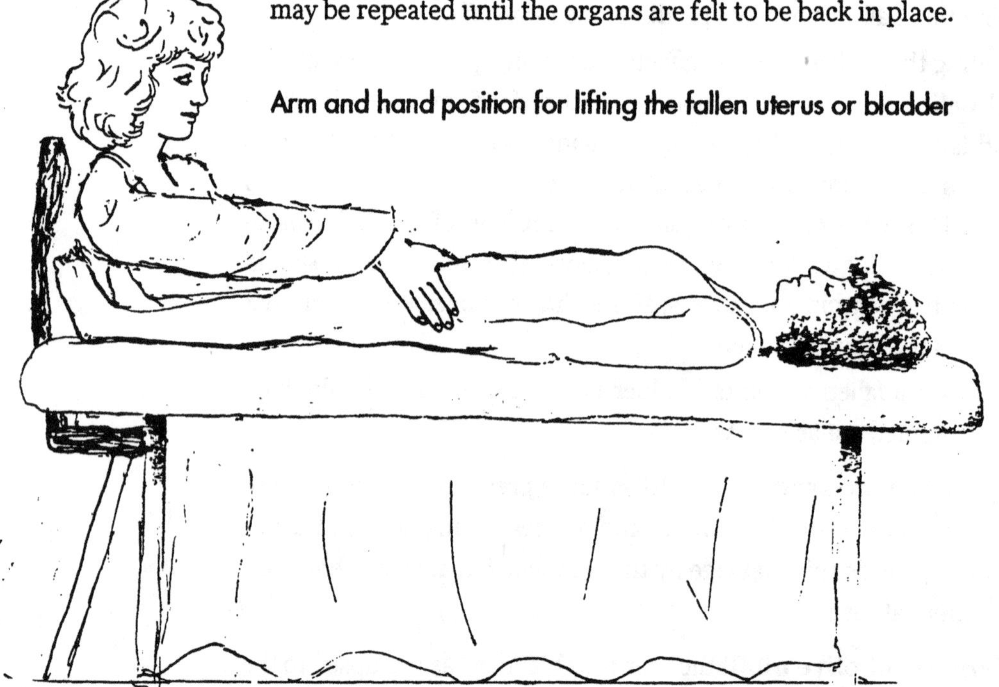

➧ **Step 4: Pressing bed wetting spots.** After performing the lift, immediately press the bed wetting spots. This causes the muscles to take hold and keep the organ in the natural position to which it has just been returned.

Tilted Uterus

With a tilted uterus, apply the same treatment. A tilted uterus is one that has not fallen uniformly, and one side has fallen while the other is still held up.

Example from Creative Healers

A mid-wife Creative Healer told of the success she had with this treatment with a new mother whose womb had come out during childbirth. She used the gentle bladder lift and everything slipped back into place without any pain.

Pain in the Vagina and Ovaries Area

The patient may complain of bearing down pain in the vagina. The condition of the muscles and nerve centers causing much pain is very similar to that described in the bearing down pain treatment.

Treat the condition of bearing down pain of the vagina by pressing the bed wetting spots. To thoroughly strengthen the lower pelvic region give also the bearing down pain treatment, page 5–37.

If the patient complains of pain during intercourse in one of the ovarian regions, it may be because the ovary is too high (up out of position). The trouble is easily remedied. Exert a gentle, gradual pressure with the tips of the index and middle fingers just higher than the ovary and directed to a place just behind or inferior to the anus. One treatment is usually sufficient to put the ovary back in place.

Polyps

A polyp found inside the labia or vagina, is nothing more than a little ruptured muscle. It is pear-shaped and to eliminate it you must cut off its source of nourishment. Trace it to its beginning where it is feeding, and if you pinch there very gently and hold the pinch for 30 seconds, it will be taken care of. In 3 or 4 weeks it will fall off when the patient is sitting on the toilet. She may never know when it falls off.

Reproductive Nerve Center Treatment

Treatments for female disorders should be completed by checking the nerve center that nourishes the reproductive organs. This center is the same for men and women and controls the organs' principal feed.

Position

The patient sits on a flat bench. The Creative Healer sits behind.

➧ **Step 1: Locate kidney feed spot.** Let your palms cup the fleshy area between the ribs and the hip bones so that the lower edge of the hands rest on the hip bones. Pull your hands to the center line so that your wrists touch and raise your thumbs straight up. The thumbs will be on the approximate location of the kidney spot.

➧ **Step 2: Reproductive spots.** The nerve center that controls the feed of nerve life to the reproductive organs is found at the first spot below the main feed for the kidneys on the spine.

➧ **Step 3: Center the nerve.** Using the quarter twist, reposition the substance on each side of the center of these vital vertebrae and the center of the spinal column.

Pregnancy and Miscarriage

Mr. Stephenson admonished his students to be very careful in treating pregnant women. Any touching, even the gentle stroking of the back of the neck, for example, might be construed by some as causing a miscarriage. Mr. Stephenson also gave strong assurance that in all his Creative Healing experience, there was no Creative Healing application that could interrupt a pregnancy, either unintentionally or intentionally. He believed there was no safe way to interrupt a pregnancy.

Miscarriage

If the reproductive organs are not strong, not quite in position, or not fully functioning, the neck of the cervix is often not capable of sustaining an airtight, closed state. If air is allowed to enter the cervix of a pregnant woman, a miscarriage may ensue.

The condition of the reproductive organs is often revealed by the nature of the menstruation. If there is spotting, this may be an indication that the cervix cannot hold its closed, airtight state. If a woman has had one or maybe several miscarriages, apply those parts of the female treatments that seem to be needed; see page 8–4. This should never be done while the woman is pregnant.

Other treatments can prepare a woman to carry a pregnancy and are aimed at strengthening the pelvic area: sciatica, page 3–23; hemorrhoid, page 5–35; bearing down pain, page 5–37; weak legs and feet, page 7–6; and the quarter twist to the entire spine, page 3–3.

Treatments Related to Pregnancy

Relief of Morning Sickness

The hook-like movement at the feeding notch for the spleen will relieve morning sickness in pregnancy; see page 5–13. Mr. Stephenson's explanation was that as the walls of the womb thicken and increase in weight, the womb wants to assume its most natural position according to gravity when the woman gets up in the morning. However, the womb is prevented from making this adjustment by the tightness of a certain ligament that is attached to it and which, by its tension, causes the agitation, leading to nausea. The feeding movement releases the ligament, allowing the womb to rotate to its natural position and thus removes the cause of the nausea.

Stretch Marks

Tearing and stretching damage to the tissues of the abdomen can be minimized by applying a warm olive oil massage gently to the skin, once or twice daily. Husbands can be taught to do this.

Binding after Childbirth

Mr. Stephenson used to say that our grandmothers knew enough to bind a woman's trunk securely after childbirth. This action assured that the ribcage would come down, be pulled in and resume its natural shape, and extra weight gained during pregnancy would be lost below the ribs.

Birth Defects

Mr. Stephenson believed that all birth defects except clubfoot, are caused by the scarring of the ovum as it descends the fallopian tube, if the tube is not free from scale and corrosion. This explains why it is so necessary to thoroughly clean out the tubes before attempting to induce action in the ovaries. See dysfunction of tubes and ovaries, page 8–9.

Mothers' Milk

If she has good milk, a mother should breast feed her baby up to 18 months. She should not, however, have the milk be the baby's sole food for that entire period.

If a mother has no milk you may bring it on by "seeing" the human fountain come into action. The milk will begin to flow.

If a woman has milk and she doesn't need any more and the breasts swell and are inflamed, use the Creative Healing principle of withdrawing heat without touching until the temperature is gone.

If the breasts are caked, remove heat and then gently massage the edges of the lumps or cakes. This may require several treatments. Husbands can learn it to relieve pain.

Mammary Glands

Mr. Stephenson saw that in all mammals the milk of the mother for the young is not manufactured within the mammary glands as might be supposed but within the walls of the womb itself. In humans, the mother's breasts serve to receive the milk from the blood stream. As long as a mother is nursing, the walls of her womb will remain in a very thickened state because of their milk production.

Breast Problems

Lumps In The Breast

Mr. Stephenson said that breast lumps are caused by:

- An injury to the breast by a blow sustained in an accident, a sudden jab by an object such as a broom handle or an umbrella, or by another person.
- Suction on the breast by other than a nursing child; blood is drawn into those chambers of the breast where milk would be if the woman was nursing. It is cut off from the general circulation and "spoils" causing little lumps to form. These might become discolored, festering sores and over a period of 2 years or more, irritations of this type could lead to more serious problems.

Position

For steps 1 and 2, patient lies on her back. Creative Healer sits to the right of patient.

For steps 3 and 4, patient sits on a bench. Creative Healer sits behind.

➧ **Step 1: Cool.** If the breast is in a badly bruised condition, either discolored or draining, it will be sensitive to the touch. Treat it first without touching, by the cooling treatment, page 8–27. Follow the contour of the breast with the hand without touching, and direct your thought toward draining out the purulent material. It will gradually make its own opening and be expelled. After this material has been expelled and the breast no longer drains, begin the next step.

➧ **Step 2: Stimulate circulation.** With plenty of oil on your fingers, let them circle around the breast just inside its outer margin. The middle finger plays the main role, so that the fingers will actually glide on the breast, but in a gentle manner. The pressure will compress the tissue only slightly. This movement creates action within the breast, which in turn stimulates circulation, which will move in a spiraling manner and eliminate any remaining congestion from those recesses and chambers that were the seat of the irritation. The hand moves clockwise on the right breast and counter clockwise on the left breast.

➧ **Step 3: Check the spine.** Check the spine, especially on the affected side, for cord-like formations that may extend from between the vertebrae on that side and continue parallel to the ribs toward the breast. Such formations are usually present on one side of the body only. Comparison of the two sides is always a valuable aid. These cord-like formations emanating from the spine may be detected by palpation, though frequently not apparent to the eye, or discernible to the superficial touch. An effective means of palpating is the scissors movement, applied from the sacrum to the base of the neck. What is felt as a cord-like formation seems to emanate from between the vertebrae. It is usually detectable for 2 or 3 inches, following a course parallel to the ribs, then buried at its end in the tissues.

➧ **Step 4: Use the quarter twist.** To correct such formations, start at the end of the cord near the spine. Bury the cord in the tissue by repeated quarter twists. Proceed in this manner as far out from the spine possible to replace displaced substance. Alternate the quarter twists with stroking movements away from the spine, parallel to the ribs in the area beyond that of the quarter twists. Also apply breaking up movements in the area beyond that of the quarter twists. By alternating these 3 movements, the whole cord formation will disappear. Repeat this treatment if necessary.

In addition, break up any muscle contractions high up under the arm between the shoulder blade and the ribs. A painful residual contraction is often found in this region and may be relieved by the treatment for contraction of muscles around the shoulder blade, page 3–15. Besides treating for lumps in the breast, this treatment has been used successfully in cases where the arm cannot be raised.

For women experiencing lumps in the breast, it is important to pay attention to proper garments. Tight shoulder straps or bands around the chest that constrict below the breast must be avoided. Marks made by a garment should disappear within 10 minutes after the garment is removed; if not, it is too tight.

Swollen Lymph Glands

If there is trouble with swelling glands in the region of the breast, consider the possibility of interference by underarm shaving or the use of antiperspirants. Any such interference must be eliminated so that the lymph system is not blocked by the interjection of unnatural agents from the outside.

A Draining Abscess

If the lump is draining, use a strong intention of the mind to visualize the cleanup from the very bottom and use the hands without touching to apply the cooling treatment, page 8–27. You may use a massage at the edges but if you heal it by heat withdrawal and the mind alone, no one can say you did any harm. Any breast lump can be massaged very gently by the breaking up movement around the edges of the lump as in the goiter treatment, page 2–20.

Discharging or Inflamed Nipples

When nipples are drawn in and a secretion is draining, do a circular movement with the palm of your hand above the body and create a drawing power of the concentrated mind to draw out the nipple. A drop of olive oil will clean it. When the nipple is elongated and inflamed, use the hand without touching to remove the heat and inflammation.

Menopause Troubles

Treating menopause symptoms can be understood based on Mr. Stephenson's view of these troubles. When the reproductive system is preparing to cease its function, the menstrual period becomes erratic, though it still follows some pattern, sometimes hard to discern and different for every woman. The body will still, from time to time, make the amount of blood necessary to rebuild the inner wall of the uterus as it did during the regular menstrual cycles. If the reproductive organs are healthy and able to release the accumulated excess blood, no trouble will arise. But if there is any congestion in these organs, the release of blood through the vagina will be delayed and excess blood will be sent to the head.

To relieve these disturbances, the basic female treatment, page 8–4, is administered and will strengthen the reproductive organs so that they can more readily release the accumulated excess blood. Clear the neck with the general treatment, page 1–8, to allow the blood channeled to the head to drain off more easily. If there is any profuse bleeding or bleeding that continues for many days you may give the basic female treatment while they are bleeding. (See explanation under menstrual pain, page 8–7.)

Abdominal Supports

Support should be like hands holding up the abdomen

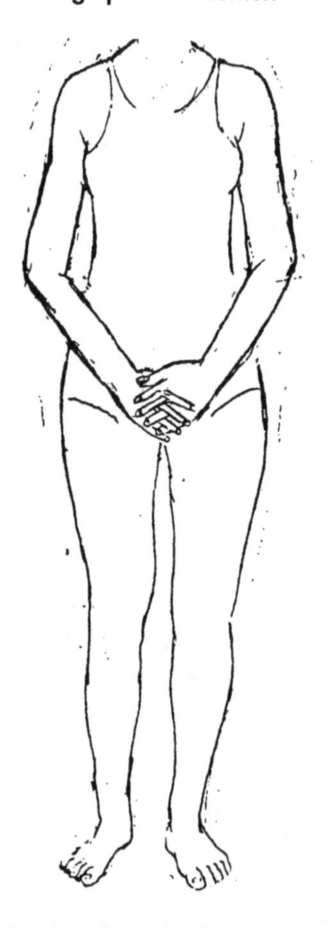

Because of the larger opening provided for the birth canal, the pelvic girdle is larger in a woman than in a man. Spanning this opening puts a greater demand on the abdominal muscles; therefore, women have more difficulty in doing heavy lifting and they are more vulnerable to a drop of the abdominal organs by straining the abdominal and pelvic muscles.

Whenever an organ is out of place, i.e., a fallen uterus or bladder, a fallen stomach or a floating kidney, the abdominal wall is poor and the patient will benefit from an abdominal support.

The muscles of the abdomen can be sprained, that is, subjected to stretching that tears the tissues, preventing them from returning to their natural position. Pain in such a case can be great and last for a long time until nature has compensated for the displaced tissues by building connective tissue rather than returning to the former natural state.

When this condition of sprained abdomen is recognized, particularly before compensating repair has been completed and when there is no pregnancy, the remedy is simple. It consists of binding the abdomen so that the tissues can move into their proper position and heal correctly. The binding will, almost immediately, relieve all aspects of pain. In lieu of a better provision, a piece of sheeting, or a towel securely fastened around the abdomen to draw it in and cradle it comfortably, will be adequate.

If the abdominal tissues are very weak, the abdomen may fall out of place when the person stands. This could happen in very heavy people, women after childbirth, or where injuries from a fall or some other reason causes a severe distension of the abdomen. In such cases, the muscle fibers may have stretched and torn such that they cannot reach against the distended abdomen to pull themselves together and heal properly. A temporary support is necessary to bring the organs and muscles back into position and hold them there until they are sufficiently strengthened. The support garment should provide a lift like that provided when the interlocked fingers are held under and against the abdomen, drawing it upward and a little inward. The support should exert pressure only over the area covered by the hands. The purpose is to lift and to allow unrestricted circulation above the supported area. Any pressure exerted at the waist would work against the purpose of the garment and would tend to push the organs down into the pelvis, like into a funnel.

Support could be a panty-type garment

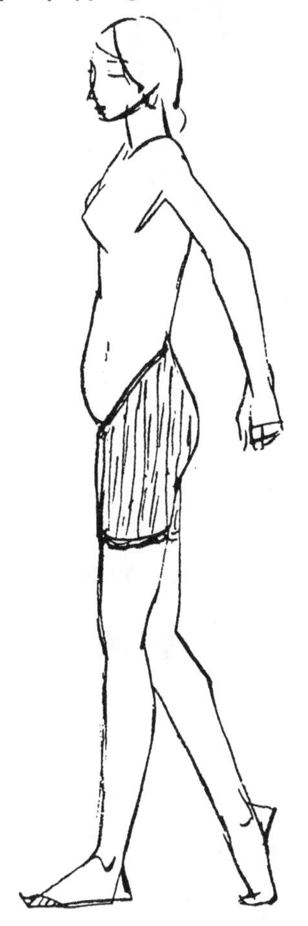

The support could be a panty-type garment made of a firm two-way stretch material and should have no bindings. It should fit snugly around the hips and over the groin. On a very thin person, the hipbones project out too far, so a body powder puff or a ball of cotton under the garment, in the depression, will let the garment have the desired snug fit. The back of the support should come up to the waist. The front should be folded over to about the groin and tacked down, so that it lies smooth. It will form a double-walled supporting sling for the abdomen to lie in. Because of the snug fit of the garment over the hips and legs, and because of the quality of the material itself, a beneficial, massage-like action is transmitted to the weak tissues as the person walks or bends.

If the person is rather fleshy, there may be a considerable bulge over the sling. Do not be concerned about it. The abdomen will soon be reshaped and the bulge will disappear. The garment need not be worn at night.

This garment may also be used when no organ is out of place, but when the abdominal wall is so weak that the skin hangs down over the upper legs. *[I believe this makes a good case for some kind of girdle: it might be beneficial to a lot of women whose stomach muscles have weakened and whose stomachs are protruding in an unhealthy way.— Ed.]*

Give any pertinent treatments once a week until the tissues are so strong that the support may be dispensed with.

For a man whose abdomen needs support, a more appropriate form of garment may be found among the athletic-type abdominal supports available in sporting goods stores.

Childless Woman Desiring a Child: Infertility

Mr. Stephenson found that if a woman desiring a child is still childless after having been married up to 15 years, she could frequently be helped by receiving the basic female treatment, page 8–4. Sometimes it is necessary to do this several times. During the later treatments, give special attention to decongesting the tubes, to remove from them all scale and corrosion until the tubes are freed from all impediments to the passage of the ovum. The fingers become so sensitive that the slightest bulge in the tubes can be detected and removed in the drainage movement. Then a gentle treatment over one of the ovaries would consist of working with a small-diameter circular motion, using the index with the middle or third fingers. In treating the ovary, use the mind strongly to create action within. Working over the left ovary tends to give rise to the birth of a female child and the right ovary a male child. Treating both ovaries with this intent, tends to promote the birth of fraternal twins, according to Mr.Stephenson.

Douches

Mr. Stephenson said that as much as 90% of reproductive organ dysfunction is caused by introducing unnatural substances into the body. The normal vacuum action within the body of any strong, healthy woman causes a portion of any foreign material, introduced into the vagina, to be drawn up into the tubes and ovaries. If foul or corrosive substances, such as feminine hygiene products, contraceptive chemicals, and antiseptics, are introduced into the vagina, the very delicate membranes of the tubes and ovaries are badly irritated and may be seriously affected. It can also happen unintentionally by improper cleaning of the anus resulting in fecal matter being deposited in the vaginal area. Even the use of vinegar and water for a douche was not approved by Mr. Stephenson.

If the three secretions of the vagina are in balance, the vagina and other female organs will keep themselves clean and will need no artificial cleanser. If aid is ever needed because the secretions are out of balance, body temperature water should be used as an irrigation.

If an occasional discharge persisted after the administration of the basic female treatment, Mr. Stephenson suggests introducing an ounce of olive oil into the vagina by means of a baby syringe. The olive oil, by its creeping action, will penetrate into the areas harboring foul material. It will loosen the deposits so that the body can let them go and they can be drained out.

Treatments for Children

Infant Diarrhea

This treatment may be used with babies who are born with good weight but then become emaciated down to skin and bones because of persistent diarrhea during the first few weeks of life. Mr. Stephenson said his treatment had never failed in cases of infant diarrhea.

Dosage : take once an hour until results are obtained:

Age	Proportions
Up to 6 weeks	3 drops of vinegar in 1 teaspoon water
6 weeks to 6 months	5 drops of vinegar in 1 teaspoon water
6 months to 6 years	7 drops of vinegar in 1 teaspoon water

Worms in the G.I. Tract

Such infestations as worms or parasites, particularly in the bowels of children are taken care of by eating carrots in any form. Small children should be fed grated carrots and fresh carrot juice. The worms will not stay where the carrot is.

Relief from Ear Pain

If the ear hurts when the child swallows, use the drainage movement of the tonsillitis treatment, page 2–12, and as the fingers come close along the jaw a taut cord may be felt. Repeat this movement until the cord dissolves.

Blue Baby

The foramen ovale is an opening in the wall between the right and left atria of the heart in the fetus. This opening provides a bypass for the blood that would otherwise flow to the fetal lungs. After birth the foramen ovale should close when the newborn takes the first breath and circulation through the lungs begins. Complete closure is accomplished by about nine months of age.

The condition known as "blue baby" is when the foramen ovale does not close and circulation to the lungs is impaired.

Treat the #1 heart spot, page 4–21, which closes the foramen ovale, as often as needed for short periods of time.

Treat the #5 heart spot each time you treat the #1 spot.

You may also treat the other three heart spots if needed.

Modified Treatment for Baby Born with "Asthma"

The baby born with breathing trouble, usually described as a "baby born with asthma," may be actually suffering from inaction of the diaphragm. The requirement is to evacuate the pleural cavity. This will bring the pleural membranes in contact, inflate the lungs, and tension the ribcage. This is achieved by applying the high and short breathing treatment, in delicate adaptation to the small body. For a child only a few weeks old, omit the heart treatment.

➧ **Step 1: Vacuum over breathing tube.** Very gently, begin to create a vacuum down the center line of the chest (four-minute breathing tube treatment, page 4–5). Perform it with the edge of the thumb, for 4 minutes as in the regular case.

➧ **Step 2: Placement of a band.** Next apply the chest band: Use a roll of gauze bandage, 1 or 2 inches wide. Slide a single run of bandage underneath the baby and continue it across the chest, so the free end of the bandage crosses on the right side of the body.

➧ **Step 3: Hand placement.** Place the hands over the band according to the instructions in step 3 of the high and short breathing treatment, page 4–2. As the baby's ribcage is held, (it can hardly be discerned but feels like a poorly inflated balloon) the hands will lie over the band.

➧ **Step 4: Wrapping band.** Now, very gently draw the ribcage in from the sides, at the same time observing the rise and fall of the abdomen, which depicts the true action of the diaphragm. Adjust the pressure of the hands, bringing them closer together or further apart as necessary, until the maximum rise and fall is felt. Then continue the band across the chest so the free end of the bandage crosses on the right side of the body and so that the safety pin holding it is not over the heart. Be sure that the band lies at the correct level: place it so that its upper edge is on a level with the lower end of the sternum; it spans the area down to the lower edge of the ribcage.

Frequency

It is best to give the whole treatment, vacuum movement and application of band, every day or at least every other day for 3 weeks. But even if it can be performed only once a week, the normal breathing of the baby will usually be established in 3 weeks.

Children With Legs Drawn Tight Together

Sometimes a child is born with its legs drawn so tightly together by the adductor muscles that the mother cannot clean it properly. The usual treatment is to use an apparatus to force the legs apart. This is not only extremely painful for the child's limbs, but that pain extends all the way up the spine and even into the head.

The Creative Healing approach is very different. The child is laid face down and a gentle quarter twist is applied along the center line of the back. On a child's body the spinous processes are quite small and close together, so that one cannot differentiate between the vertebrae. The thumb might span several vertebrae at a time but each quarter twist is contiguous or even overlapping and the pressure is straight down.

Start at the sacrum and work with quarter twists up to but not including the neck. As this treatment is performed, the little body responds with sounds like the cracking of bones. Mr. Stephenson reassured the mother that the sound had nothing to do with bones but was due to the breaking up of tensions of over-tightly drawn ligaments.

The treatment is repeated until nothing more is felt or heard and then the child is turned over on its back and the legs gently pulled apart. The treatment might be done in as little as 15 minutes. A child 2 years old or more may immediately start to walk once the legs are separated.

As stated, this treatment applies only to the spine. It does not include the neck. If the neck also needs help, the general treatment with delicate adaptation to the small body will usually take care of the problem.

Example from Creative Healers

A mother, who is also a Creative Healer, was helping a neighbor by caring for her two-year-old child who had great difficulty walking. She said she heard a swishing sound as the child walked toward her and it made her think of this treatment. When it was time to change the child's diaper, she decided to do the work on the back. When she finished and placed the child on the floor, he walked in a perfectly normal way. The mother could scarcely believe her eyes when she returned.

[I have spoken to nurses in London who say that this problem happens with newborns and the treatment is to break the hips to separate the legs. I hope this is not true. Ed.]

From the writings of Joseph B. Stephenson

Child Born with Legs Tight Together

When I saw the child she was seven years old. She had been born with legs so tight together that the mother could not keep her clean. The parents had taken her to the hospital and doctors there put weights on each leg to hang over the bed to pull her legs apart. It hurt the girl so that she screamed night and day until the doctors could stand it no longer so they sent her home. The weights were pulling her spine tighter together and locking it even more.

When the mother checked her daughter out, the receptionist advised her to see Mr. Stephenson in Johnstown and gave her my address. The next day she came to see me and told me of the case and the hospital experience.

"I will be at your home at 8:30 tomorrow morning."

As soon as the child saw me she began to scream so I sat down on a chair. She would not stop screaming. The door opened and two men rushed in and said, "What the hell are you doing to the child?"

I said, "Nothing yet, but if she could be persuaded to keep quiet for 15 or 20 minutes I could put her on her feet."

"Well I'll be damned. I believe you." He grabbed a towel and put it in the girl's mouth. "Where do you want her?"

"On the table, on her stomach and keep her down," I said.

I started to work at the bottom of her spine. As I worked my thumbs up each side, you could hear everything breaking loose, just like breaking thin china.

"You sure you know what you are doing?" one man asked.

"Yes, I have already done it. Turn her over." When they did, I took hold of each leg, pulled it gently and her legs came apart. I massaged the front of her legs for about five minutes.

The child, who was quiet now, said, "I cried because I was afraid you would hurt me like the doctors did, but when you did not hurt me I wasn't afraid."

Then I asked the men to put her on her feet and show her how to use her legs. They did and with a little help she walked. When I left they were all using their hankerchiefs.

Bed Wetting

Bed wetting, or any involuntary form of release of urine, is due to improper functioning of the sphincter muscle. This muscle acts as a valve for the voluntary control outlet of the bladder. This valve functions hydraulically by gravity, that is, the proper weight of blood or pressure flow must act on the sphincter muscle to give it the strength to fulfill its valve function without fail.

For a child less than 5 years old, it is reasonable to give the child the benefit of the doubt. The child may not be trying to control the bladder. But an older child usually makes a genuine mental effort to effect that control. If unsuccessful, it is generally due to a failure of the sphincter muscle to function properly. The same is true for adults who wet their bed. Bed wetting, or any other involuntary release of urine that may occur during excitement or a fright or hearty laughter, is generally because of a malfunction in this valve.

The sphincter muscle valve may be restored to proper functioning by the pressing of two spots, the bed wetting spots. These spots are found in the same location for both male and female.

➧ **Step 1: Locate spots.** To locate them for the male, have the person lie down and stand to the patient's right. Place your left hand on his right shoulder and place the palm of your right hand on his lower abdomen. Your fingers are extended toward his feet, and the axis of the index finger is parallel to the spine. Curl the index finger over the pubic bone next to and to the right of the penis.

The first depression or cavity encountered is the right bed wetting spot. The left one is found in the corresponding manner. In a woman, the spots are located as in the male, allowing for the separating width of a penis.

➧ **Step 2: Press to restore muscle control.** When the index finger has contacted the cavity, pause for a moment to make sure that the person is relaxed. Then press quite firmly, toward the head, parallel to the spine, using the pad of the index finger and release at once. Repeat on the left side.

When treating a child for bed wetting, apply only half the pressure employed in treating an adult and never treat a child under the age of five.

With a male body it is possible that the cords extending from the testicles into the body lie across one of the cavities. Be sure to push them aside before applying pressure.

The pressing almost always causes a sharp sensation that produces an involuntary recoil within the body, which is desired, as it is the restorative action. It causes the muscles to be drawn up and reestablishes their control.

It affects not only the muscles surrounding the sphincter of the bladder but also other muscles on the floor of the pelvis and the muscles fanning out from there on each side. The sharp sensation caused by the pressing usually subsides within a minute or so. On the rare occasions in which the pain is still felt 5 minutes after the initial pressure, press the spot again, this time sustaining the pressure. This will cause the painful sensation to vanish.

The bed-wetting spots are useful whenever there is dribbling of urine because the valve of the urethra does not completely shut off.

Frequency

The treatment usually needs to be applied only once. It may be repeated within a week or even sooner, however, if necessary.

Undescended Testicle

The bed wetting spots have another application for males. Occasionally in young males, one or both testicles do not descend out of the body into the scrotum.

To treat, place the left hand palm down on the abdomen, the heel of the hand on the navel, the fingers extended toward the pubic bone. Give the hand a rocker-like shape. Exert a downward pressure moving down to the pubic bone. Start the pressure from the heel of the hand and rock as you move the hand downward. This will cause the testicle to descend.

Sustain this pressure, particularly just above the pubic bone, while the right index finger molds the cartilage surrounding the bed wetting spot on the side from which the testicle descended into this cavity, as though pressing it over the edge of a crater.

Retracted Penis

If the penis of a young male has not fully developed so that it does not extend but seems to be retracted into the body, the rocker-like pressure described above in undescended testicle will cause the penis to extend, but when the pressure is released, it will again be retracted into the body. This serves to illustrate the helpful effect of the pressure action, but also shows that the pressure must be sustained. The entire rocker-like pressure need not be sustained but only the pressure on the navel. The sustained pressure at the navel may be achieved with the help of a reasonably cushioned pad of gauze or cloth with rounded edges, a diameter of 1 to 1 1/2 inches and a thickness of up to 1/2 an inch. Hold this pad in place on the navel with a simple bandage. In this way a sustained inward pressure upon the navel is brought about. The boy should wear this bandage for several weeks or maybe months, until the penis remains normally extended.

Foreskin

It was Mr. Stephenson's thought that the foreskin of the penis should be left alone and not tampered with. It was his feeling that circumcision is not desirable. The important aspect of care is to keep the mucous membrane, under the foreskin, clean at all times.

Delayed, Stunted or Slow Growth

The name constitutional glands and the concept that it represents are uniquely Mr. Stephenson's. If slow, delayed, or stunted growth occurs in childhood without detectable reason, it is due to a dysfunction of these glands.

Examine the area lying along the median at the back of the neck. Also examine the areas lying between the median and the cords of the neck. If you can detect a corrugated, laterally serrated, washboard-effect when stroking downward with the flat sides of the fingers, this is the significant discovery because the back of the neck should be smooth.

Give one or several very thorough high blood pressure treatments, page 2–37. This will clear away these formations. The constitutional glands will be restored to full, normal function and normal growth will take place.

Crossed Eyes

Give the feeding treatment for the eyes, page 2–22, and at the end of the groove, use the thumb and finger to toe in if the eyes are crossed inward. If the eyes are crossed out (wall-eyed), the thumb and finger toe out. This treatment can be applied with expected success until the age of 25.

Treating Infectious Childhood Diseases

In Mr. Stephenson's view, the effects of measles, smallpox, chicken pox, scarlet fever and whooping cough can be borne more easily in childhood or early life than in later years and not everyone is heir to each of these diseases. Those to which an individual succumbs, depends on hereditary factors.

A characteristic of these five diseases is that each produces a persistent fever that is hard to take out with the hands. And if one succeeds in taking it out, it will soon return. A fever of this type is a sign that the illness is one of the five childhood diseases even before the particular features of the disease are apparent. When the disease becomes apparent and the fever is running high, allow it to do so. Watch over the patient carefully and prevent chilling. Keep the child as comfortable as possible, but make no attempt to cool the body. Do not lower or remove the fever. Allow it to burn out. This establishes immunity to the disease for the rest of the person's life.

If, on the other hand, the case seems to linger and the temperature rises and falls erratically, encourage the fever to rise and stay at a consistent level so it can burn itself out in the shortest possible time. Give the child lemonade that is quite warm, but not too hot and will be acceptable with comfort. For a grownup, it may be useful to add some alcohol. Never use a more vigorous means of raising the fever such as a hot electric blanket.

Problems in the Mouth

Abscessed Tooth

A certain type of abscessed tooth occurs in children, where the gum line around the tooth becomes inflamed, sore, and swollen.

To treat, grasp the gum high up on the inside and outside of the tooth beyond the root with the index finger and thumb Firmly "milk" or strip in the direction of the projection of the tooth, out through the gum. This causes a drainage channel to burst through and open into the mouth.

For adults, port wine is recommended as a mouthwash to complete the drainage and start the healing. With a small amount in the mouth, swish the wine around for 2 or 3 minutes and then spit it out. The wine will draw the poison from the tissues. Often this will appear in the form of curdled masses of dark material. If the tissues are too sensitive, the port wine may be diluted with water as much as 50% at first. Gradually work up to full strength. Three days of applying the mouthwash several times a day are usually sufficient to complete the healing.

This procedure is not to be used in place of proper dental attention, but only as an emergency measure.

Crooked Teeth

In a young child's mouth up to a certain age the condition of crooked teeth can be rectified by grasping the teeth firmly with the thumb and finger and setting them straight.

Cleft Palate

A cleft palate is an incomplete formation of the roof of the mouth caused by arrested development. Mr. Stephenson would treat a child born with this condition if it had not normalized by the time the child would begin to speak.

By using the thumb on the existing forward part of the palate and, in a sliding motion, perform gentle strokes from front to back with the intent of getting the palate to lengthen and extend, prompting its growth to start up again and develop to completion.

Harelip

The harelip that frequently accompanies cases of cleft palate will also yield to the treatment of the palate.

Pigeon Toes

The conventional treatment for pigeon toes is the application of casts. However, Mr. Stephenson saw that the cause of the problem was in the head and could be treated. He saw that the body is put together in such a way that if a person moves a finger, it is the result of nerve endings in the opposite side of the brain that are brought into action by thought. To each segment of a finger there is a corresponding segment of these nerve endings and when the brain segment moves, the finger segment moves in unison. Mr. Stephenson said that if the nerves did not cross at the back of the skull, man could not be smoothly balanced in walking, but would hop like a frog or a kangaroo in overcoming gravity. This view of the body's functioning makes one more aware of the connections between obstructions anywhere in the body and corresponding nerve endings in the head.

This applies to all the motions of the body and the reason for the feet to turn in is that the tips of the nerve endings that correspond to the last segments of the toes were too weak and tended to fall inward. Treatment for pigeon toes is done on the back of the neck to feed the nerve endings so they have the strength to fully extend. With the patient seated, use the thumb on one side and one or two fingers on the other side about 1 inch from the center line, to stroke upward. The strokes start at the base of the neck and extend to the base of the skull and are continued for 15 minutes. Five or more treatments may be needed.

From the writings of Joseph B. Stephenson

In Johnstown, Pennsylvania, a physician brought his 17-year-old grandson to Mr. Stephenson to get help for his severely pigeon-toed condition. Several attempts with casts had failed but when Mr. Stephenson began to work on the back of the boy's neck and continued for fifteen minutes, the grandfather exploded saying it was ridiculous to try to straighten feet by massaging the neck and left with his grandson. Mr. Stephenson refused payment from the grandfather but told the boy to return in 3 days. When he returned he reported that he had better control of his feet. He received five treatments at three-day intervals. On the Sunday after the fifth treatment, the grandfather, sitting on his porch, saw his grandson coming up the street with his feet straight. He immediately went to Mr. Stephenson to apologize and to pay his bill.

Miscellaneous Treatments

Cooling Treatment Without Touching

Temperature is determined in Creative Healing by the palm of the hand. By touching several different areas of the body it is easy to determine whether heat exists in any one place or the abdomen. If heat does exist, the treatment that should be applied is called a cooling treatment.

Position

The patient lies down. The Creative Healer sits on a chair that is a comfortable height. It should be high enough to allow whichever arm is used to operate freely above the patient, without strain to the healer. It is comforting and reassuring to the patient if the hand of the healer that is not being used for treatment, rests quietly on the patient's arm or the side of the body during the treatment.

➧ **Step 1: Use of the hand.** In the cooling treatment the hand is not in contact with the body. Instead, it moves over the body about 1 inch above it. The fingers are together and the hand is not rigid but should be relaxed and it will assume a slightly cupped shape as it moves in arc-like circles over the entire area.

➧ **Step 2: Mind and hand work together.** Perform 40 to 50 strokes a minute with the strong thought and intention of drawing the heat out of the inflamed body. As the palm passes over the area, visualize it grabbing heat and pulling it away from the body or visualize that you are creating a cooling breeze. As the palm returns for the next stroke, it is cooled by the air. This is not a fanning motion. The strokes are long and uninterrupted and extend over the entire area in whatever direction they are performed. The treatment may require the stroking to continue for 15 to 20 minutes or until the body, when gently contacted, feels to be at normal temperature.

➤➤➤CAUTION: If this treatment is given for cooling the abdomen and if, after the treatment, the abdomen persists in the original inflamed condition, do not continue the treatment but urge the patient to seek a specialist's help without delay. In any case, even if you have succeeded in removing the heat, do not proceed with any further treatment that day.

Cancer

[The following is Mr. Stephenson's explanation of what we call cancer and what he "saw" as the causes for this condition in different parts of the body. These explanations make a better case for prevention than for cure. In some situations however, he felt it could be dealt with.—Ed.]

Mr. Stephenson said, "What has been named cancer is what I call the death germ which is present in every body. The death germ comes to life by the death of the human body **and in any part of a living body** where death may occur to cells. Most causes are from the human race not knowing the consequences of their actions. If something is named cancer and operated on and the person lives more than two years, it was not cancer. Hundreds, maybe thousands of women have had breasts removed for cancer, which was not cancer. My advice is, if you are sure it is cancer, then hands off."

Cancer in Women

He goes on: "For example, especially in this country cancerous breasts are more prevalent. This problem can be brought on by the husband using them to create a vibration or sucking. Blood is drawn through glands where there is no milk. This blood cannot go back where it came from and it dies for want of circulation. This brings the death germ to life in the blood cells and that germ has life and has to be nourished so it throws its poison ahead of it to kill the flesh. That is what I call 'eating cancer.' It may take years to develop into actual cancer from the time the breast was tampered with."

"Cancer of the womb has two causes: it cannot develop a cancer of itself. The first cause is from unfinished menstruation and the first sign of trouble in the womb in a mature or older woman is pain before menstruation. If the pain before menstruation is in its infant stage it can be removed in a short time with the Creative Healing female treatment. Not enough air is going into the womb to open the mouth of the womb and let all the blood out. The blood congeals and becomes solid (clots) and these clots cannot get through. A little more blood is left in each month and eventually dies and the death germ begins its work of decomposition. This can go on for a period of years before showing itself. The first symptom is an odor which only the person herself can smell. After the odor, a slight discharge may begin, greenish-yellow and thick. This is some of the decomposition being discharged and the odor can be detected by others. After it has become cancer, the walls of the womb begin to give off blood and marrow and then it is beyond help. The second cause of cancer of the womb is that the afterbirth has not all been removed."

"Vaginal cancer begins with burning and itching until scratching draws blood and the whole area becomes infected. Over-douching washes out the natural secretions and the vagina becomes dry and walking causes friction when the walls of the vagina rub together. The friction causes heat and heat brings on inflammation and a discharge and agitation which is the forerunner of cancer."

"Another cause may be the size of a man's penis or artificial means that go beyond the safety margin to blood vessels, causing obstructions, and that blood cannot get back into the blood stream."

Cancers Common to Men and Women

Mr. Stephenson said that cancer of the stomach would occur more often in men (from age 40 up) and that young people would not often be affected. He said, "Cancer of the stomach comes from a discharge that drips from the brain cells. It is swallowed year after year until a ball of mucous forms that will not digest. It will take in small particles of food that do not digest and instead die: an invitation to the death germ to come to life. An agitation of the stomach that causes an ulcer to form, if not taken care of can kill the life of part of the stomach."

"Cancer of the nose is started by some small part of the nose being affected by a finger nail cutting into it, drawing blood where it ferments and dies."

"In general, cancer can begin anywhere where there is a pinch or constant sore, a heavy bruise, or an unclean cut that draws blood into any small part that cannot get nutrition. This breeds infection and kills the flesh, allowing the death germ to come to life."

From the writings of Joseph B. Stephenson

Twenty Days to Live

I called next and a man and wife came up the stairs. The wife looked very sick. I put them in my room and in a few minutes when I walked in they were both crying.

The wife said, "The doctor told me I have just 20 days to live. He said I have cancer and it is eating up into my heart. I have just 16 days left to live and I keep watching the clock hands and counting the hours of each day and the days I have left every time I look at my five children. What torture; I have lost 20 pounds in four days. Death is nothing compared to the torture of hell I am going through."

I said, "Do you love your children? And do you love your husband?"

She said, "I do."

Then I turned to the husband, "Do you want your wife to live?"

He said, "Yes, sir. How would I get along without her?"

Then I said to the wife and mother, "Lie down on this bed."

I used the power of creation alone—I did not lay my hands on her or touch her in any way. I said, "You may dry your eyes and come and see me in 21 days. The doctor served you a sentence of 20 days. I prolong your sentence to live until you see your family grow up and leave your home to make a home for themselves."

On the 21st day I called next and the same two came up the stairs. Both were smiling. As I followed them into the room she said, "Here I am and I have gained 17 pounds since I was here last."

Two more treatments by the power of creation and she was a well woman and still is.

The doctor who sentenced her to death is taken care of by the law. The man who restored her to her family is punished by the same law—something wrong somewhere. [This happened during the time Mr. Stephenson was being harassed by the American Medical Association.—Ed.]

Venereal Diseases

Mr. Stephenson was very careful to announce that he never treated venereal diseases. This was because they were contagious and must properly be reported to the state. But, he would tell a patient seeking help what to do so that they could carry out the treatment for themselves and then go to be checked by their physician to see whether they were free of the disease.

Gonorrhea

Gonorrhea is a disease affecting the mucous membrane. It causes severe inflammation and infection resulting in purulent material draining from the penis or vagina. Mr. Stephenson recommended the use of olive oil to heal this disease.

For a man, a rubber prophylactic with a spoonful of olive oil poured into the tube and taped into position over the penis so that the head of the penis is immersed in the oil, is the treatment. As the purulent material leaves the body, an exchange of flow takes place. The olive oil enters the body as though responding to a vacuum. There is an action of natural attraction when olive oil comes in contact with a mucous membrane. This attraction causes the oil to creep and climb and spread throughout the region so that it will, in time, search every nook and cranny to smother the germs and expel every pus pustule from the body.

In the case of a woman, olive oil can be introduced into the vagina by means of a small syringe.

Syphilis

Syphilis is a disease of the blood stream caused by a very persistent, spiral organism. The blood naturally fights and works to expel it. This causes skin eruptions at an early stage of the disease.

Mr. Stephenson's way of healing the body of syphilis was to have the patient eat dried figs, according to a certain scheme. He recommended figs coming from the lands bordering the Mediterranean, such as Greece, Turkey, France, Morocco,

Italy and Spain. These figs are sun dried, not artificially heated. The desirable feature is their large seeds that contain a powerful vacuum when the figs are dried as described. California figs would, in general, not be effective because they are developed to produce very small seeds or no seeds at all. The Mediterranean figs are still, as in former years, packaged on strings, but more recently the strung figs are curled up into cellophane wrappers.

The figs may be thoroughly washed in preparation for use, but neither heated nor soaked. Both of these processes would destroy the vacuum. The patient is instructed to eat 1/2 pound (dry weight) of these figs twice a week. That is 1 pound per week. The 1/2 pound should always be eaten at one time, in place of a meal. It is important that a quantity of seeds be present in the small intestine at one time. In the small intestine, through exchange, the syphilitic germ is drawn from the blood stream into the seed. In this way, it is passed out of the body.

Continue the fig treatment until all tests are negative. In this manner the body can be completely cleansed of the disease.

Mr. Stephenson's method in his day was far superior to any other known method in that it would not drive the organisms into the nerve or bone tissue of the body causing the stricken person, years afterwards, even though the blood had been cleaned, to develop crumbling bones or end up as a syphilitic insane.

Chapter 9 ♦ General Problems

The General Problems chapter covers a variety of problems that are not necessarily found in only one section of the human body. Most of the problems can occur anywhere in the body and the treatments proposed are applicable to the problem wherever it occurs.

The following anecdote from the journals of Joseph B. Stephenson illustrate the simplicity and effectiveness of Mr. Stephenson's gentle methods.

Example from the writings of Joseph B. Stephenson

A University Professor's Reaction on his First Treatment for Itch

Indiana, PA. I called "next" and a man, six feet two or more came up the stairs. He said, "I am a professor in the college here. The doctors say I am having a nervous breakdown, but I don't feel that way. I work all day and rest until bed time, but as soon as I get warm in bed I get a stinging itch all over my body and I cannot get to sleep sometimes until five in the morning and I feel it telling on my nerves. Can you do anything for me, Stephenson?" I said, "Why not: just stand there." I put my hands above his head, brought them slowly down over his body three times down the front, three times down the back then took each arm in turn and went down each arm three times. It took about a minute or so to do this then I said, "Come back next week." I just felt his mind say, "The hell I will. I was a fool to come to you in the first place." However, next week came and so did the professor. With a smile, he said, "I don't know what you did last week but I have slept every night since without any signs of itch." So I gave him another treatment and a third one, and in thanking me he said, "Stephenson, I'd give a lot to know as much as you."

Skin Problem Treatments

Acne, Boils, Carbuncles, and Other Skin Eruptions

The dried fig treatment is effective for acne, boils, carbuncles or other disturbances that cause skin eruptions. The figs used in this treatment come from countries bordering the Mediterranean: Greece, Turkey, France, Morocco, Italy and Spain. These figs have large seeds, are sun dried, and are usually packaged on strings and curled up into cellophane wrappers. The large seeds in Mediterranean figs contain a powerful cleansing action when they are sun dried. The large vacuum in the seed draws germs from the blood stream into the seeds, which are then excreted from the body. California figs, with small or nonexistent seeds, would not be effective for this treatment. The Mediterranean figs may be thoroughly washed in preparation for use, but not heated or soaked. Both of these processes would destroy the cleansing action of the seeds.

One half pound (dry weight) of these figs must be eaten at one sitting, once a week, in place of a meal, because it is important that a large quantity of seeds be present in the small intestine at the same time. In the case of boils, for instance, the person suffering from them will never be subjected to them again. Once the blood stream has been cleansed in this way, it will no longer try to cleanse itself by forcing eruptions through the skin. Acne will be helped but diet and external hygiene must also be taken into consideration.

All Over Itch

In this type of itch the prevailing disturbance does not manifest itself on the outside of the body, but this itch extends over the whole body and can be so severe as to deprive the person of sleep. It is most frequently observed in elderly and senile people, but can occur at middle age or even earlier. Nothing is apparent on the surface of the skin, nothing detectable even for a dermatologist except perhaps the abrasions from scratching.

Position

The patient stands and need not be undressed; the Creative Healer stands also.

➧ **Step 1: Downward action of hands on body.** Hold your hands with thumbs touching each other, and the fingers of each hand extended and stretched away from the thumbs as far as possible. Then, with hands a few inches from the body begin at the top of the head and draw the hands down to the feet. Do this 3 times over the front side of the body and 3 times over the back of the body.

➧ **Step 2: Downward action of hands on arms.** Let the patient extend an arm and rest the fingertips lightly on your own and make 5 or 6 similar drawing down movements over each arm with one of your hands, commencing at the shoulder and carrying the strokes beyond the fingertips.

Other Itches

The palm of the hand may be used to stop the itch from a mosquito bite, nettles and many other cases of a sudden itch that one begins to scratch. As quickly as you become conscious of the itch or of the scratching, cup the hand slightly and without touching the skin, begin several inches above the itch and draw your hand down over the itching place 3 times, without touching the skin. If you have something that tingle-itches, it means the cells are being rapidly replaced; it is a good sign.

Eczema

Most needs will be answered by the simple mechanical, hands-on, Creative Healing treatments to the body. But there will be those exceptional cases in which contact on the patient's body is not the right approach. In such cases, Mr. Stephenson said, "We use the power the Creator gave us to cause a cool breeze to come from the hands, which draws out heat and inflammation so that nature can go about her healing work."

Mr. Stephenson made that statement in reference to a condition of eczema. Massaging or contacting someone with ecxema would be unwise and undesirable, both for the patient and the Creative Healer. For the patient because, while the disturbance must actually be drawn out away from the body, massaging with contact would drive it inward causing an inward manifestation in addition to the outward one. It would be unwise for the Creative Healer because he/she would be touching infection with clean hands.

Thus, in such a condition the need arises for a natural way of healing other than by contact and that is the cooling treatment. It is preferable, when treating an inflamed area, to have that area exposed, but this is not an indispensable condition for the application of the Cooling Treatment. Thus, it can be applied to treat cases in which such exposition would not be practicable.

During the treatment, a "contact" will be felt with the movement of the hand over the inflamed area of the body. The treatment should be continued until this contact dies out—the signal to cease that application of the treatment. During this treatment, you must work with a positive mind. Mr. Stephenson would say, "It takes a positive mind to do this."

Cooling Treatment for Ecxema

Position

The patient sits on a chair or a child can stand on a table at a comfortable height for the Creative Healer to operate the arms freely; the Creative Healer stands.

➧ **Step 1: Use of hand.** Temperature is determined in Creative Healing by the palm of the hand. The hand is not in contact with the body. Instead, it moves about 1 inch above it. The hand is not rigid but should be relaxed and assume a slightly cupped shape as it moves in arc-like circles over the area. The fingers are together.

➧ **Step 2: Mind and hand work together.** Perform 40 to 50 strokes a minute with the strong thought and intention of drawing the heat out. As the palm passes over an area, visualize it grabbing heat and pulling it away from the body. As the palm returns for the next stroke, it is cooled by the air. This is not a fanning motion; the strokes are long and uninterrupted and extend over the entire area in whatever direction they are performed. The treatment may require the stroking to continue for 15 to 20 minutes.

This is one of the Creative Healing treatments where the patient may seem worse before getting better. Drawing the heat out of the body also draws the pustules and redness to the surface. This is the intent of the treatment.

Frequency

Several treatments may be needed before the skin becomes clear. Sometimes the red spots drop off all at once as in the following account from Mr. Stephenson's writings.

From the writings of Joseph B. Stephenson

A Case of Skin Disease from Head to Foot

The girl was seven years of age and she was corruption from head to foot. She not only had a skin disease but the aroma that came from her smelled like sulphur and was the color of the same. The mother told me she had taken her to all the skin specialists in and around Pittsburgh, their home. No one understood the case or tried to do anything for her. While sitting in yet another specialist's office she overheard a conversation in which one woman was telling a mother who had a child with eczema to take it to Mr. Stephenson in Johnstown. She had seen wonderful cures he had done. She got my address and came to me the next day. The mother said, "Did you ever see anything like this?" "Yes," I said, "There is nothing the human body is heir to that I have not seen before. Stand in front of me, little girl." Then I gave her a treatment, turned to the mother and said, "Now this week, she will appear to get worse, but that will only be on the outside. You must bring her back next week." When she came the next week she could hardly bend her joints: she was a solid scab and as she walked the sulphur fell from her. The mother felt worried. After treatment, I told her, "When you take her home this time, keep her in her room. Lay papers on the floor and do not listen to your friends or neighbors because they do not understand. Your daughter will feel the difference." After seven treatments the last of the disease was gone and her skin was clean.

Bruises

All bruises that produce black and blue marks are serious and should be attended to promptly to disperse the blood that has been confined. The use of tiny, breaking up circles around the perimeter only will begin the dispersal outward from the bruise, and the blood will spread and be absorbed safely. Each day the bruise will decrease in size as the breaking up circles are used. The center of the bruise should not be touched. After a severe bruise has been suffered, it is important after 2 or 3 weeks to check at those places where the bone is prominent, to see if flesh may have loosened from the bone by the blow. If a pocket of fluid has formed separating the flesh from the bone, treat to remove the fluid. This treatment might eliminate the threat of tuberculosis to the bone or inflammation of the bone marrow (osteomyelitis) that might breed in the pocket of fluid.

➧ **Step 1: Find the fluid pocket.** To find a pocket of fluid, use the technique of palpation: with the tips of two fingers or a thumb and finger, contact points located on opposite sides of the painful area. Without breaking the contacts, quickly alternate the pressure between the points of contact, first at one side then at the other. This palpation causes any fluid present between the two points of contact to fluctuate and the extent of the fluid pocket can be determined.

➧ **Step 2: Breaking up treatment.** Perform tiny circles around the pocket along the outside perimeter. The intent is to cause the circulation to absorb the trapped fluid in a gradual manner and carry it away. Allow adequate time for nature to do its part. As the treatment continues, the perimeter will shrink, gradually coming into the center of the area. Finally, work on the center of the area. Soon there will be no fluid left. When this is done there will again be between the bone and the adjacent tissue a substantial cushion of healthy tissue that firmly adheres to the bone.

Frequency

This may require more than one session.

Arthritis Treatments

Arthritis is essentially a disease of the joints. Mr. Stephenson thought it occurred in two forms, systemic and nonsystemic. Systemic is at large in the system and can attack any joint. This he called rheumatoid arthritis. Non-systemic is more localized and is commonly called osteo or wear-and-tear arthritis and can be due to traumatic injury.

Osteoarthritis: Non-Systemic Arthritis

Osteoarthritis is a localized condition. Each affected joint must be treated separately (see finger treatments, page 6–13) and the joint must never be force-flexed, twisted or subjected to any kind of motion not natural to it until healed. Hinge joints like fingers and knees must be protected against any action that goes beyond what is acceptable in the plane of the hinge action, such as not using the fingers to unscrew a fruit jar lid or turn a stubborn faucet or window lock.

Mr. Stephenson mentioned isolated cases of osteoarthritis like that of a man contracting this disease after having waded in an icy cold mountain stream to fish for a prolonged period of time, or that of a woman whose car has stalled on a cold winter day and who has to walk a considerable distance for help and becomes chilled. Severe cases of chilling can give rise to osteoarthritis. Keeping the body at normal temperatures has applications for the joints.

If the number of joints affected by osteoarthritis is high enough, attacks of rheumatoid or systemic arthritis may develop by way of the poisons released into the bloodstream from the affected joints.

Rheumatoid Arthritis

Rheumatoid arthritis stems from a leaking heart. According to Mr. Stephenson, a trickle of blood forms on or above the heart and makes its way through the heart tube into the stomach and into the bowel. The blood forms a coating in the stomach and bowel and because humans cannot digest their own blood, the blood remains in these two organs, decomposes, and becomes poisonous to the body. As the poison enters the circulation and is carried through the body, it attacks the joints.

If the disease has not persisted for more than 2 years or if the pain has not all ceased, there is hope for restoration; this may be partial or complete. Attempting to treat cases of longer duration might be a waste of time. If treatment is given, it is hard to predict how much bony cell tissue deposit is permanent and how much can be reversed to be carried off by the blood stream. It is often possible to help those in the latter stages of the disease, but real restoration is not achievable.

Rheumatoid arthritis develops through four stages:

1. The joints very suddenly and pronouncedly swell up and give off heat. This is the stage of inflammatory rheumatism. Usually one or both knees are swollen and give off heat. Even the bones may be swollen.

2. If the swelling is not properly taken care of, it will break the seal of the joint and rupture the capsule. This allows the "joint oil" to seep into the flesh. Because joint oil does not belong in the flesh, it acts there as a poison; this is called the neuritis stage. It involves severe pains, even beyond the joints. Neuritis (nerve inflammation) pains can be most agonizing.

3. This is the corrosive or destructive stage when the joint is destroyed. If the disease progresses without treatment, the oil continues to flow out of the joint. A partial vacuum will be formed in the joint. This vacuum will draw blood into the capsule enclosing the cartilage. The blood attacks the cartilaginous surfaces of the joint, destroying them and penetrating to the bone. Empty spaces are created within the joint. As the disease continues, these spaces are filled in with compensatory bony cell tissue, or calcium.

4. If the disease runs its course it becomes the terminal stage. All damage is done that is going to be done, especially if pain ceases. The condition becomes benign in that no further destructive action will take place as far as this particular sequence is concerned. But the condition may start up again at another time. It may involve a more extensive range of the body or the same joints. The fourth stage can take on two forms. In the first, ankylosis (abnormal bone fusion), bony cell tissues from opposite surfaces of the joint grow together and grow into each other. They interlace and interlock like two heads of cauliflower growing into each other, and the joint becomes immovable. In the other form of the fourth stage, opposite surfaces of the joints become so deformed that they can no longer articulate, destroying alignment and usefulness. An example of this terminal form of rheumatoid arthritis is that of the fingers of the hand pointing in all directions as a consequence of destruction of the finger joints.

➧ **Step 1: Leaking heart treatment.** In any active stage of the disease in which inflammation is present and heat is given off, give the treatment for leaking heart (see page 4–25) and continue with this treatment as long as the inflammation exists.

➧ **Step 2: Treating each joint.** Treat each joint that is affected. Each joint must be treated individually according to what is found, with the vision of eventually compacting the joint and replacing the cartilage completely. See the ligaments as strong, and the circulation coursing smoothly through it. With a badly swollen joint, one cannot replace the cartilage immediately. Work to remove heat, inflammation and swelling (as in the preparatory work for replacing cartilage in the knee, page 7–19). Once the cartilage can be replaced, one is well on the way to restoring usefulness to the joint and having it truly heal.

Persons suffering from rheumatoid arthritis are frequently opinionated and locked up within themselves. They are often disturbed emotionally, mostly to a high degree. This disturbance affects the solar plexus by keeping it continually agitated. Such agitation can lead to a heart leak.

Agitation also affects the digestion. There is an important nutritional aspect to the treatment of arthritis. The body must be unloaded so that it burns cleanly what is fed to it. Incomplete combustion of food is the essential cause for the accumulation of poisons within the body. Such incomplete combustion results in overloading the eliminative organs, which then fail to function normally and wastes that should be eliminated remain within the body and turn into poisons.

In all instances, if the body is to be restored to true balance, the vital organs must be restored to normal function. Restoration of normal function is the strong point and sole endeavor of Creative Healing. From the point of view of Creative Healing, there is no substitute for normal function. When normal function returns, the person becomes healthy, and is not dependent on anything administered from the outside.

Muscle Treatments

The Muscles

The great importance of the muscles for the total wellbeing of the body should never be overlooked. Particular attention should be given to what is known as muscle tone, which is a measure of comparison between the condition of the muscle in its fully relaxed state and its fully contracted state. The greater the difference in feeling between the muscles in full contraction (balanced firmness) and in their relaxed state (uniform smoothness and pliability), the better the muscle tone is considered to be.

A muscle works only by contraction, unless outside forces are applied to it. One muscle rarely acts alone. In studying the action of muscles one is concerned with groups of muscles, though the groups may be difficult to delineate. But in any motion there are always many muscles involved. In its present use, the word muscle refers to muscle groups. A muscle (muscle group), when fully relaxed, feels uniformly smooth and pliable. There should be no residual contractions. These are felt as ropy, knotty or stringy formations, dispersed randomly beneath the surface. On the other hand, a muscle group in full contraction presents a high degree of firmness. All of the muscles in the group should be equally involved and in perfect balance. When a few predominate, there is imbalance and failure of the muscles to work in perfect harmony.

Good muscle tone indicates that the best possible conditions for circulation exist. The importance of good circulation cannot be overemphasized, since the circulation carries nourishment to the muscles. Muscles cannot receive full benefit of circulation while in the contracted state, but receive full circulation only if adequately relaxed. Alternating contraction and relaxation can actually enhance circulation if there is adequate resting time between contractions. Visualize alternately squeezing all the fluid out of a sponge and allowing it to reabsorb the fluid. If successive compressions of the sponge are too rapid, the sponge will never be able to absorb its full capacity of fluid. This example illustrates the importance of an adequate interval between two successive contractions of a muscle.

Constant contraction, such as holding the arms in a fixed position for a long time, precludes circulation to such a degree that adequate nourishment is impossible. The only way for the muscles to recover their power is to allow relaxation. Prolonged activity of any kind, even watching television, ironing or knitting may be sufficient to cause the body harm. One should listen to the body and give in when it signals fatigue. Prolonged sitting still, for example, can impose work on the muscles and if it does, circulation will be impaired.

Under severe, prolonged contraction, fuel can only be partially replenished. No one, not even the best trained and conditioned athlete, is exempt from the effects of exhausted muscle tissue, which react with involuntary contractions, such as spasms, cramps, severely reduced work capacity or reduced endurance. Often an attempt is made to remedy the situation by imposing more elaborate exercise, which usually backfires because the capacity of the muscle is greatly diminished. Muscle exhaustion precludes adequate circulation. As long as adequate circulation cannot replenish the muscle, recovery cannot take place. To reverse this situation, the first step is to improve circulation. Often this cannot be accomplished without massage.

To establish conditions that are favorable to adequate circulation for a weak or exhausted muscle, wisely applied exercise is indispensable. This is in addition to or in combination with massage, as necessary. To improve muscle tone, muscles must be used. If the proper conditions exist, nature will always respond by increasing the strength of a muscle to meet an increased load when this increase is judiciously imposed.

Muscle Injuries and Adhesions

When muscles have been injured, healing is often unsatisfactory. Adhesions may form. There may also be a separation of muscle fibers so that the muscle is unable to unite in its full-bodied length. When muscle fibers are torn, the muscle heals by connective tissue repair. Muscles do not regenerate. In severe injuries, some permanent impairment is inevitable because connective tissue has to replace muscle tissue and connective tissue cannot contract. Massage can do much to improve and minimize such impairments to recovery.

Muscle injuries resulting from compressive forces, severe blows that pinch the muscle against bony structure, pressures from ill-fitting garments or casts and braces, can leave muscles in a deformed state. Muscles that have been overstressed by overloading or overextending are left in a condition commonly described as sprained muscle.

To fully understand the condition of the muscles in these cases, one must realize that no muscle is composed of a single body of muscle fibers. Muscles are composed of many minute bundles of muscle fibers known as the "fasciculi." Each enclosed in their individual sheath of connective tissue, these fasciculi join to form the whole muscle. Most muscle injuries involve a slippage or a displacement of the fasciculi, which prevents them from returning to their natural adjoining positions. Such slippage and displacement can occur even within the muscle fibers of a bundle.

Adhesions

Such a disturbance causes nature to make a compensating connective tissue repair. It is only a partial healing, however, not a full recovery. Full flexibility is not regained. These natural repairs are commonly called adhesions. To reduce an adhesion and make it more flexible, the breaking up circle is the best tool. Use small, even tiny breaking up movements. Deep or heavy movements may actually cause a reinforcement of the adhesion. This circle is directed strictly to one spot, not to a whole area. It is applied successively from spot to spot. Use a gentle touch until it produces no more change.

Do not limit yourself to using only the circle movement in repeated treatments. Use also other movements such as kneading, raking and stroking (described in leg treatments, Chapter 7). These applications will help the muscle fibers lie smooth, long, and parallel to each other.

Water Immersion Treatment for Voluntary Muscle Control

Prolonged inactivity causes muscles to lose their voluntary response. This occurs when the body has been paralyzed or immobilized to any degree. An example of this would be when one has been in a full body cast for an extended length of time. The voluntary response is lost because the muscles atrophy or waste away. This condition can be compared to that of a declining fire, when the embers are only a faint glow. Heaping on more fuel would smother the embers, so would opening a draft wide. Embers must be nursed along to bring forth a little flame and that can then be nurtured into becoming a strong fire. In a similar manner, weakened muscles must be gently and slowly coaxed back into activity. To accomplish this, water offers a dimension that is not available in the routine massage. If the principles of Creative Healing are applied to a person immersed in warm water, more can be gained than with the same amount of time in the routine massage.

The following are outstanding advantages of water immersion treatment.

1. Water is buoyant. The smallest power present in any muscle can be taken advantage of because it is relieved greatly of the effects of gravity. Its "small flame" can be more easily detected and nurtured by appropriate massage and exercise.

2. Water offers a wide gradient of resistive force. Water offers practically no resistance to slow motion. As the speed of the motion increases, so does the resistance. Thus, resistance can be used progressively as the strength increases.

3. The water temperature can be kept constant. The temperature of the water, for any given application, should be governed by the comfort factor. Use water as warm as can be tolerated up to the threshold of comfort. Keeping the water at a constant temperature more quickly improves circulation and frees the body to return to normal function.

4. Technical aids are available. Mechanical aids such as whirlpools, jets and Hubbard tanks may be used when needed. Additional benefit may be derived from the chemical/mineral composition of the water. Mechanical aids such as slings, supports of any kind and safety conveyances that prevent inadvertent immersion of the nose and mouth should always be considered.

Paralysis Treatments

Paralysis

When nerve control to the muscles has been cut off, nerve impulses directing the muscles don't reach them and they hang completely limp. If the paralysis is of sufficiently long standing, the muscles will have deteriorated such that in an arm joint, for example, the ball can fall downward away from the socket under the effect of gravity and the sag will cause further deterioration.

While voluntary muscle response is reduced, there may still be unconscious responses to certain stimuli. If the paralysis is extensive, these involuntary responses indicate areas where nerves are more intact, areas that are therefore more fertile for the reestablishment of conscious voluntary control.

Conscious voluntary control must be regained. When it is firmly established, it will gradually be transferred to the subconscious, and involuntary responses will take over. The redevelopment of conscious, voluntary muscular control is a process known as muscle reeducation. Hydrotherapy, utilizing the graduated resistive forces of the water, has been able to allow some persons to overcome the paralysis. However hydrotherapy is not always available and Creative Healing methods can be done by anyone.

➧ **Step 1: Skin tissue massage.** The Creative Healing work must enhance and sustain circulation and keep the skin tissue from deteriorating. To accomplish this, all heavy compressive movements, tugging or pulling must be avoided and massage must always be directed upward. All massage must gently lift, mold, and reinvigorate the skin upward. Where possible apply this upward movement with the hand held in an almost cupped position and covered lightly with oil. At first the hand scarcely touches the skin of the affected parts as it moves upward, the oil attracting the hair and imperceptibly lifting the top layer of skin tissue so that blood circulation will increase just below the first layer, bringing more natural color to the skin.

➧ **Step 2: Arm paralysis.** Supporting the arm in a sling will delay deterioration caused by sagging muscles. In addition, the gentle upward massage in Step 1 becomes important; the skin tissue massage enhances and sustains circulation to keep the tissues from deteriorating. The patient reports that in attempts to move the paralyzed arm, there seems to be a response although no observable motion is detected. Support the arm comfortably and grasp the hand. Rotate the forearm by moving the hand to and fro.

We assume here that the patient's sensory feedback mechanism is intact so that when you ask whether contact on the skin and motion on the paralyzed arm are felt, the patient can answer affirmatively. You can then ask the patient to consciously direct attention to all the muscles that are involved in the motion you are doing, and to attempt to move these muscles. This will allow one of the attempts at moving the muscles to produce an observable response that you the Creative Healer can feel, encouraging the patient, which immediately becomes a resistive type feedback. The patient will then become conscious of using muscles and will begin to use them actively to consciously contract them. This response capability will increase rapidly in a short time and the patient's delight in the accomplishment is a valuable factor in ongoing progress.

The patient's understanding and cooperation are indispensable; furthermore, the patient must want to get well, have a strong desire to regain conscious control and cannot remain passive. Full participation will gradually reinstate a feeling of control even if it is remote at first. With resistive exercise training, this feeling will eventually develop into fully conscious voluntary control. At first the response may not be constant but if the response happened once, it can happen again and expand, and we must be careful not to force or tire the response. If, at this point the body can be suspended in water, the effect of gravity can be reduced and the feeble responses enhanced.

➧ **Step 3: Rest and balance.** Allow adequate intervals of time during each session for the patient to rest, not only the muscles but also the mind, which is greatly taxed by the required concentration. Eventually the delicate and erratic response will be under full voluntary control. As the work progresses, the patient must become aware of every muscle involved in a particular motion so that all can be brought to a fully balanced response. When we have achieved a certain response we aim to develop the opposing one, that is, if the mind can consciously move the muscle that lifts the arm, it must also learn to consciously move the muscle to let the opposite occur, to eventually regain automatic control. Our guideline will be to successively develop opposing responses and thereby increase strength development.

If paralysis includes an arm and a leg, start with the leg first and concentrate on developing responses there; you can then expect the arm to respond spontaneously. This may occur by way of reflex mechanisms activated by the responses in the leg. However, the arm must be prepared so that it is ready to respond: support the arm with a sling and massage the skin with light, upward, barely-touching strokes. The general pattern that the conscious responses of the leg induces almost subconsciously in the arm, seems to rest on the fact that the leg is needed as a foundation of the body, and the arm will respond later due to the counter-balancing movements of normal activities.

Polio: Infantile Paralysis

Mr. Stephenson saw polio, or infantile paralysis, as a disease that attacks only young people 18 years of age or younger. It is not passed from one person to another. He said that polio is one of only two diseases that he knew to be caused by an outside agent, yellow fever being the other. Polio's cause, he said, is a tiny insect that flies into an open mouth to the back of the throat where it severs the nerve to the leg.

According to Mr. Stephenson's view, polio is identified by the following four characteristics.

1. Polio can only be contracted out-of-doors during a critical time of day and a certain time of year. The critical time of the day is 5:30 pm until 7:30 am, from before dusk to after dawn, independent of geographic location. The critical time of year depends on geographic location. To understand the concept, visualize the North American continent covered by four bands, each with an approximate width of 800 miles. They extend roughly parallel to the East Coast. The first band begins on the East Coast and extends approximately 800 miles westward. In this area, the only dates polio can be contracted are from August 15th to September 15th. September 15th to October 15th is the critical period for the area covered by the second 800-mile band. The period for the third band is October 15th to November 15th. The last band is the area extending from the Rocky Mountains to the Pacific Coast where the time period is from November 15th to January 1st, each year. This involves a time span of 1 1/2 months as opposed to 1 month in the other areas. In Stephenson's day, many parents were advised that if their children were kept indoors during the critical periods, they would not contract infantile paralysis. In those families that heeded this advice, no cases of infantile paralysis occurred. The time and date that the paralysis occurred is a way of identifying a polio leg.
2. Infantile paralysis develops to its full extent within 48 hours, and all the paralytic damage done by the disease is done during that time period. In every case, the damage begins with dropping of the foot. If the condition is arrested early, by the treatment below, the dropping is only slight.
3. If a person who suffers an attack of infantile paralysis is not placed in an iron lung, only one or both legs can be paralyzed because if the disease involves the whole body, including both arms and legs, death is inevitable, unless the person receives the support of a respirator, which offers the only possibility of survival.
4. The groin test will help the Creative Healer identify a polio leg. The patient lies supine. Lightly rest your hand on the groin of the paralyzed leg and ask the person to raise this leg. The person, of course, cannot do this. Still the request will call forth a certain response, and if the hand, resting on the groin, feels even the most delicate twitch or motion, the paralysis is **not** infantile paralysis. In infantile paralysis, the life line to the paralyzed leg has been severed by the outside agent and this has caused the paralysis.

Twice while treating a parent for something, Mr. Stephenson noticed the twitching of the leg in a child who was present. Mr. Stephenson immediately administered the treatment below, which stopped the twitching and stopped the damage.

➧ **Step 1: Positioning.** The patient lies on the stomach on a massage table with a head drop, which allows the patient's neck to be straight. The patient may also be in the sitting position, which is how Mr. Stephenson gave the treatment now to be described. The patient leans the head forward and rests it against your abdomen. If the left leg is paralyzed, the nerve channel will be on the right side of the neck 1 inch from the center line.

➧ **Step 2: Unite the severed nerve.** With the index and middle fingers held together, use the pads of the fingers (not just the tips) and beginning at the base of the neck, move up this most sensitive channel; this will be the channel to the legs, 1 inch from the center line, as in the pigeon toes treatment, page 2–52. Draw the fingers with a strong, positive, lifting pressure, upward along this pathway until they stop at the base of the skull. Well before this point is reached, start the same movement in exactly the same manner with the index and middle fingers of the other hand. Their lifting contact is well established by the time the first 2 fingers have reached the skull. Again start at the base of the neck with the first hand and in this manner, both pairs of fingers are in lifting contact most of the time during the treatment. Continue this movement for 12 minutes.

This is the key part of the treatment. The disease caused by an outside agent severing the nerve to the paralyzed leg at the base of the skull, causes the lower part of the nerve to sag downward. Therefore, the treatment must be performed with the strong intent of drawing this lower part of the nerve upward so that it can again join the upper part.

If both legs are paralyzed, work on each side of the neck separately, at first. Then, work on both simultaneously although this necessitates breaks in the lifting movements. If both legs are paralyzed, treat longer than 12 minutes.

➧ **Step 3: Strengthening massage.** For the second part, the person lies supine. Massage with medium pressure upward over the thigh of the paralyzed leg on its median and anterior sides from the knee through the groin for 10 to 15 minutes. Hold your hand in flat contact with the tissue, the thumb adjacent to the fingers, the fingers leading and the palm following. The entire massage movement must be slow, especially approaching the groin, to give the tissues time to respond. If heat, swelling or inflammation is encountered draw out the heat and swelling with the palm. As the hand reaches the groin, move it laterally outward, following the natural fold of the groin. This strengthening massage is done with the thought of removing the downward sag in the nerve channel.

Next, work for 10 minutes on the lower leg from the ankle to the knee. Hold the thumb extended on one side and the fingers (as a unit) on the other side of the shin bone. In both of these movements, envision taking sag out of the nerve in order to further lengthen it and to help it to reunite.

➧ **Step 4: Back of the leg treatment.** The person lies prone as you apply a 10-minute massage that consists of continuous sweeping movements from the buttocks all the way down to the ankle. This also lengthens the nerve and facilitates its reuniting. As treatments progress, you will notice a twitching in the paralyzed leg. This usually occurs while working on the back of the neck. It can be seen in the region of the ankle and foot, and appears like a spasmodic dorsal flexion. This verifies that you are on the right track. As you visualize lifting the nerve upward and the severed ends come nearer to each other, it is as though nature suddenly draws them together. Simultaneously, as this occurs, the foot begins to twitch. The twitching that takes place as the severed nerve begins to reunite, is the reverse manifestation of that which is observed when the nerve is being severed. As the connection is reestablished, it is at first intermittent. It flickers like a light bulb flickers when contact in the socket is not secure. This means only that the work must continue.

Frequency

The full treatment must be given at regular intervals until the nerve path to the leg is once more firmly established. It should be administered at least once a week.

Complete healing may be expedited by employing hydrotherapy to bring about the balanced recovery of the muscles.

Environmental Problem Treatments

Allergy

The intolerance of a body to a certain agent is commonly called an allergy. People have, through genetic inheritance, become tolerant of many things in the natural environment. A fully functioning body should not complain when subjected to a reasonable amount of dust or pollen naturally occurring in the environment.

Mr. Stephenson believed there are several reasons for intolerance.

1. When the body lacks full strength and function it becomes oversensitive to, and intolerant of a great many things it would normally accept. From the point of view of Creative Healing an allergy is caused by something that does not agree with the body at a particular time for the condition of the body. The same body functioning fully, will not be subject to these irritants and will ignore them. One need not have an allergy forever.

2. Bodies are wittingly or unwittingly subjected to things they are not able to tolerate such as unnatural agents that have been introduced into modern life. Bodies cannot be expected to accept man-made molecules, particularly products designed as anti-life agents, and should never be exposed to these things.

3. Allergy may also be caused by chest congestion. In some cases, the temperature may not seem to be above normal at the start. But as the heat withdrawing treatment is applied to the chest, red blotches can be seen on the surface of the skin. These areas give off heat and testify to a smoldering inflammation beneath the surface of the skin. Treat as for pneumonia (see page 4–7) and make certain to give the four-minute breathing tube treatment (see page 4–5).

To overcome a weakened condition of the skin, an irritation or deterioration blamed on allergies, a person should avoid skin contact with strong detergents, which often include powerful disinfectants. Degreasing agents can burn the natural oils out of the skin and even impair the natural production of the oil glands.

Allergy treatments are applied depending on type of allergy, remembering that many people have multiple allergies and many areas of the body may need treatment as they affect each other.

Treatments

• Adenoid treatment, page 2–5.

• Sinus or hay fever (from dust, grass, pollen, fumes): hay fever and sinus treatment (page 2–2), as well as throat (page 2–11) and chest (page 4–10).

• Asthma: asthma treatment (page 4–13), plus chest (page 4–10), sinus (page 2–2), throat (page 2–11), and digestive tuneup (page 5–14) treatments.

Food allergies: give digestive tuneup, page 5–14.

Skin allergies: digestive tuneup, chest treatment, pages 5–14 and 4–10; treat without touching, page 8–27.

Synthetic Fibers

The usual synthetic fiber has little compatibility with, or friendliness toward, the human skin, when compared with natural fibers. Synthetic fibers often have a chilling action that cause the surface circulation of the skin to shrink back.

Such chilling action imposes an additional liability on a body that is struggling to establish normal temperature. Mr. Stephenson warned quite generally, but especially in chest cases, against wearing synthetic fibers next to the skin. He recommended wearing a rather snug garment of natural fiber in the daytime, and even at night in bed, so as to keep a warm blanket of air next to the body, directly over the skin. With a looser, non-absorbent garment, the slightest amount of air reaching the skin might have a chilling effect and would be a serious threat to a body with temperature above normal.

Because they interfere with the body's circulation, Mr. Stephenson felt that synthetic fibers can be far more detrimental to the body than most people are likely to suspect, not that these fibers are, in themselves, injurious, but that they block the biological functioning of the body and by and large, they are non-absorbent. They absorb moisture only to the point of equilibrium with the humidity of the atmosphere.

The body expels waste through the skin. The amount of material expelled can be as much as 2 pounds a day, whether the person is conscious of sweating or not. The non-absorbent nature of synthetic fibers allows the excreted substance to dry and glaze over the surface of the body, tending to seal it off.

Example from Creative Healers

A man in an executive position with heavy demands of lecturing and on his feet all day, found himself suffering intense pain, arising from his feet, through his back and to his head. After exhausting all other possibilities, a Creative Healer recommended he wear natural fiber socks and underwear. Not only did the pains cease but after a few months he found that a chest congestion and cough he had for several years had disappeared. It is easy to verify that the tackiness of the feet is much greater when synthetic hose are worn than when absorbent hose are worn. It thus becomes evident how unwise the use of synthetic fibers on the body can be.

Electrolysis Action Hurts Hands

The weak galvanic current coming from the flow of water past a metal nozzle of a garden hose can cause a damaging electrolysis. The damage, evidenced within the joints of the fingers, is caused when bare hands are used to grasp the nozzle and the finger or thumb is clasped over the hose to control the flow of water. Sensitive people can feel this current. Its effect, combined with whatever chilling may be caused by handling the hose in this manner, can have a detrimental result. It is wise to hold the hose by its rubber or plastic part. This protects the hands from the electrolysis and chilling.

Severe chilling can give rise to osteoarthritis. Wading in an icy cold mountain stream to fish for a prolonged period of time or walking a considerable distance on a cold winter day without adequate protection can set up conditions for osteoarthritis.

If the number of joints affected by osteoarthritis is high enough, attacks of rheumatoid or systemic arthritis may develop. This is caused when poisons are released into the blood stream from the affected joints.

In treating arthritis, it is important to remember the principle of bringing the body to normal temperature and keeping it there. This applies to the joints. Treat the joints so that they are brought to normal temperature. The person, then, must keep them at normal temperature.

For a detailed description of treatment of individual joints, see pain in the forearm and hand, the fingers and the knee, pages 6–2, 6–13, and 7–19.

Fallout

One or two months after the so-called infantile paralysis epidemic in March 1946 in the Los Angeles area, Mr. Stephenson made the following observations about this illness. He questioned people who had worked on cases in the hospitals at that time and assembled facts about the development of the disease.

1. Both adults and children had been stricken with the disease.
2. Often the person had gone to bed in good health and awakened the next morning to find legs or arms or neck paralyzed.
3. After three days of intensive care including hot fomentations and other physical therapy treatments plus injections with new medicines then believed to heal polio, the patient could be released with as much as a 90% recovery.

None of these facts fit Mr. Stephenson's concept of infantile paralysis. Atomic bombs had been dropped in Japan the year before, and he had observed clouds circling the earth carrying atomic particles or fallout. He saw the cause of the epidemic as fallout. He observed that if a large particle were breathed in, it would knock out only certain brain centers temporarily.

To Mr. Stephenson, stimulating the heart and circulation and keeping the blood stream coursing strongly through the body until the involved brain centers could recover seemed the most sensible path to follow. He suggested an ounce of whiskey or brandy, several times daily would achieve this stimulation until the brain centers could again take over.

Miscellaneous Treatments

Home Remedies Suggested By Mr. Stephenson

Low Calcium

If the body is known to need additional calcium, this can be obtained in a form readily accepted by the body by using powdered eggshell and sprinkling it over foods so that its bitterness is kept from being offensive.

Rheumatic Pains

Rheumatic pains evidenced in cool, damp weather are caused by a condition of the blood stream. To ease the pain, dissolve 1/4 teaspoon cream of tartar in a little hot water, add juice of 1/2 lemon, add more water, warm or cold, to make the drink palatable. Take this once a week at first and once a month when the condition has improved.

Nervous Chills

Nervous chills occur when nerve life is not fed through to the spine—no amount of external heating will warm up the body. Treat as for asthma, by applying warming strokes down the spine with the palm. If the heat treatment cannot be applied, a little whiskey will prove helpful, according to Mr. Stephenson.

Typhoid Fever

As Mr. Stephenson saw it, typhoid fever causes the walls of the stomach to swell, coating them over heavily with a gelatine-like substance. The stomach is thus unfit to receive solid food, and a fast is indicated. As the body struggles against the disease, it must be helped in the process of eliminating the poisonous wastes arising from the shedding of the stomach coating.

Twice in his life, Mr. Stephenson suffered an attack of typhoid fever. Both times, he recovered quickly and both times attributed his rapid recovery to his use of *Eno*. He regularly sipped tall glasses of water to which very small quantities of *Eno* had been added and took no other food or drink. The cleansing effect prevented a stagnation of the eliminating process.

Insomnia

People who experience a restlessness and sleeplessness not caused by any pain, physical discomfort, or mental agitation that they are aware of, can be helped to more relaxed sleep by wearing their shoes to bed. This may be necessary only for a short period, after which the person will regain normal, relaxed sleep.

Anemia

Two ounces a day of Guiness Stout can help rebuild an anemic person's strength.

Weight and the Rib Cage

The shape of the rib cage, besides being vital for breathing, is the biggest single factor governing the weight tendency of the body in a strong healthy person. A healthy person, when lying down after a meal, will show the abdomen being level with the chest. Such a person will tend to have firm rather than flabby flesh, regardless of weight.

When the ribs part at the end of the sternum at an obtuse angle (exceeding 90° but less than 180°), the rib cage will be short and deep and it will take a considerable quantity of food to fill the abdomen and keep the contour line level. The abdomen and chest will be more barrel shaped, and this person will be heavy all over. When the ribs part at an acute angle, (less than 90°) the rib cage will be long and shallow in depth and the person will need much less food to eat to sufficiency, and to keep the abdomen filled and level with the chest. Less food eaten and less flesh formed and this person will tend to remain thin except for a possible potbelly.

For the acute-angled parting of the ribs, there is a rarer case in which the ribs separate at the sternum but as they continue they meet again and are tied together by cartilage. The thorax is extremely long, almost meeting with the hips and extremely shallow. The person with this type of ribcage will have a lean and lanky build, and can be strong and wiry and never seem to lack stamina. On this type of ribcage there is an oval-shaped opening between the end of the sternum and the lower cartilage through which the thumb can enter so that the heart and breathing tubes can be contacted for treatment.

In the intermediate ribcage shape, there is more latitude. The person may be a little more on the heavy side or on the lean side and still remain strong and healthy. When the body is not level at the juncture of the chest and the abdomen, and a hollow has developed there, whether caused by illness, dieting or after childbirth, trouble of different kinds and degrees of seriousness is invited, because the ribs have remained up or high while the abdomen has shrunk.

To avoid trouble, the ribs must be brought down and in to meet with the abdomen. Use the treatment for high and short breathing, page 4–2, and recommend wearing the band described there.

These principles can be applied to voluntary weight control without the loss of health or strength. If, while lying supine the abdomen rises higher than the chest, the food intake should be reduced and the band should be worn day and night until the abdomen is of lesser height that the chest. With the band on, the amount of food required to eat to sufficiency will be much less than when eating without wearing the band. Once the trend to take in less food is established, it will continue to develop and weight reduction will be automatic. Also, the person will remain strong and healthy and his flesh firm.

Mr. Stephenson said that nature never deviates from the patterns described above, which express the connection between the weight tendency of the body and the shape of the ribcage.

Absent Healing

Mr. Stephenson found that in his later years much of his treating was in the form of absent treatment and that his work in this form was even more efficient than his work with massage. He would always stress that the absent treatment required great positive intention of the mind, even more than described in giving the cooling treatment. He would often be called on the telephone late at night by someone needing help. He would listen to the person's description of his trouble and say, "I'll take care of it," then immediately hang up and go back to sleep, knowing that relief and healing had set in at the other end. Proof of this ability is available from dated telegrams from a family in Pennsylvania after Mr. Stephenson moved to California. These documents are in the Joseph B. Stephenson Foundation archives.

But over and over again Mr. Stephenson emphasized that treating without touching, both in the form of the cooling treatment and in absent treatment, should be used only when the circumstances preclude treatment by contact.

Mr. Stephenson dictated the following to Mabel Gunderson:

To Heal From a Distance

As you begin to heal from a distance you will soon know that distance means nothing but I must stress one point "Leave the mind of your patient alone." When you get a message or request from any distance, relax your mind completely, your vision will travel and you will see the part of the body affected.

Understand when I say "see" this is a different kind of "see." It is not seeing the house on the other side of the street, it is seeing the body miles away. If it is a hemorrhage, you see the artery close. If it is high temperature, you see the temperature evaporate from the body. If the body is too cold, you blanket it with the power of warmth. The three laws of Creative Healing:

1. Touch when necessary.
2. If the body cannot be touched, give the power from the hands.
3. If the patient cannot get to you over 30 miles away, you go to them.

Index

A

B

C

D

E

F

G

H

I

J

K

L

CPSIA information can be obtained
at www.ICGtesting.com
Printed in the USA
LVHW101635180121
676812LV00031B/286